The Time of Secrets
and
The Time of Love

Marcel Pagnol was born in the small Provençal village
of Aubagne on 28 February 1895 – the very place and
date on which Louis Lumière showed the first
cinematic film. 'The cinema and I were born on the
same day, in the same place,' Pagnol observed. Hailed
by fellow directors Rossellini, Godard and Truffaut,
Pagnol was called by Jean Renoir 'the leading film artist
of his age', and his film *The Baker's Wife* was said by
Orson Welles to be the most beautiful he had ever seen.
Pagnol's work also includes a number of plays and
several autobiographical volumes.

Marcel Pagnol died in 1974.

Also by Marcel Pagnol in Picador

My Father's Glory *and* My Mother's Castle

The Water of the Hills
Jean de Florette *and* Manon of the Springs

Marcel Pagnol

The Time of Secrets

translated from the French by Rita Barisse

AND

The Time of Love

translated from the French by Eileen Ellenbogen

PICADOR

The Time of Secrets first published 1962 by Hamish Hamilton Ltd
The Time of Love first published 1979 by Hamish Hamilton Ltd
First combined edition published 1991 by André Deutsch Ltd

This edition published 1994 by Picador
a division of Pan Macmillan Publishers Limited
Cavaye Place London SW10 9PG
and Basingstoke

Associated companies throughout the world

ISBN 0 330 33258 9

3 5 7 9 8 6 4 2

A CIP catalogue record for this book is available from
the British Library

Printed and bound in Great Britain by
Cox & Wyman Ltd, Reading, Berkshire

To my son Frédéric

M.P.

PUBLISHER'S NOTE

With this publication of *The Time of Secrets* and
The Time of Love, Picador has the privilege of
bringing together in one volume the final two parts
of Marcel Pagnol's memoirs, *Les Souvenirs
d'Enfance*. *The Time of Secrets* was originally
published during Pagnol's lifetime, but *The Time of
Love* was published posthumously. Details on how
these later chapters came to be discovered, edited
and published are to be found in the appending
essay by Bernard de Fallois, Pagnol's editor and
friend.

PART ONE

The Time of Secrets

CHAPTER ONE

THE dreadful affair of the Château, when we had been held up at gun-point by the vast game-keeper and his repulsive dog and accused of trespassing on the Baron's land, had not been an auspicious start. But after Bouzique, the canal-pricker, had induced the keeper to part with the report that he had prepared for the School Inspector, detailing my father's supposed villainies, and had victoriously announced that it was now mere confetti floating down the canal, happiness settled down at the little *Bastide-Neuve*, and the long summer holidays began.

The first day, however, was unlike the one I had lived through with such tremulous anticipation. Lili did not call for me at dawn, as he had promised, and I slept soundly till eight o'clock.

It was the gentle scraping of a joiner's plane that awakened me.

I hurried downstairs to see what was going on.

I found my father on the terrace: he was squaring a door that had been warped by the winter, and a pile of wood-shavings shaped like bishop's croziers was curling right up to his chin.

Deep in his work, he gestured with his finger towards a sheet of paper, tied with a length of raffia on a low-hanging branch of the fig-tree. I recognized my dear Lili's hand-writing and spelling.

We cant go for the snaires thiss morning, Ive gon with my Farther to harvist Pastans feeld. Cum there. we'll eet under the plumtree. Cum. Dont hurrey. We'll bee ther all day. yor friend Lili. Weve got the miule. You kan ride on it. Cum. yor frend Lili. Its the feeld where the pipits was lasyear. Cum.

My mother, who had just come downstairs too, was already singing in the kitchen.

While I was enjoying my coffee-and-milk, she was getting

7

my haversack ready: bread, butter, hard sausage, a pie, two raw chops, four bananas, a plate, fork and glass, and some salt in the knot of a reed-stem, corked with an acorn from a kermes-oak.

With the haversack on my shoulder and my stick in my hand, I set out by myself towards the enchanted hills.

To reach the 'field where the pipits was' I had only to walk across the small plateau of Les Bellons and go down into the valley: by climbing up again along the fault beyond, I could get to the distant field in under an hour. But I decided to make a detour over the hilltops, crossing by the shoulder of Tête-Ronde—Mt. Roundhead—whose black pine-wood fringe loomed above the three bands of white rock against the morning sky.

The powerful July sun made the cicadas chirp: along the sides of the mule-path cobwebs were glistening between the gorse bushes. As I climbed slowly towards Baptiste's Pen, I set my sandals in my last year's footprints, and the landscape recognized me.

At the turning of Redouneou, two crested skylarks, big as blackbirds, startled out of a terebinth: I put my stick to my shoulder, took careful aim (like Uncle Jules) and cried: 'Bang! Bang!' I decided that I had killed the first but had aimed too low for the second one, which vexed me greatly.

The old sheep-pen had lost half its roof; but the fig tree by the crumbling wall had not changed. The tall dead branch above its green crown still reared up, stark black against the blue.

I hugged its trunk in my arms amid the humming of the bees that were sucking the honey from the wrinkled figs, and I kissed its elephant hide, murmuring words of friendship.

Then I followed the long cliff—the *barre*—that overlooks the sloping plain of La Garette. . . . On the edge of the steep drop I rediscovered the small heaps of stones that I had piled with my hands to lure the white-tails or the mountain larks. . . . At the foot of those perches we used to place our snares the previous year, that is to say in days of old . . .

When I got to the foot of Mt. Taoumé, I sat down under the tall, leaning pine tree and gazed at the scenery for a long time.

Far, very far away to my right, beyond some lower hills, sparkled the morning sea.

Before me, at the foot of the mountain range of Marseilles-Veyre, bare and white like a sierra, a light mist was floating above the long valley of the Huveaune. . . .

On my left, at last, the high, stratified *barre* of the Eagle Plateau upheld the vast tableland that rose in a gentle curve right up to the neck of Mt. Garlaban.

A light breeze had just risen: it suddenly wafted the scent of thyme and lavender to me. Leaning backward, propped with my hands on the ground behind me, my eyes closed, I was inhaling the burning fragrance of my homeland, when I felt beneath my hand, through the carpet of pine-needles, something hard that was not a stone. I scratched the soil and brought to light a brass snare, a snare for thrushes, blackened by rust: one of those, no doubt, which we had lost on the day of the thunderstorm at the end of the holidays. . . . I looked at it for a long time, moved as an archaeologist who discovers, at the bottom of an excavated site, the tarnished mirror of a long-dead queen. . . . So it had remained there a whole year beneath the small, dry pine-needles, which had slowly dropped on it one after the other, while the days had been dropping on me. . . . It must have thought it was lost for ever . . .

I kissed it, then opened it. It seemed to me that the spring had retained all its strength. I rubbed it against the earth: a slender gold thread reappeared, and I saw that it would be easy to bring it back to life: I got up, put it into my haversack and galloped down towards Passe-Temps, where Lili the Reaper was waiting for me.

*

I found him in the middle of a field that stretched in a narrow strip along the bottom of the valley, wedged in between two high walls of rock. It was bordered on the right by some well-cared-for olives and, below the cliff on the left, by a tangle of bushy trees: they were plum trees, laden with round fruit that was beginning to turn purple.

François, his legs wide apart, was swinging his scythe. Lili was following him, binding the grain into sheaves . . .

9

It was buckwheat, the poor man's corn. The ears were sparse, and there were even wide gaps where the rabbits like prodigal sons had eaten the green corn; then, after the demise of the scarecrow, which the rats had stripped of its clothing, the nuthatches, magpies and partridges had devoured the ripening corn at their leisure.

As I was deploring these ravages, François began to laugh, saying: 'Don't weep over the lost corn: they've paid for it!'

Lili told me that his father had, in fact, caught two or three rabbits a day in this field, to which had been added, when the corn was in ear, a dozen young partridges.

'I do that every year,' said François. 'Afterwards I pick up what's left for the chickens.'

It seemed to me that on these remote and barren lands this was the only imaginable form of agriculture.

I emptied my haversack onto the grass, while Lili spread the contents of a leather game-bag on a piece of sack-cloth.

We made a hearth below the cliff by putting three big stones close together; then, over a crackling fire of myrtle and rosemary, Lili placed my chops and three sausages on a square of chicken-wire he had brought. They shed sputtering tears of fat, and the thick, savoury smoke made my mouth water like a puppy's.

The lunch was delicious, and the table-talk, broken by long masticatory pauses, was also most instructive.

François carved his chunks of bread with a knife and ate gravely, with bulging cheeks, in an almost solemn silence. But suddenly he noticed my china plate and began to laugh, as if at a surprising joke. Throughout lunch he came back to it several times: he would point to it with the tip of his knife and laugh again noiselessly: his shoulders were bobbing up and down under his ears.

When we got to the bananas, he peeled his and said: 'I've had ones like that before, at Marseilles, during my military service.'

Then he gazed at it, laughed once more, and swallowed his banana.

Just then a very big green lizard crossed the field in a leisurely way, not far from us.

François pointed to it.

'Do you know what that is?'

'Of course! It's a *limbert*. Last year we caught a dozen of them with our snares, quite unintentionally!'

'When I was little,' he said, 'I ate at least fifty of those. My father used to skin them, gut them, and then ten minutes' grilling on the fire . . .'

'Were they good?'

'Not bad. But one must be used to it. At any rate, it's better than snake . . .'

He corrected himself, as if prompted by a gourmet's scruple:

'. . . Mind you, I'm speaking for myself. It's just as some folks like foxes. But personally, I think they smell, and I much rather prefer badger . . .'

He picked his teeth with the tip of his knife, snapped it shut with a loud 'click', and went on:

'. . . Squirrel too isn't bad, if you don't mind the taste of resin. But in the end, none of them's a patch on hedge-hog.'

Finding it hard to believe that he stuck to such a strange diet, I asked:

'Have you really eaten all those animals?'

'Of course!'

He turned to Lili.

'Townspeople are always surprised that we eat hedgehogs. And yet *they* eat sea-urchins!'

After this triumphant reply, he seemed to ponder for a moment, then suddenly added:

'And it seems that there are even some dirty fellows who actually eat frogs!'

He opened his mouth wide and slowly closed his jaws again as if cracking a batrachian between his teeth.

'Oh!' cried Lili, with a pained grimace, 'don't talk about that, it makes me sick!'

François got up.

'Never mind,' he said philosophically, 'as the saying goes: everyone to his taste—and *I've* a taste for hedgehogs. Now, off we go. To work!'

He picked up his scythe, and Lili the rake; I was set to

gleaning after them, making small bunches of ten ears or so which would later serve as lures for partridges.

These rustic labours lasted till sunset, and made a pleasant day. Going back, we climbed right on top of the sheaves piled in the cart while François led the mule by the bridle.

We passed through the cool shade of the valley. High up along the cliff-top, the rays of the setting sun were gilding the pines that leaned towards us, and our passage put swarms of cicadas to flight.

Lying flat on our stomachs in the rustling straw, we started to exchange confidences.

Without looking at me, Lili said in an undertone:

'I was longing to see you.'

'So was I.'

The jolts rocked us back and forth amid the fresh scent of bearded grain. He went on:

'Tomorrow morning we can set snares, but I'll have to get back early.'

'Why?'

'To crush out this corn on the threshing floor. And in the afternoon, I've got to flail the chick-peas that are laid out to dry in the granary.'

He seemed worried and wistful.

'My father,' he continued, 'wants me to help him now almost every day, 'cos I've got hair on my legs!'

He stretched out his leg to show me the dark fuzz on his calf, which was threatening his freedom.

'I'll come and help you,' I said.

'That won't get me much forrader, because even after the chick-peas it won't be finished. There's always something to do in the country at this time of year. But that's no reason for you to waste your holidays. I'll give you my winged ants: I've got some lovely red ones, from down the trees. You can go and set snares by yourself till the first day of the shooting season, because after August 10th my father has promised to leave me free in the morning and after five at night.'

'No,' I said. 'All by myself it won't be any fun. I'd rather come and work with you.'

He looked at me for a moment; his eyes sparkled, and it seemed to me that he was blushing.

'I thought so to myself,' he said. 'But still, it makes me glad.'

*

That his how that year I learned to crush buckwheat under the ancient, grooved stone roller, dragged by the precious mule; then, with the pitchfork, made from the wood of the sorb tree, I would toss the tired straw into the wind: the naked grains would rain down at my feet, the straw would fall further away, and the light chaff would fly off in long white streamers across the branches of the olive trees. I flailed the chick-peas, encased in their dry pods like the marble in a jingle-bell. Then we made *canisses*, which are rush-mats on which figs are laid out to dry. Every night we also had to draw water from the well for the love-apples (which the French flatly call 'tomatoes'), tie up the lettuces, cut grass for the rabbits, and change the mule's bedding straw. We tried to set snares in the fields next to which we worked, under the olive trees or among the stubble. But our catches were paltry: indignant magpies, deceived sparrows, or hedge-warblers which were so small that the snare, passing over their heads, had snapped their rump ends.

We soon gave up these attempts and waited for the return of Uncle Jules, so difficult to pry loose from his native Perpignan.

CHAPTER TWO

ONE morning my father decided that it was high time to cut the blond curls of little Paul, who had been clamouring for this sacrifice for a long while.

'At school,' he said, 'some of them call me "the girl"', and I don't like it.'

He was therefore installed on a chair surmounted by a small box. A cloth was put round his neck, exactly as at the barber's. I had been commissioned to steal a suitably-sized saucepan from the kitchen and, for safety's sake, I had brought two.

I placed the closer-fitting one on his head like a hat, and held the handle; meanwhile, my father, with a pair of scissors, cropped the curls close along the rim: it was done with magical speed, but the result was not very satisfactory, for when the saucepan was removed the patient's hair looked strangely crenellated. So when he called for the mirror, my father cried: 'Not yet!'

He produced from his pocket a brand-new pair of clippers and very deftly shaved the nape of my brother's neck, like a prisoner's, over the coloured cover-page of *Le Petit Journal*. Then, with comb and scissors, he endeavoured to trim the hair evenly on both sides of the head. He managed this rather well, but with such numerous corrections that its length was eventually reduced to nothing. Paul gazed at his reflection and admired himself, although he was left with only a fringe on his forehead. He strove to assume a manly air, compressing his lips and knitting his brow: and it is true that to me he looked transformed. Triumphantly we went and presented him to Augustine, who was much shaken but declared that one had to resign oneself to losing a baby in order to have a little boy; and she finally agreed that 'it suited him very well'. In short, everybody was happy, and

Paul promptly started sewing his curls round a circular piece of sheeting to make a scalp.

Unfortunately, this first success lured Joseph into a rash adventure.

His elder sister, Aunt Marie, had one day advised him to have our little sister's head cropped close in order to thicken her future tresses, and the local barber had confirmed that this was an excellent method. So Joseph had mentioned it at home without, however, volunteering his own opinion on the value of this advice: the moment he caught the look in Augustine's eyes and without giving her time to protest, he declared that it would be barbarous to shave such pretty curls, ending up that 'the child had quite enough hair as it was'.

But there were those brand-new clippers in his pocket . . . It is well known that beautiful tools attract the hand and that they clamour for action because they know that rust lies ready to pounce on them. Joseph could not resist them. His vanity as a barber's apprentice persuaded him that it was his duty to apply the treatment advised by a professional, and that no absurd sentimentality, bordering on fetishism, should prevent a father from ensuring the capillary future of his child.

He therefore carried out the deed in secret, not in the hope of silencing Augustine's reactions but in the certainty of rendering them ineffectual, since they would come after the irrevocable act.

And come they did, just at the very moment when he was already regretting having bought those clippers. The stark view of that childish skull, which seemed enormous, naked and as fragile as an egg, was really disturbing: one could see the fontanelle throb as though a chicken were about to emerge from it.

My mother's reaction was spirited. She tore the clippers from Joseph's hands and ran all the way to the Boucan well, into which she flung the offending implement. My father laughed, but mirthlessly. Paul was delighted, and chanted:

> *Shorn he was, and humbled, see!*
> *Bitten by a bumble-bee!*

As for me, I was rather upset but wondered in what way

the drowning of the clippers could help to restore the sacrificed locks.

Meanwhile, the victim herself, with her curls in her hand, had climbed all alone on to a chair in front of the fireplace, and was peering into the mirror at this rosy water-melon which was opening wide big black eyes. When she realized that this was herself, her chin suddenly trembled and she let out a long wail of terror and despair. My mother, back from the well, was walking as if in her sleep, with fixed gaze and clenched jaws. Without uttering a word, she took those howls under her arm and carried them into her room. My father followed her, his moustache drooping, a guilty smile of confusion on his face, his arms held wide with repentance.

Paul said to me, still laughing: 'A good thing she threw the clippers away, or he'd have had a go at you, and at Mama too!'

*

My little sister emerged from the room under an old fur toque that my mother had fitted to the size of her head, to shield her—so we were told—from sun-stroke and draughts.

She climbed on to the chair again, took another look at herself in the mirror and, as she already had a weakness for fashion accessories, seemed perfectly happy.

My mother, however, sadly wrapped one brown lock in a piece of tissue-paper and put it into a lacquered box where it joined one of Paul's fair curls.

*

It so happened that on that very day, towards four, Uncle Jules and Aunt Rose arrived without warning, in a cart they had hired from a market-gardener at Saint-Marcel.

Our little sister—with her toque—ran out to meet them. Uncle put down his two suitcases and lifted her in his arms. So, to thank him and show her joy, she gaily sang in her treble voice a ditty composed by a party agent for the municipal elections:

Down with Chanot,
A beggar is he!
Without more ado
String him up on a tree. . . .

Since that hang-worthy Chanot was the Catholic mayor of Marseilles, Uncle Jules frowned, put down our little sister, picked up a suitcase in each hand and, walking up to Joseph who was just coming towards him with a smile, reproached him sarcastically for having started somewhat early on the political education of that infant.

My father, who was delighted to resume their pleasant quarrel, replied that he did not know the song himself—though he quite approved its rough frankness—and that it was the child who had taught him the ditty—which was quite true. As she did not yet go to school (source of all knowledge), nobody ever found out where she had learned it.

This first argument was cut short, in any case, by a stifled cry from Aunt Rose, for my little sister, in order to make her a big bow of welcome, had just removed the toque. My aunt must have thought for a moment that we had scalped her or that typhoid fever had claimed this sacrifice. But my mother threw herself laughingly into her sister's arms, and they both went upstairs to their rooms to resume their whispered conversations, impish bursts of laughter and mysteriously indignant 'Oh's'.

CHAPTER THREE

FROM Roussillon Uncle Jules brought back grapes in brandy, honey-cakes that stuck to your teeth, a goose liver as big as a calf's heart, brandy dating back to before the Flood, and his 'R's' refurbished.

Cousin Pierre's bulk had become considerable; the family were as glad of it as if we meant to eat him. Aunt Rose herself had put on a little flesh; her new cheeks became her very well, and provided room for kissing her.

It was a very happy day of reunion, and laughter and singing could be heard in every room.

Then the previous year's life started all over again. We made cartridges, polished the shotguns, and to me fell the honour of mapping out the sportsmen's route for the Opening Day of the Season: this was a great success, almost a triumph. The game-bags bulged with partridge, Lili and I had a rabbit in each hand, while Uncle Jules, like the Good Shepherd carrying the Lost Sheep, had slung a buff-coloured hare, as big as a dog, across his shoulders. He informed us that this was a 'migrant', a German hare that had no business to be here in the month of August, for they arrive in winter and leave again in the middle of spring. Its presence was thus inexplicable. But Joseph likened this case to that of a barber from Berlin, who had come to Marseilles for three days on a trade union mission and had never left since.

This glorious beginning held the promise of a brilliant hunting season. Uncle Jules calculated the profits in advance and estimated they would pay for the rent and, perhaps, for a Breton spaniel for the following year.

I soon realized, however, that my passion had lost its violence, and it seemed to me that the sportsmen themselves were no longer consumed with the same ardour.

To be sure, there were still some lovely days: but the feats of the ever infallible Uncle Jules were merely interesting repetitions, and his rare misses now assumed more importance than his hits.

Similarly, Joseph was merely satisfied when a well-aimed shot plugged a woodcock in the dusk, or the white tail of a soon-to-be-jugged hare. As for me, my heart no longer beat so fast when I made my round of the snares, and the sudden flush of a covey of partridges no longer conjured up the apparition of a monster, but rather a panic in a hen-roost. . . .

Experience, 'precious' experience, had disenchanted my hills and depopulated the black pine-woods: no more lions, no more grizzly-bears, not even a solitary lynx. They had all returned to their lairs in the illustrated pages of my *Natural History*, and I knew quite well that they would never leave them again.

Every day at eleven we left the sportsmen up in the hills: Lili went down to his agricultural tasks. Whenever my help could bring them to a speedier end, I would join him after lunch. But most of my afternoons I spent at the Bastide-Neuve.

After some minor domestic chores (a trip to the Boucan well, preparing 'soft wood' matches, tidying up the storeroom), I would lie down flat on my stomach under an olive tree, my elbows propped on the dry grass, my head between my hands, over a book by Jules Verne, whom I had just discovered. His fabulous imagination made up for the inadequacy of my own, and his inventions replaced the lost fairyland of my hills. I read and re-read with fervour *The Children of Captain Grant* and, above all, *The Mysterious Island*, whose characters were just as real to me as my father or Uncle Jules.

Paul often tried to re-awaken my Comanche soul by hurling fierce challenges at me from afar, aggravated by Pawnee insults: but I had disowned Gustave Aymard, and the tomahawk was buried for good. . . . I would sometimes reply—without even raising my head—with curses (in Comanche), and I might still scalp him now and then, but really just to please him. . . .

He would sit at the foot of the 'sycamore of his ancestors' (which was merely an old almond tree) and smoke in solitude a clematis pipe of peace, between two fits of coughing. His cheeks and forehead were adorned with swirls of powdered chalk held on with library paste. From his belt hung his own shorn locks, next to the scalp of a doll that had died of old age.

From time to time he would interrupt his meditations and cock an ear to the breeze. He would bound to his feet, emit a fierce war whoop at the sight of an invisible enemy, throw his tomahawk against the wind and vainly shoot arrows without any response. . . . But however much he tried, his glory was gone . . . He was no longer the feared chief of a ferocious Pawnee tribe, and his way of moving rather evoked the fatigue and melancholy of the last of the Mohicans.

This enjoyable life which, it seemed to me, might have gone on for years, was suddenly troubled by a tragi-comedy in our family, which might have contained a very valuable lesson for me, had I understood it. But I was still pretty young and only on looking back on it from very far have I been able to reconstruct it.

CHAPTER FOUR

ONE night I was suddenly awakened by the neighing of a horse which seemed to be outside the door. For a moment I wondered whether that long, tremulous cry had not come out of a dream. But as I listened, I could hear a great to-do in the house which the doers were trying to muffle: steps on tiptoe, whispers, murmurs, doors closed with caution.

I got up noiselessly and opened the shutters a crack: day was breaking and in the still uncertain light I saw a hackney carriage, yes, a hired cab standing near the house, on the stony slope. This was quite an extraordinary event, and the first vehicle of its kind, no doubt, that had ever ventured up there.

On the box sat a coachman, giving a long yawn. Who could have come to waken us at dawn, and why?

I opened my door very gently, and knew right away who was there: my aunt Fifi, one of my father's elder sisters. She was a woman of great authority. Since the age of twenty-five she had been the headmistress of a higher school: she reigned there as a well-loved despot and was completely dedicated to her mission, which was to teach, educate and train virtuously anti-clerical young citizenesses. As the idle Thursdays seemed to her a criminal waste, she had founded the Acorn Society, which aimed at re-afforesting the hills of Estaque: once a week she would therefore drag across the stony *garrigue* her general staff of elderly spinsters, followed by a battalion of bewildered young girls.

Deployed like riflemen and stopping at the word of command, this gang of prisoners would scratch the gravel and bury an acorn beneath a handful of pebbles. That is why the newspapers wrote about my aunt, a fact that filled the whole family with pride. As she also busied herself with the Anti-Tobacco League, the Association for Female Suffrage, and the Crusade for Maternal Breast-feeding, she was often received by the Mayor, and even by the Prefect; so much so that well-informed people said she would eventually be awarded the *Légion d'Honneur*, and every year we looked forward expectantly to this glorious event.

In short, she was a woman of importance, which did not prevent her from being good-looking and nice-smelling.

I could recognize the sound of her voice in certain bursts of talk but could not understand what she was saying: after a moment, however, I could grasp the word 'papa'. So she was talking of my grandfather, and I had a premonition that this practically nocturnal visit heralded some misfortune.

I loved old Master André very much indeed, but I knew that he could die any moment since he was eighty-six years old. I even considered that such an extraordinary age—a tree's age—was almost excessive and that every new day of his life represented a *tour de force* on his part and a gift to his family.

That is why the grief which his loss would certainly cause me had already been spread over several years of my childhood until it had been practically 'written off', as it were, like a depreciated old estate.

As I was about to liquidate this account with two big tears, I heard my father's voice saying with great seriousness:

'Now look, Fifi, you're joking!'

She answered in a low voice, with a great many words, then Uncle Jules said gravely:

'At that age, it may be more serious than you think!'

Aunt Rose gave an unintelligible reply which ended in a burst of laughter.

I was immediately reassured: no, grandfather wasn't dead, since she was laughing.

'Anyway,' my mother said suddenly, 'since he wants to see us, we must go to him at once.'

'He's been asking for Marcel above all!' said Aunt Fifi.

'I'll go and wake him,' said my father's voice.

I hurriedly closed the door, jumped into bed, and pulled the blanket over my face; then, timing my breath to the rhythm of Paul's, who was fast asleep, I feigned the peaceful slumber of innocence.

Joseph came in without making a sound, carrying a light that shone right through the coverlet.

He called me softly: I answered with a deep sigh and turned to the wall. Then he put his hand on my shoulder. I gave a start and suddenly opened my eyes wide, with an air of bewilderment.

'Come on,' he said, 'get up and put on your good suit.'

I rubbed my eyelids with my clenched fists, as custom requires, and said—in a sleepy voice:

'Wha's the matter?'

'Your grandfather is ill, and urgently wants to see us.'

With an anguish that was only half feigned, I cried:

'Is he dead?'

'No, no!' said my father. 'Since I'm telling you he wants to see us!'

'I have to go too?'

'Yes, you too, he's been asking for you.'

'Is he very ill?'

'I don't think so,' said my father. 'I believe it's mainly psychological. That's why we must go and comfort him. Hurry up.'

*

Aunt Fifi clasped me to her heart, that is to say, against the whalebones of her corset, and told me with a certain solemnity that my grandfather was doing me a great honour by calling me to his bedside as the eldest of his grand-children: because it would fall to me to be the head of the tribe after my own father's death, of which she spoke with icy serenity while pulling on long, coffee-coloured gloves. Uncle Jules and Aunt Rose, meanwhile, exchanged mysterious sentences such as: 'It's appallingly funny!' or else: 'In all my life, but all my life, I've never heard anything like it!' As for me, I thought that 'in all my life' I'd never ridden in a hackney carriage, and I ran and climbed into it without more ado; the cushions were of downy softness and I was sorry I had not Uncle Jules' backside to make more ample use of them.

This admirable vehicle had rubber-covered wheels, and once we were on a good road one could hear nothing but the horses' clop-clop. My father and Aunt Fifi were sitting facing us, and I was nestling against my mother, who was as warm as a bird. Nobody was speaking . . . With my eyes closed and on the point of falling asleep, I imagined that I was on horseback but, without knowing it, I was galloping towards the *dénouement* of an adventure that had started forty years earlier.

CHAPTER FIVE

IN 1870, during the five months of its siege, and afterwards in the terrible days of the Commune, Paris had been heavily bombarded.

Naturally, the shells fired by the cannon in those days did not yet have homing warheads or atomic loads: still, they caused a lot of damage. Several bursts of shell-fire hit the Paris Town Hall, whose delicately chiselled pinnacles were the glory of our stone-carvers. Almost all of these graceful masterpieces were scarred or damaged, and some of them collapsed in pieces on the roof.

When peace had returned and the country recovered its strength, the city of Paris decided to restore this monument. It was a difficult job. The government therefore appealed to the stone-carvers guild, which asked the masters and journey-men to nominate the most skilful among them in each *département*.

The Guildsmen of the *Bouches-du-Rhône* thereupon selected my grandfather: a supreme honour of which I am proud even today.

*

In those days, Paris was much farther from Marseilles than Moscow is today.

There were three days' and three nights' travelling, some hundred stops at railway stations, and over fifty tunnels—Monsieur Thiers predicted that all that could ever come out of them would be train-loads of smoked corpses.

However, my grandfather André did not for a moment consider refusing such a glorious mission. He kissed his dear wife, then his four children, gave his blessing in advance to the fifth that was about to be born, and walked to the station, accompanied by his craft-brothers who sang lustily as they carried his two heavy crates full of tools.

On a fair summer morning, the steam-engine eventually

25

stopped at a huge station from which, visibly, it could pull out only by moving backward, and Master André, red-eyed and starving, realized that he was in the 'modern Babylon'.

With genuine relief he saw waiting for him under the station clock three journeymen, wearing the guild's cockade. They embraced him and led him—on a beribboned wagon —to the Inn of the Building Companions: there he was to remain for over a year with other stone-carvers, masons and carpenters.

As was then the custom, a 'Journeymen's Mother' ruled over the entire household.

This particular one was the young widow of an iron worker who had fallen from a steeple on which he had just fixed a cross.

My grandfather was forty years old. The Journeymen's Mother was thirty.

Grandfather was a Provençal. He sang Christmas carols beautifully and serenades even better. He laughed easily, and during the short evenings at the fireside he was good at telling love-stories.

The Journeymen's Mother came from Roubaix. She was tall, golden-haired, and of average virtue: but she had never seen such black eyes, nobody had ever crooned *Magali* to her, and what had to happen did happen.

Hence Grandfather was amply fed, carefully clothed, tenderly fussed over, and he congratulated himself every day on the fact that the Town Hall had so many pinnacles, for he was as happy as a pope—a Borgia pope, I mean.

But one day, a companion passing through Paris—not a good companion, as will be seen—a stone-mason, of course —was silly enough to get annoyed at seeing the best morsels going straight from the cooking pot onto the plate of Master André, who was sitting at the head of the table.

He didn't dare to pass a remark, but harboured a grudge about it which kept growing every night and, above all, at midday on Sundays.

He slept in the room next to grandfather's: the partition was made of 'thirty mil slabs', which are very thin and hollow bricks, thus rendering it permeable by the faintest sigh. That was not much of a drawback in this particular

26

case, for the stone-mason went to sleep early and did not even hear his own snores.

One night, however, the famished glutton was awakened by the painful memory of a hazel-grouse he had seen disappear between Master André's jaws: he then heard such heartfelt moans that he thought someone was murdering a woman and dashed to the poor creature's rescue. The Journeymen's Mother answered through the door 'that nobody needed him' and inquired, in somewhat crude terms, if he were a virgin. Whereupon my grandfather added a piece of advice that was easy to follow and might have calmed him at little cost. The silly fool, who couldn't see the joke, was terribly vexed by this, and resolved to have his revenge.

At the end of the week he left for Marseilles, where new docks were being built—and one fine Sunday morning he went to pay a visit to my grandmother, on the pretext of bringing her news of her husband.

And so he did, and very precise news at that, for no sooner had the children gone out than he spilled the whole story. And as she was still fresh and buxom, he offered his collaboration for a prompt revenge.

Grandmother answered him with a deft blow from her knee, and while the traitor was painfully picking himself up she rebuked him for his vileness, predicted he would die a cuckold, and unceremoniously pushed him out.

*

She did not quite believe in her André's betrayal, but doubt began to gnaw at her.

In her letters—which she dictated to her eldest daughter —she did not give the slightest hint of the informer's visit; but she spoke of the sadness of their home, the dangers that lurked for young girls in their father's absence, the neighbours' insolence, and the distressing withering of her charms condemned to uselessness.

My grandfather felt a twinge of remorse; but since duty must come before sentiment, he polished off the last pinnacles, which required all of three months.

Three times he jumped down from the railway carriage to give the Journeymen's Mother a last kiss. She shed torrents of tears, as prescribed by Châteaubriand (whom she had never read) and clung to him: but the indignant locomotive whistled with all its might and Grandfather André, wiping away a guilty tear, only just had time to jump onto the footplate which was moving away.

CHAPTER SIX

HE found his wife much beautified by her sorrow, which had reduced her weight, and rather impassioned by her year's widowhood. They were as much in love as on the first day and happier than ever.

The children had grown: the boys were sturdy, the girls pretty and demure, and an architect brought him the plans for five modern buildings which grandfather was to erect around a piece of wasteland called the *Cours du Chapitre*. Very busy with his work and his wife, he forgot all about the Journeymen's Mother.

But grandmother didn't forget.

*

One Sunday morning, when he was shaving, and while she was offering him alternately the bowl of lather and the towel, she told him of the treacherous journeyman's visit. But she related the story jestingly, and concluded by saying: 'He made me laugh, he did!'

Grandfather did not take it as a laughing matter. On the contrary, he turned quite pale and his hand trembled so much that he cut his chin three times. Whereupon he gave up shaving against the bristle, put on his best smock, picked up his heaviest walking-stick, and said:

'If I find that bloke, there won't be enough left of him to make a stew.'

The horrified family waited the whole day. He only got back very late, but without carrying the smallest morsel of the traitor under his arm: the villain had left for Brittany. My grandfather, who believed that Nordic province to be something like Greenland, consoled himself with the thought that the polar climate would put an end to the fellow before the year was out. So he never spoke again of that wretch who had frozen to death. But my grandmother started to play a comedy which was to last for forty years.

At five in the morning, when he was drinking his coffee, or at night on the pillow, she would gently lead the conversation on to the city of Paris (is it true that it rains there every day?), to the pinnacles (what kind of stone were they?), the excellence of the craftsmen's guilds (they were really one big family, weren't they?)—and my surprised grandfather found himself talking about the Journeymen's Mother.

Then grandmother would smile ironically, and with a pursed mouth and a shake of her head she would say:

'André, I know very well that the journeyman lied to me. But what astonishes me is that you can't help talking of that woman!'

And Grandfather would blush so deeply that it showed through his beard.

Up to then he had answered only by shrugging his shoulders or raising his eyes to heaven, but without saying a word, for his guild-name was 'Truthfulness of Marseilles'. He soon realized that, in the very interests of his dear wife, it was his duty to lie just for once, and solemnly.

That is why one Sunday morning, when she was asking him with a naïve air whether he thought her coffee was as good as the coffee in Paris, he declared that this business was getting on his nerves and that it was better to have it out 'frankly': in the shelter of this adverb, Truthfulness of Marseilles plunged headlong into a lie.

He began by swearing on his Square—at the risk of putting it out of true for ever—that he had had no guilty intercourse with the Journeymen's Mother. My grandmother threw her arms round his neck and there were tears in her eyes. But, flushed by the success of this first perjury of his life, Master André added:

'Besides, she was almost fifty and weighed at least fourteen stone. Moreover, she was a bit squint-eyed, had a chignon no bigger than a walnut, and since she was born in the Far North, nobody could understand her language.'

That was an irreparable mistake on the part of Truthfulness of Marseilles, for Grandmother had made inquiries.

Other journeymen, recently returned from Paris, had told her in all innocence that the Journeymen's Mother was a very beautiful creature, and a plasterer from Saint-Barnabé had even declared that 'if one made a cast of her, the Venus of Milo might go and dress herself, for all anyone cared'.

Grandmother flung into his face these testimonies from honourable men, which it was impossible to deny, and the unhappy Truthfulness of Marseilles, getting ever more bogged down in his deception, cried:

'So mine must have died, the poor thing! It's true she had a heart disease . . . When one's so fat, one doesn't live to be old . . . Still, it's a pity, for she was a great cook . . .'

But Grandmother didn't believe a word of it.

So he sent for a devoted friend, an ironworker and a perjured witness, who confirmed the sad news and even told at length about the funeral of that gigantic Norsewoman, whose transport to the churchyard had exhausted six undertakers' men.

Grandmother appeared to believe him and, for a few days, seemed to have calmed down. But over dinner at night she began to give advice to her daughters, who were of marrying age:

'Above all, be careful of ginger-haired women! Don't ever invite one of them to your home, once you're married. They're spineless, they're slatternly, and they have a stale smell, rather yellowish, like Gruyère cheese: but there are men who like that!'

She held forth about their deceitfulness, their lewdness, sloth and gluttony, watching out for Master André's reaction all the while. He was pretending not to hear, and was pencilling keystones and scarf-joints on the oil-cloth.

*

Some time later she changed her tactics and began to make generous, understanding remarks.

For example, she approved of neighbour Benjamin, who had started courting his housemaid hardly six weeks after the death of his wife.

'There's no denying it,' she would tell her daughters, 'a man of forty, if he's hale and hearty, can't live like a monk

31

for three months! Nature has made him so, and one would be silly not to understand it!'

Another time the butcher's wife, a stout termagant, caught her husband in the back shop busying himself with a tenderloin that was neither beef nor pork. She made a dreadful hullabaloo, and someone had to wrest from her the knife that she wanted to stick between her own prime ribs.

'Good lord, how stupid she is!' my grandmother declared. 'It isn't nice for a man to deceive his wife, but after all it doesn't matter as much as all that. It's a thing that happens every day, and no reason to kill oneself!'

Then glancing at Grandfather, who pretended he had not heard:

'Now if he lied to her, that *would* be serious—if he hid from her what everybody knew . . . All the rest is a mere trifle!'

'That's just words,' said my grandfather. 'And if I ever cuddled another woman . . .'

'*Bou Diou!*' exclaimed my grandmother, 'my poor André, is it possible that you should know me so little? If you'd ever deceived me with a hussy, just in passing, it would upset me of course. But you'd only have to tell me and I'd forgive you. And if you didn't tell me, I'd think you'd just had a moment's weakness, and I'd NEVER talk of it.'

But she never talked of anything else, even when one thought she did, and the cross-examination, which started in 1871, lasted till 1907.

＊

For several years now, they had been sheltering their old age in a small farm-house, near Roquevaire. They had kind neighbours, who cultivated strawberry-beds, fig-tree orchards and small olive groves.

He was eighty-six years old, and she only two years younger.

Grandfather, after the fashion of guildsmen, had kept his long curls and his square beard: its frizzy bristles were as thick as in the distant days of his youth, but they had become white as snow around his shrunken face.

Grandmother had put on weight. She was stout and heavy. But her face, below the small, yellow-white chignon, had remained fresh, because the fat stretched her wrinkles.

32

Her big round eyes were always merry. She had only one tooth left, and it pushed up her upper lip. A single tooth, but remarkable for its size and sparkle: big, bulging and white as a peeled almond, it roused the admiration of my brother Paul who was sometimes allowed to touch it with his finger-tip.

*

On that night, as on every night, they were both sitting in front of a very small fire of olive-wood for, despite the summer heat, Grandfather found that there was 'a nip in the air' in the evenings, and he ascribed this new-found harshness of the season to the passing of some invisible comet.

They were talking of small things: the black hen didn't want to lay any more and it was high time to put her into the pot. The pail for the well was getting rather heavy, but Fifi had promised to bring them a smaller one, with a rope instead of a chain.

As they talked, both were slowly sipping an infusion of thyme, strengthened with a small drop of local *marc*.

Grandfather had never touched a drop of alcohol in all his life. A litre of wine per day, yes—because for a stone-cutter who always works in the open air wine is a food: but never an *apéritif*, and he always refused distilled spirits.

When he had laid down his hammer Grandmother, who was pampering him, observed that he no longer ran the risk of falling off a scaffolding, and asserted that a drop of *marc*, which came straight from the vine, sustained the heart of old people, and they got into the habit of having every night a little dash of alcohol in their herb-tea.

That evening Grandmother had overstepped the dose, and Master André, despite his toughened tongue, realized it at once.

'Eugénie!' he said, 'you've put in too much.'

'Never mind!' she answered. 'You have a bit of a cold. It'll only do you good.'

He had merely protested for form's sake, for he drank the reinforced brew with pleasure, talking of that black hen, so mysteriously blocked, and of the well-rope that would be lighter than the chain and make less noise, too.

Meanwhile, exhilarated by the *marc*, he gradually grew merry and declared:

'Eugénie, alcohol is the very devil, and I've only just discovered that I adore it! You're lucky I didn't find out sooner!'

'You're right,' said Grandmother. 'I certainly wouldn't have cared to go and fetch you from the tavern every night. But now it doesn't matter any more, and I'll show you something that is even better!'

She went and opened the ancient sideboard and took from it a thick bottle which shone black behind its golden label.

'What's that?'

'That? That's called Champagne.'

'Do you intend to go on drinking?'

'I do,' said Grandmother emphatically. 'And it pains me that you don't know why. Doesn't this wine remind you of anything?'

'It does indeed! It reminds me that we drank some at our wedding. My fellow-journeymen brought us two bottles of it! The big Féraud was there, Cazenave, Remoulins, Ricard, and the one we called Banaston. Do you remember Banaston? He had a hairy wart right in the middle of his forehead, and his two eyes weren't the same colour . . . And then—'

'And then,' said Grandmother, 'you haven't forgotten Banaston, but you *have* forgotten that it's just sixty years today that we got married!'

Grandfather's gaiety dropped at once and he opened his eyes wide.

'Oh, my beautiful Eugénie! Is it possible? Is it the twenty-fourth of July today?'

'It is,' she said, 'ever since this morning, and you haven't said a word about it.'

'Oh, my darling! Forgive me. I can see I've really hurt you there, but it isn't altogether my fault . . . You must allow for the fact that for some time now—ever since I ate those mussels from Martigues, which weren't quite fresh, perhaps—I tend to forget people's names, and dates . . .'

'Never mind, I forgive you!' cried my grandmother. 'But on condition that you'll have a glass with me in memory of the most beautiful day of our lives . . .'

34

It was hard to open the bottle, and Grandfather uneasily stopped his ears for fear of the detonation. But Grandmother, who was skilful and strong, managed it very well.

When the golden wine was sparkling in a big glass, Grandfather said:

'Eugénie, you mustn't be annoyed if I don't drink it all.'

'But why?' asked Eugénie, with a touch of peevishness. 'Are you afraid of becoming a tippler? At eighty-six you won't be one for long! Tonight one would almost say you're doing everything you can to put my back up!'

'All right, I'll swallow half of it,' Grandfather said, 'and if I drop down stone-drunk, *you'll* have the trouble of putting me to bed!'

He took a big draught: the yellow wine bubbled on his tongue, tickled his nostrils, and the wedding-table, lit by clusters of candles, suddenly stretched out before him.

His fellow-craftsmen were thumping the benches in honour of Rouqueyrol, a fair, bearded carpenter, who had just sung *Ah! a curse be on wars!* and now it was grandfather's turn.

He got up and, in a voice a little hoarse with emotion, champagne and the weight of so many years, sang *The Song of the Golden Corn*.

At the end of the third verse he had to raise his glass to the health of the honourable company; he clinked glasses with Grandmother, who was quite as moved as he, and emptied his glass at a gulp.

Then he put his arm round the beautiful Eugénie and, on his spindly old legs, tried to make her dance a polka.

Now she knew that he was done to a turn: after four dance-steps she said that 'her head was turning', made him sit down opposite her, and drew the two armchairs close together.

'My handsome André,' she said, 'let's not give way to folly. At our age, it wouldn't be wise to hop around like youngsters . . .'

'My head isn't turning,' said Grandfather, 'and I feel as if I were twenty!'

And his feet, under the easy-chair, went on dancing the wedding-polka.

'It's true,' she said, 'that you're extraordinary for your age! It's a long time since I was twenty, and I often realize that I've got one foot in the grave.'

'Why no! Not at all!' cried Grandfather, merrily.

'Why yes! It's true!' my grandmother asserted. 'One of these days I'll die, and it may be this very night, perhaps, because my heart is as tired as that of the old clock; but I prefer to be the first to go: what would I be doing without you?'

'True enough,' said Grandfather, 'there's little chance of your finding another beau!'

'*Bou Diou!*' cried Grandmother. 'And what use could I make of him? I've had my share: a good husband, good health, fine thighs, beautiful children, and a lot of milk: no, you see, I'd leave happy if there didn't remain the least doubt between us.'

'What doubt?' Grandfather asked gaily. 'What's this about a doubt?'

'André, I didn't want to tell you, but you're forcing me to speak about it.'

'I? I'm forcing you?'

'Yes, you are, since you won't tell me!'

Truthfulness of Marseilles opened his eyes in amazement.

'And what do you want me to tell you?'

'You know quite well. You know that at the moment of dying there's something that'll irk me, a small doubt that will spoil my agony: it's that business with the Journeymen's Mother!'

'Oh, bugger!' said Grandfather. 'That again?'

'Well, yes, that again! I know, after all you told me, that she's been dead a long while, and that she was as ugly as sin, that she weighed fifteen stone, and that your friend the iron-smith, with that hypocrite's face of his, felt sorry for the undertaker's men . . . I know that you didn't fancy her at all, except that you fancied her beef-stew and onions . . . Come on, André, don't take me for a fool. I've known the truth for forty years, but I'd like you to tell me so.'

Grandfather was gazing at her, his head inclined on his right shoulder, and he was smoothing his beard with his left hand, but he did not answer. She went on, in a tone of friendly wisdom:

36

'André, what can it matter, today? This sort of thing doesn't interest us any more, it even seems silly to us . . . What remains is our friendship. And if in a forty-years-old friendship you leave a little lie, it's like a sharp pebble in a postman's shoe . . . André, tell me the truth!'

He gazed at her for another moment, then gave a resigned little smile:

'Why tell it, since you know?'

Grandmother, who was quite pale, became pathetic:

'How awful that you won't understand! It isn't truth I love, it's you! I want my husband not to be a liar any longer! André, if you don't speak up, you'll have stolen something from me!'

In spite of her creaking arthritis she went and knelt down before him and put her old white head on the only faintly beating heart which pumped the transparent blood along the frail and brittle pipes.

Grandfather, deeply moved, stroked the coarse white hair. The candle had just gone out, but the olive-logs threw small blue flames. At first he talked to her as to a child.

'Why, of course, big silly,' he said. 'Of course I had a fling with her. I was forty, and you were far away . . . But you know very well that I never loved anyone but you, and that you are the mother of my children.'

'Ah!' said Grandmother, smilingly, 'you're taking a weight off my heart! At last you've said it!'

She gave a great sigh of relief and immediately went on:

'And how did it happen? Not on the first day, I hope?'

'Oh no!' said Grandfather. 'The first day, I didn't as much as glance at her face. I was only thinking of you. Besides, you know me: I had all those pinnacles on my mind, and I was worrying on account of the Paris stone, which isn't the same as ours, and there was a chance it might break my chisels . . . So, as there happened to be a journeyman from Nogent who knew how to work that stone, I talked to him all the time so that he would tell me his secrets . . . Imagine, they have tools that are half chisel, half needle. That is to say, it is a round chisel flattened at the end, and the cutting edge is toothed like a saw . . . And I don't know how they do it, but they only temper the tip of the teeth, so that the hammer-stroke is softened by the handle, which is made of cast steel: and so . . .'

'I'm sure,' Grandmother said, 'that she was the one who started it.'

'You've guessed right,' said Grandfather. 'Not that it was a difficult guess: she did to me just what you did.'

*

And he began to tell the story, which has always been the same ever since there have been men and women. The first glances, the lowered eyes, then the fleeting smile on a face that is blushing.

While he spoke he saw her again, he lived again those vivid last moments of his youth.

And Grandmother kept putting questions. So he told her how one night she had come into his room, how she had bitten him while she was scratching his shoulders, and how she had fallen off the bed laughing, her lovely feet up in the air . . .

*

We reached the farm at Roquevaire just as the sun was rising above the hill.

In front of the low house, beneath the big fig-tree by the well, there stood a group of peasants and their wives.

Four men were holding Grandmother back by her wrists and shoulders, and several women were forming a barrier before her, with outstretched hands. She was straining forward, pulling the men along, against the women who were pushing her back . . . She had a madwoman's staring eyes, she was strong as a blacksmith.

My mother placed herself in front of me. Fifi said to my father: 'Go and see Papa . . .'

And she ran towards her mother while we walked into the farmhouse.

In the large Provençal kitchen there were more people. In the centre of the circle Grandfather was sitting on a chair. He was bare to the waist. There was long white hair on his lean chest. Bending over him was a bespectacled doctor, armed with a watchmaker's pincers and digging about in his bleeding shoulder. He was searching for the tooth, my grandmother's magnificent tooth. She had plunged it into André's shoulder and the doctor showed it to us at the end of his pincers, white, bulging and smooth, with a bloody tip.

My father pushed me forward. I hugged the lean chest and buried my forehead in the white beard.

Grandfather stroked my neck and, talking to me alone, said:

'Ah, women! Don't trust women, my lovely boy! Women just don't understand.'

I, too, didn't understand. But I could hear Grandmother outside, howling like a she-wolf, and flinging herself, with lowered head, against the circle of neighbours, at whom she was gnashing her gums and who were gently pushing her back.

'Joseph,' said Grandfather, 'lock the door . . . Hurry! If she comes back, she'll finish me . . .'

'Come, come, Father,' said Joseph, 'you surely don't believe . . .'

'I do! I do! I'm telling you she wants to kill me! If the neighbours hadn't come to my rescue she'd have slaughtered me! You don't realize she's gone mad!'

My mother, who was sitting next to him, said softly: 'Don't you believe it, Father, she isn't mad.'

She was slim, pale, fragile, her hands were crossed upon her knees. She was smiling wistfully.

There was a long animal howl, a howl trembling with rage and despair.

'Listen to it!' said Grandfather. 'Don't you call that raving madness?'

'No,' said my mother. 'That is love.'

CHAPTER SEVEN

WHEN Joseph told the story to Uncle Jules he omitted to
mention the tooth, and thus reduced the whole business to a
puerile quarrel of a couple of old folk fallen into second
childhood. But to me it was a tragedy, in which my grandfather had lost his prestige, since he had been bitten . . . As
for Grandmother, I agreed with him that she had gone mad,
which considering her age did not seem to me surprising;
but I was afraid that his own case might be even worse. For
when one person bites another, one must immediately think
of rabies: that is why I thought it would be prudent to send
them both to that Monsieur Pasteur who had cured the
shepherd Jupille in my *General Knowledge* book; otherwise
there was a good chance that their lives would end in a
horrible battle of rabid dotards, and the papers would write
about it. That would be a catastrophe for the whole family,
and above all for Aunt Fifi, on account of her *Légion d'Honneur*
which surely could not be awarded to someone who came of
a family stricken with rabies. I communicated my anxiety to
my father. He replied that Grandmother had already asked
her husband's pardon on her knees, and that the loss of her
last tooth ensured future peace and quiet in the household.

My mind was thus set at rest on this count, but my
mother's final words left me with an insoluble problem.

She had said: 'That is love!' and she hadn't meant it as a
joke. I could not understand. I would have found it quite
natural to bite an enemy fiercely, but to bite someone because
you love him was an act completely contrary to common-
sense. What then had she meant? I did not dare ask her. But
it sprang to my mind that a red-haired woman had sung in
the street one morning, to the sound of a guitar: 'Love is a
madness', with rolling eyes and waving her arms like a madwoman—and the people who had been listening hadn't
looked at all surprised.

40

Then there was that business with the baker's wife: she had half murdered her husband in his sleep, and Aunt Rose had said, to excuse her, that he had 'deceived' her and that she 'loved him to madness'.

So there was some relationship between love and madness. But was it love that made those people mad, or was it madness that exacerbated their love?

For my part, I loved my mother with all my heart, and yet I was not mad since I had got second place in the high-school scholarships. . . . Naturally, if someone had harmed her I should have gone berserk, but she wasn't the one I'd have bitten . . .

I finally came to the conclusion that the love that drives you mad was a business of grown-ups, more especially of women.

*

I was still rather uninformed about the habits and customs of the weaker sex. I only associated with my mother and my aunt, who weren't women but a mother and an aunt. Of course, in the streets I often saw some of those creatures, topped by hats laden with useless things that would have been very much in the way if they'd had to doff their hats in greeting. I had noticed, in particular, that their backsides swayed as they walked, and this filled me with a kind of alarm. There was even a friend of my mother's whose face was all covered with flour, like a raw sardine, who had a painted mouth and sooty eyelids.

She would kiss me very nicely, and I did not dislike it: but when she had gone I had to have my face washed and my father would open the window, because the place smelt like a hairdresser's, only more so.

One day my mother had said:

'It's not her fault if she's gone wrong . . .'

I understood that where the lady had gone wrong was merely in indulging in her mania for painting herself to deceive people about her looks, which indeed did not seem honest to me.

I had, however, a certain experience with girls: it was based on the daily sight of my little sister, my very occasional meetings with a nice little cousin, and my Thursday games in the deserted schoolyard with Clémentine, the caretaker's daughter.

*

My little sister was an agreeable person, but one who, to my mind, occupied far more room than her small size warranted. She cried when her hair was being combed, furiously pushed away her soup, then clamoured for it sobbing, and suddenly burst into laughter. She claimed the right to join in our games, but burst into tears when Paul, to amuse her climbed onto the table and dipped her doll into the copper, or when, playing hide-and-seek, we locked her up in a wardrobe among the clothes filled with moth-balls.

One day, I even shouted to her through the door, for fun, that we had lost the key, and Paul added, as a consolation, that the locksmith would come and set her free next day.

She gave such heartrending screams that I opened the door at once, but too late: my mother had rushed in and boxed our ears with both hands simultaneously, like those boxers who 'throw punches in all directions'.

While she was comforting the stupid darling and Paul was rubbing his cheeks, she told us very earnestly that girls were fragile creatures, that they mustn't be jostled and that it was dangerous to vex them because they were much more nervous than boys, and a fit of rage could make them sick.

*

My cousin, who was two years younger than I, was extremely pretty and had very big black eyes, constantly lowered, for she was rather shy and never opened her mouth except to answer.

When she felt someone was looking at her she turned quite crimson, and when you pulled her hair—even for a joke—she cried without making a sound.

One day, however, when her parents had come to lunch with us, I caught her unawares in my mother's bedroom, and she was so busy she did not notice me.

Standing all alone in front of the wardrobe mirror, she was dropping curtseys, daintily holding the hem of her dress. Then, inclining her head now to the right, now to the left, she exchanged with her image a considerable variety of roguish smiles, as if she were trying out which was the best.

At last, pursing her mouth into little simpers, she came quite close to the mirror and three times kissed the reflection of her own lips!

I closed the door noiselessly, convinced that I had unwittingly stumbled on a secret mental derangement and that it was better not to talk about it to anybody. I should have been ashamed to mention it, anyhow.

Another time, at dinner, she suddenly got into a state over a fish-bone that had stuck in her gum, on the edge of her throat.

She coughed, whimpered, groaned, choked, while everybody slapped her on the back.

My father said to her, amid the general hullabaloo: 'Scratch your throat and spit!'

She did not know how to do one or the other, and when the fish-bone had at last been dislodged, thanks to a pellet of bread-crumb, her mother was not ashamed to confess: '*I've never been able to spit either!*'

*

As for Clémentine, my Thursday girl-friend, and sometimes my Sunday one too, she was eleven years old when I was nine.

Her father was a keeper at the Zoo, and we sometimes went and admired him at his heroic job: standing on the roof of a cage, on the brink of an open trap, he would drop huge chunks of meat into the roaring mouths of the lions.

Her mother was the caretaker of the school.

They lived near the entrance gate, in a poorly lit but fairly large caretaker's lodge, which was always fragrant with the smell of stew.

Clémentine's hair was long, red and lank. Her blue eyes, set in a fringe of long ginger lashes, looked at you in a strange and even a somewhat disturbing way, since they didn't turn in the same direction at the same time.

I used to admire her straight little nose, but her white cheeks were covered with freckles. Mangiapan asserted that when she was a baby she must have fallen asleep in the sunshine under the shadow of a colander. This explanation,

43

which was quite new to me, seemed to me only semi-scientific, and I asked Mangiapan if it was a joke; but he maintained his mother had told him about it while talking about a similarly speckled woman neighbour of theirs who, it seems, had 'swept Father Mangiapan off his feet'.

*

Sweeping was a major occupation of Clémentine's too: she did it with a bent brushwood besom, collecting the dead leaves in the courtyard into four or five little mounds to which I would set fire one after the other. When I think of her today, I see streamers of blue smoke and can still smell the sweet, russet odour of bonfires of autumn leaves.

In winter I would help her fill the schoolroom stoves with wood and coal; in summer we would give the yard a good sprinkling with a copper-nozzled hose. The jet of water—constantly broken by belches and splutterings—carried far enough to rise over the wall and drench some passers-by in the street, whom destiny picked at random and who sometimes came to complain.

On those occasions Clémentine's mother would bar the way to danger: with her fists on her hips she would upbraid the intruder for his evil temper and end by saying: 'Only people who do nothing never make mistakes.'

By the time these chores were finished Paul—always a late-comer—would eventually arrive, and we would play hopscotch or marbles or have a ball-game.

Clémentine was very skilful, but she cheated impudently and always refused to admit that she had lost.

Moreover, she would lie constantly, for no reason, just for the fun of it.

For example, she would come on tiptoe to meet me and announce in a whisper, with a horrified air, that the headmaster had fallen gravely ill and that several doctors were at his bedside. Five minutes later, while I was sadly imagining the stately funeral of this mighty chief, the Head himself would be passing through the yard, quite fit and gay, his stick in his hand.

Another time, a superb Senegalese rifleman—a sergeant, at that—had gone to see her mother to ask for her—

44

Clémentine's—hand in marriage, she said, 'because in his country girls get married at the age of twelve'. Naturally, her mother had refused 'because it's too hot in Africa and because they make women carry the parcels there'.

'Anyhow, I'm engaged,' she added, 'to an American prince. He makes so much money that he has huge crates to put it in. But I'm not allowed to tell you his name.'

One evening as she was coming home from shopping, a huge man with a black beard had followed her in the street. It was dark, and she had run as hard as she could.

'If he'd caught me, I don't know what he'd have done to me!'

Paul suggested he may have wanted to make her dance in a circus or perhaps force her to sell wicker baskets in some foreign place such as Toulon or Avignon.

Thereupon she shook her head several times, gave a low giggle and cast a sidelong glance at me. Then she said: 'He's a child! He doesn't understand!'

For my part, I didn't understand either—I never understood her.

Quite often, in the middle of a game of dominoes, she would burst out laughing, with her head thrown back and her mouth wide open.

'What's the matter? Why are you laughing?'

But instead of answering she would leap to her feet, run and fetch a broom-stick and dance around with it.

One day, in a spurt of friendship, I said: 'You'd have lovely eyes, if they were alike.'

Whereupon the idiotic girl burst into tears, with heart-rending sobs and hiccups.

To calm her down I explained that this was a compliment, and that I thought two single eyes rather more becoming than a pair. Quick as a cat, she scratched my cheek below my ear; I retaliated by slapping her face with resounding success. She remained stunned for a moment, then ran towards the plane tree and, with her forehead against her arm, set up such a loud howl that it seemed wiser to me to effect a fast withdrawal.

When she reached the age of twelve she became even more bizarre and began to let me into mysterious secrets.

45

Sitting next to me on the bench in the covered walk that ran along one side of the empty schoolyard, she said to me one day:

'I have a friend who often comes to play with me. He is nice, and awfully handsome. Only I think he's stupid.'

'Why?'

'Because I know quite well that he adores me, but he's afraid to tell me so and he doesn't dare to kiss me.'

'And do *you* like him?'

She threw her head back, raised languorous eyes to the ceiling and sighed:

'Oh, I do!'

'What's his name?'

'Marcel, like yours. And he's also got brown eyes, like you. I often try and make him understand, but it's no good.'

I was furious that she had given her heart to that fellow who had the cheek to look like me and to have my Christian name.

'Where do you play with him?'

'Right here, at school.'

I immediately triumphed.

'Well, you're a big liar, my girl! If he came here, I'd see him because I often look out of the kitchen window! You're just making this up because you think it will make me jealous. But I can tell you that I don't care—I just couldn't care less! And you needn't trouble to tell me any more about it because I won't even listen to you!'

Thereupon she got up, clasped her hands, turned her eyes heavenward, and screamed in a shrill voice:

'How stupid he is! Gosh, how stu-upid!'

And she ran away.

A few days later—on the following Thursday—while I was playing five-stones by myself in a corner of the yard, she walked up to me very slowly and gravely.

'I must tell you something very important.'

'And what's that?'

'Well, it's this: for the moment, I can still go on playing with you. But you'll have to be very careful.'

'Careful about what?'

'About bumping me in the chest. Even ever so little. It could be VERY DANGEROUS.'

46

I was amazed.

'Why? Do you cough?'

She tittered.

'No, not at all! But you mustn't touch my breast any more, because now I've got one.'

'Got what?'

'Breasts.'

'So what?'

'Heavens, how stupid he is! Look!'

She put her hands on her hips, tightened her waist, and breathed deeply to make her chest swell.

'They're starting!' she said. 'My mother says I'll soon have to put on a corset!'

I gazed at the two small bumps (swelled with much effort) and felt a kind of uneasiness and a surprise that was all the greater because she seemed to be proud of this new infirmity which would compel her to wear a corset.

She looked at me sideways and said:

'You'd like to touch them, perhaps. But let me tell you that that isn't done. It's forbidden.'

I was very glad of it.

'Still,' she added, 'they aren't made of sugar, and if you like I'll have a wrestling-match with you.'

'Not today,' I said hastily, 'I haven't the time, my mother's calling me . . .'

And I ran towards the house, a little sickened by the thought that the match she so uncautiously suggested might well have ended in a pool of milk.

From that day onward, she began to dress like a lady, to twist her hair into a ludicrous chignon, and to simper and grimace so much that I couldn't recognize her any more. Within a few weeks she had outgrown me by five years, and her father would go and look for her every night, for on leaving school she would go and play with street-arabs on the banks of the Jarret.

She told me one day, full of pride:

'I'm going with a fellow now.'

When I asked my mother the meaning of this verb without an adverbial object, she answered obscurely that 'this might get her into deep water' and my father declared that 'the poor thing' would doubtless end up as a 'draggle-tail' —which made me think of Queen Brunehild. Whereupon they both agreed to forbid me to speak to her. This ban was easily respected, for I no longer interested her, and she now scared me.

*

Thus my personal observations of the behaviour of girls had not yet enabled me to form a conclusive judgment, when my father one day, in my presence, used an expression that gave me the key to the secret.

Talking about Monsieur Besson's niece, who had broken her arm when falling from a tree, he said: 'That girl is a *garçon manqué*!'[1]

I understood this phrase in my own way, which no doubt was not the right one: but this was not the first time a great discovery was the fruit of a misinterpretation.

For me, the words *garçon manqué* meant that girls were merely a *faux-pas* of Nature, the result of a mistake in the course of creating a boy.

That was why they blushed without cause, giggled over nothing, cried for even less, and scratched you for paying compliments; that was why, unable to whistle or spit, they fell out of trees, made up perfectly useless lies and secretly indulged in simpers in front of looking-glasses . . .

They were boys that had gone wrong . . .

I, a boy who had 'come off', never blushed, didn't laugh without cause, and nobody (except my mother) could say they had seen me cry. I was strong, and Clémentine called me when she had to carry a pail full of water; I could whistle like a bird with my tongue rolled back under my two fingers. As for spitting—I may say it without undue modesty—I almost equalled Mangiapan who, on his good days, could hurl shooting stars of saliva up to five or six yards away—and I had never fallen from a tree, like a fragile *garçon manqué*.

However, everybody was interested in girls, and without being able to understand why, I had to admit I rather liked them.

In the course of a meditation at night in my bed, I dis-covered several reasons that justified their existence.

[1] *Garçon manqué* (a boy that's gone wrong) = tomboy.

In the first place, their shortcomings lent lustre to my qualities and enabled me to appreciate their worth . . . Compared with my father or Napoleon I didn't amount to much, whereas the mere existence of Clémentine brought me closer to those great men, and this certainly deserved some gratitude.

On the other hand, I loyally admitted that Nature, as if to disguise her failure, had taken a lot of care over their outward appearance: big eyes, long lashes, delicate hands, silky hair, graceful movements and small, musical voices. They were often very pleasant to look at. But taken all in all, in daily life they could only serve as admirers or as confidantes. But even there one had to be on one's guard.

In the course of that year's holidays, I was to have an opportunity to get to know them better and to discover the childhood face of Love.

CHAPTER EIGHT

ONE morning I saw Lili arriving at a run. The straps of two haversacks crossed over his chest, and on his shoulder he was holding the neck of a sack that hung down his back. I saw he was rather excited: Mond des Parpaillouns—Butterfly Ted—had just told him about an extraordinary fly-past of migratory birds.

'He has seen,' he told me, 'white-tails, Corsican black-birds and flights of *darnagas*—cross-bills. They are on the slopes of Tête-Rouge, but they won't stay there for long. Let's hurry!'

He was carrying in his luggage the eight dozen snares that constituted our entire armament, plus two dozen borrowed from his brother Baptistin, and six *vertoulets* (which are net-traps for catching birds alive) lent by Mond des Parpaillouns.

We laid a great many traps, and this kept us busy till nightfall.

As we were walking back, Lili said to me:

'The worst of it, I won't be able to do the rounds with you tomorrow morning.'

'Why not?'

'Because my father's taken it into his head to clean the well at Four-Neuf. He'll climb down to the bottom and I'll have to help Baptistin pull up the pails. So I won't be able to come before five. But we can't leave so many snares all by themselves till tomorrow night, 'cos otherwise we'll have worked for the fox, the rats and the ants. Let alone the Lame Man from Allauch: he's scared of the *gendarmes* because he can't run. So he goes and swipes other people's catches. Be sure to go up there tomorrow morning. Not too early, so as not to disturb the birds. As long as you get there by ten, it's all right. And then we'll go back together at five or six, and I promise you we'll come back weighed down!'

50

Next morning, after a delicious coffee-and-milk, I settled down on the terrace in a chaise longue to wait for half past nine and the departure for the great snares inspection. I was reading *The Mysterious Island* for the third time and, for the third time, was greatly and happily surprised by the unexpected torpedo which had just blown up the pirate ship under my eyes at the very moment when I thought we were lost.

Paul had not yet started his hard day's work as a foe-less warrior: squatting near the fig tree, he was inspecting a small cage in which a dozen cicadas were milling around. On the authority of the good poet La Fontaine, he had prepared for them a feast of 'small morsels of flies or worms', to which he had added, on his own initiative, half a dried fig and a bit of cheese-rind. For he claimed that those insects' extremely short life span was due to undernourishment, and he had decided to teach them to eat.

Meanwhile my mother appeared on the doorstep, looked at us for a moment, and said to me:

'The thyme that's left is falling to dust. You'd better go and get me some fresh sprigs if there are still some about.'

'I know where there are some,' I said. 'And it isn't far. It's at the bottom of Rapon Valley. I'll go there presently, when I'm making my round of the snares, as soon as I've finished this chapter.'

'You'll finish it later. I'm in a hurry, the jugged hare is for lunch.'

It pained me to have to abandon Pencroft, Herbert and Cyrus Smith in the middle of their fight, and it seemed only fair to barter this sacrifice.

'All right,' I said, 'I'll go right away but you'll have to give me two biscuits.'

She did not argue over my price and brought me a couple, but she was weak enough to give another two to the squatting cicada-watcher, who never did anything useful and deserved them all the less as he accepted them absentmindedly, without even raising his head because he was so busy.

While I was passing my hand through the leather strap of my shepherd's stick, she went on:

'Try and find some fennel, too, but not as big as the last you got. They were as tough as a reed, and as dry as a fishing-rod. I used them to light the fire!'

I refrained from answering that Joseph himself had chosen them and, munching my biscuits, set off towards the Rapon's lonely wilderness.

The morning was already very hot: the cicadas were chirping frantically, and a big red buzzard was hovering high up in the air, in the middle of a golden halo.

I was running along the slope of the hill, amid the dry summer grass, preceded by a blaze of red and blue grasshoppers that fanned out like fireworks.

Rapon was a valley in the hills: it rose between two wooded slopes which met high up at the top, just at the border of the sky.

The bottom of the valley was a small lake of earth—a *planette*—where the rugged farmers in the old days used to grow vines, buckwheat and chick-peas. But ever since the sad invention of compulsory military service their sons, when freed from the barracks, had remained captives of the cities, where they had founded dynasties of level-crossing keepers, road-menders and postmen: with the result that, from the very day the old fellows died, the hills that had only been waiting for this moment had launched against the abandoned fields concentric waves of thyme, then of fennel, and then of rock-roses and hawthorn.

There remained, however, right in the middle of the dell between two hedges that had turned into thickets, a rather meagre vineyard; some of its stocks, unexpectedly, still produced huge bunches of grapes, just as small sickly women will sometimes give birth to a rugger husky or a wrestling champion. The fact was that its owner, old Niéni, would occasionally come and defend it with a bill-hook against the invaders, and bring it a few mouthfuls of dung, carried on the back of the very donkey who had manufactured it.

I therefore decided, as I trotted behind my team of flying grasshoppers, to go and pilfer one or two grapes provided I could find some ripe ones.

Without climbing down to the foot of the valley, I followed along the left the base of the cliff and soon found what I was looking for: a long ribbon of thyme, which was flowering late into the summer, in the shadow of the cool rock-face.

I had no trouble in pulling up some fine clumps, and tied them, one at a time, along a piece of string whose ends I then twisted into a knot, to make a cross-belt.

Thus fitted out I walked down towards the 'dell' and disappeared under the golden-grained clusters of a forest of fennel. It was much taller than I, and I could not see a yard ahead. So I went down on all fours and, for a moment, imagined that I was an ant in a meadow, so as to have an idea of the feelings—and, perhaps, the philosophy—of those mysterious insects.

Then with my shepherd's knife I cut the tenderest shoots just above the ground. I was promptly surrounded by a delicious green smell, that of aniseed drops. I tied up the stalks with another string; then, with my bundle of fennel under my arm, my garland of thyme slung across my chest, and my precious stick in my hand, I emerged from the redolent forest to pay a vist to the lonely vineyard.

But as I came out onto the path, I stopped still, openmouthed: on a big white boulder, in the shadow of the low-hanging branches of a pine, there sat a strange creature.

CHAPTER NINE

SHE was a girl of my own age, but she did not in any way resemble the girls I had known so far.

On her long, gleaming black curls, she was wearing a wreath of poppies, and she was clasping to her heart an armful of white clematis mingled with wild iris and long, pink foxgloves.

She was looking at me motionless, silent and quite pale; her eyes were enormous and violet like her wild iris.

She did not seem to be either frightened or surprised, but she was not smiling, and she said nothing, mysterious as a fairy in a picture.

I took a step towards her: she jumped lightly down on the carpet of thyme.

She was no taller than I, and I could see she was not a fairy, for she had white and blue sandals just like mine on her feet.

She asked me seriously, with her chin raised:

'Which is the way to Les Bellons?'

She had a pretty voice, very clear, with a kind of sharp accent, like that of the saleswomen at the *Nouvelles Galeries* store, and her large eyes were absolutely alike.

I promptly answered:

'Did you get lost?'

She took a step backward, gazing at me through her flowers.

'Yes,' she said, 'I got lost, but that's no reason for addressing me as "*tu*". I'm not a peasant-girl.'

I thought she was rather uppish and concluded that she must be rich, which seemed to be confirmed by the cleanness and sparkle of her clothes. Her white socks were well pulled up, her blue dress shone like satin and, through her flowers, I could see she was wearing a small gold chain round her neck, from which hung a medal.

'Well,' she said, 'which is the way?'

I pointed to the cross-roads at the end of the valley and said:

'The right-hand one.'

'Thank you.'

I watched her move away: she had pretty round calves (like rich people) and the iris towered above her head.

I climbed up to Niéni's vineyard. The grapes weren't ripe yet, but after searching hard I discovered three clusters that were almost blue.

I began to peck at them voluptuously, despite the tartness of the grapes which burst between my teeth.

I wondered who the girl might be; I had never seen her around. She had mentioned Les Bellons: that was the hamlet to which the Bastide-Neuve belonged, but the few houses that made up the village were rather far apart, and ours was buried in an olive-grove on the edge of the pinewood. Then it occurred to me that she must be living on the other side of the hamlet, near Felix's cottage. Or perhaps she was a girl just up from town for the day on an excursion with her parents?

I was half-way through my first bunch of grapes when I saw through the hedge the bouquet coming back towards me.

I deliberately turned my back to her and continued to munch the grapes.

I heard it pass through the hedge, then she called:

'Psssst . . .'

I did not move.

She started again.

'Psstt! Psstt!'

I turned round.

'Are *you* making that noise?' (This time I was calling her *vous*.)

'I'm calling you!' she said, rather sharply. (She too was using the courtesy form.)

'Didn't you find the way?'

She answered indignantly:

'You know quite well that it is barred by enormous cobwebs! There are at least four or five spiders, and the biggest one tried to jump at my face!'

'All you have to do is walk round the cobwebs. The valley is wide enough!'

'Yes, but I should have to walk among that long grass (she was motioning to the fennel) and that would be even more dangerous! I saw a huge animal running in it, it was long and green!'

She looked at me reproachfully, as if I were in charge of the safety of these grounds. I realized that she had seen a *limbert*, but as she was irritating me I said very casually:

'It must have been a snake. This is the valley of snakes. They feed on rats; and as there are a lot of rats, there are also a lot of snakes.'

She remarked suspiciously:

'That isn't true! You're saying it to frighten me!'

But she was inspecting the grass all round her. I went on:

'That's nothing to be frightened of, they're harmless grass snakes. They're cold-blooded, but they aren't poisonous. You only have to make a noise, and they'll be more frightened than you.'

Without moving a foot, I pretended I was closely examining my bunch of grapes, as though I considered the conversation was closed. After a long silence, she said sarcastically:

'No boy who was a *gentleman* would abandon a young lady in such a dangerous place.'

I munched the last grapes and did not answer. I was thinking. It must be past ten; I had to take the thyme home and leave for Tête-Rouge: Lili had left me with the entire responsibility for our most important hunting expedition to date, for which we had even been loaned snares, a thing that is never done. But he had advised me not to go there before half past ten: slaying those spiders wouldn't oblige me to make a big detour.

She too must have been thinking matters over, for she said:

'To get it over with, I authorize you to use the familiar address two or three times if you come and drive the spiders away.'

She was still talking like a princess, but I saw there was fear in her eyes. I realized that to avoid those insects she might even take the road to Passe-Temps and get lost in earnest.

'Let's go,' I said. 'But I don't need to address you as "*tu*" for that.'

I tossed the picked grape-stalk into the hedge (for if Niéni had found it, he would have been grieved). I picked up my bundle of fennel and waved my stick.

'I had better walk in front.'

And I resolutely strode ahead of her.

When the myrtle bushes began to close in on the path I turned back to the girl and raised my hand: she stopped, behind her flowers.

Then I beat the bushes with my stick, emitting fierce shouts; when I was certain that the brushwood was untenanted (for I was afraid I might meet the snakes I had just invented) I passed through it noisily.

I soon reached the danger spot.

A large cobweb, in the shape of a hexagonal kite, was blocking the path. In its middle, clothed in black velvet with yellow stripes, gleamed the owner of this enterprise. He was as big as a walnut.

I stopped. I signalled to the bouquet to approach and slightly touched the beast with the end of my stick: it began to shake its net furiously, and the cobweb billowed out backward, then bulged forward, with a gathering speed, as if gathering impetus to thrown itself at me; but I knew this was just make-believe and that it would do nothing of the sort: I therefore remained impassive. The bouquet, however, was recoiling step by step, with little screams of terror . . .

After a minute of this heroic game, I raised my stick for the death-blow, and with a single stroke slashed the fragile silk web in two; the spider fell into the grass; I crushed it under my heel and continued on my way without deigning to turn round.

The girl dashed across the scene of this victory, while I walked on, beating the bushes right and left like the conductor of an orchestra.

At the crossroads I stopped to wait for her.

'That's your way: at the turning, down there, you'll see Les Bellons.'

'I'm very much afraid I'll get lost once more,' she said. 'I authorize you to escort me home.'

CHAPTER TEN

Now that wasn't possible. For one thing, my mother was waiting for the thyme. For another, up there below Tête-Rouge, there were the fox, the rats and the ants perhaps nibbling away at our innumerable catches, or else the treacherous Lame Man of Allauch, whom I imagined making the round of the snares in my place.

'If it were some other day, I might,' I said. 'But today I can't.'

'Very well.'

Then, as if peeved:

'Thank you all the same.'

She threw her flowers onto the grass and sat down on the edge of the path, her hands clasped around her knees.

She was really very pretty. Her dark eyelids, which fluttered from time to time as if she were doing it on purpose, had a fringe of thick lashes that gracefully curved up towards her forehead.

I walked up to her.

'Are you going to stay there?'

'Naturally,' she said. 'I'll wait for someone to pass by.'

'Nobody passes by here.'

'Well, then, when my mother sees that I'm not coming home, she will tell some peasants and they'll come and fetch me. Since you're in such a hurry you can go away.'

For a moment the idea occurred to me of telling her about my snares and my responsibility towards Lili. But snares are a secret. You don't tell about them.

'You understand,' I told her, 'my mother is waiting for me! If I come home too late, she'll scold me.'

'If you explain to her that you've rescued a lost young girl, she'll have no right to scold you. It isn't every day that you have the chance to save someone!'

I told an impious lie:

58

'There's something you don't know. She's awfully strict!'

She gave an ironic little laugh, and cried:

'In that case, I don't advise you to tell her that you deserted a young girl among snakes and spiders!'

Once more I pondered. The shadow of the pine trees was gathering around their feet, and above every white stone a column of air was swirling like transparent smoke. It was probably past eleven. For the thyme I would not be awfully late. Besides, the story of this encounter, suitably elaborated, would furnish me with a romantic justification. As for the snares, suppose I went there straight after lunch? There was no need to tell Lili at what time I had gone on my round.

As I stood there scratching my head, she smiled at me sadly, then pulled a face as if she were about to cry ...

'Come on,' I said, 'let's go.'

She rose, picked up her flowers in silence.

I got going. The footpath had widened into a mule-path. She was walking at my side. I took the second bunch of grapes, which I had hung on my cross-belt of thyme, and handed it to her a little awkwardly.

'Do you like grapes?'

'I adore them,' she said, 'but (she shook her head gravely) I'm too well brought up to eat stolen grapes.'

She was beginning to simper all over again.

'Well, *I* think they're better!' I declared cynically.

'Oho! I'm sure you're wrong, because you'll end up in prison that way. You won't be so cocksure when you're locked up in a cell and your family disgraced. That sort of thing is printed in the newspapers. I can assure you of that, because my father is on a paper that is called *Le Petit Marseillais*.'

'That's the one my uncle reads every day, on account of politics.'

'Oh!' she said, rather disdainfully, 'my father doesn't concern himself with politics! He's much above that!'

'Is he the editor?'

'Oh! More than that! He corrects the articles of all the others! Yes, he does! And what's more, he writes poetry that gets published in magazines in Paris.'

'Poetry that rhymes?'

'Yes, sir, exactly! He finds thousands of rhymes. He thinks them up in the tram.'

I had learnt poetry at school and had always been surprised by the rhymes, which arrive unexpectedly at the end of a line. I believed that poets capable of such *tours de force* must be exceedingly rare and that they must all, without exception, figure in my schoolbook.

I therefore asked:

'What's his name?'

She answered proudly:

'Loïs de Montmajour.'

'What?'

She repeated, enunciating it clearly:

'Lo-ees de Montmajour.'

No, he wasn't in my book.

I knew Victor Hugo, Louis Ratisbonne, Françoise Coppée, Maurice Bouchor, Eugène Manuel, La Fontaine, Clovis Hughes[1] but this name wasn't in it.

I did not dare tell her, and I was struck with awe at the thought that she was noble, since there was a *de* before her name; perhaps she was the daughter of a count—or even a marquis: that's why I was not allowed to address her as *tu*.

'And what does *your* father do?'

'He's a professor.'[2]

'Professor of what?'

'Of everything. He's at the Chemin des Chartreux school.'

'An elementary school?'

'Of course. The biggest one in Marseilles!'

I waited for the effect to be produced by this revelation. It was disastrous.

She pursed her lips in a pretty little *moue*, and assumed a superior air:

'In that case, let me tell you he isn't a professor. He's a schoolmaster. That's all right, but it's less than a professor.'

Struck to the heart, I now wanted to crush her conceit to

[1] He enumerates higgledy-piggledy school-book poets ranging from famous bards to ephemeral versifiers.

[2] *Professeur*, in French, applies to secondary school teachers as well as to University professors.

gratify mine and present Joseph to her in all his glory by telling her the epic tale of the *bartavelles*.

I skilfully sidled up to the subject.

'Does your father go shooting?'

I smiled despite myself, for I was sure of scoring a hit. She opened her eyes very wide, assumed a horrified mien, and cried:

'My father? Oh no! He wouldn't kill a little bird for anything in the world! He even says he'd much rather shoot at a sportsman than a rabbit!'

This declaration rooted me to the spot. Fire at a sportsman! The man was undoubtedly insane, and I must warn Joseph and Uncle Jules at once. But she went on:

'Of course, he's never tried to. But when he reads in the papers that a sportsman has injured himself with his gun, he says it serves him right.'

As if the subject were exhausted, she moved on to other things:

'Do you go to school in town?'

'Yes. I'm starting at the *lycée* next October. In the Sixth Form.[1] I'm going to start Latin.'

'I've been at the *lycée* for ages. I'm moving up into the Fifth this year. How old are you?'

'Almost eleven.'

'Well, I'm eleven and a half, and I'm a year ahead of you. And Latin is just what I'm best at. I was first in translation, and second in composition.'

She looked at me for a moment, then added casually:

'Not that it matters to me, anyhow, because next year I'm going to sit for the Conservatory of Music, to study the piano. My mother is a piano-teacher, and she makes me practise not less than two hours every day.'

'And *can* you play?'

'Quite well,' she said, smugly. 'And even very well for my age. Only my hands are still too small. I can only just manage an octave.'

Confronted with this technical term I felt once again in a state of inferiority and changed the subject.

'So you're on holiday here?'

[1] The Sixth is the lowest class in French secondary schools, and the First the highest but one.

'Yes,' she said. 'But I'd remind you that I gave you permission to address me as "*tu*" up to Les Bellons. I wonder why you don't make use of it.'

I tried to regain the advantage.

'Because it's too late now, and anyway, one never says "*tu*" to people of the nobility.'

She gave me a long sideways glance, then laughed a little, and declared:

'I think it's rather because I overawe you.'

'Me? No you don't!'

'I do, I do! What overawes you isn't me, but my beauty. It's like that with all the boys. I can make them blush whenever I want!'

I was stung to the quick, for boys are the ones who make girls blush!

'Well, it would take more than that to make *me* blush!'

'You think so?'

She barred my way, placed herself in front of me, and looked into my eyes from quite close, slowly leaning her head back. Her mouth was slightly open, and her nostrils were quivering.

I felt angrily that I was blushing, and I made an effort to laugh.

'There you are!' she cried, triumphantly. 'He's blushed! He's blushed!'

She raised her arms to the sky and danced with her bouquet, calling to witness a very dear old olive tree of mine.

'It's the faces you pull that make me blush,' I said.

'Come, come,' she said, 'don't be ashamed. One day, I heard my father say to my mother: "She'll wreak havoc at twenty!" Yes, my dear boy, "havoc". And my father knows all about it, because he consorts with lady poets. He calls *me* Princess. But, of course, that isn't my name. My name's Isabelle. I'm telling you, and you'll never forget. What's yours?'

'Marcel.'

She made a little *moue*.

'Not bad, but it isn't as pretty as Isabelle. Anyway, that isn't your fault.'

She moved to face me again, dropped her flowers on the grass, and said suddenly:

62

'Give me some grapes!'

'You're no longer afraid of eating stolen grapes?'

'A moment ago I didn't want them. Now I do. Give them to me, one by one!'

She put her arms behind her back and opened her mouth. Her perfectly even little teeth sparkled like mother-of-pearl, with a faint blue glint, and her full lips were finely drawn, like a bow with two even curves. I put my herbs on the ground and, with my fingertips, put the first grape into the childish mouth that was turned to me.

She munched it with every sign of delight and murmured:

'Delicious! It bites like vinegar! More! More!'

*

Ten times over I gave her a mouthful, and always with the same success. But she suddenly opened horrified eyes and gave a scream of terror:

'Oh, those hands! You dare to offer me grapes with such dirty hands? They're like a beggar's! Now perhaps I'll get some awful illness!'

'Not at all,' I said (quite ashamed, for my hands were really pretty grimy), 'it's clean: just earth . . . It's because I pulled some thyme!'

'Still, you've a pretty good nerve to approach a young girl's lips with such hands, and I don't compliment you on it!'

She turned her back on me and walked away, holding herself very straight and putting one foot exactly in front of the other, as if she were walking on a tight-rope. I picked up my herbs and was going to leave her there when after ten yards she stopped short, swivelled round on her toes and cried in a peevish voice:

'Well, *are* you coming? I must introduce you to my mother! Since you wished to escort me, that is compulsory!'

I ran after her.

The little village of Les Bellons was looming up beyond the turning. I asked her:

'Which house do you live in?'

She looked at me with pity:

'The biggest one, of course!'

CHAPTER ELEVEN

She stopped behind the cottage, which was long and low like the ancient Provençal *mas*, without any opening at the back.

She went round the first corner of the house, but before she reached the second one, she motioned me to stop:

'Wait here. I'll call you.'

She disappeared.

Then I heard a woman's voice, deep and musical, and it was saying:

'There you are at last, Babette! I was beginning to wonder whether the wolf hadn't eaten you!'

I thought: 'That must be a housemaid, since she's saying *vous*.'

But the young voice answered:

'My dear Mama, I had a hair's-breadth escape!'

So it was her mother who was using the formal address! Always that nobility!

She went on:

'Just imagine, strolling from flower to flower, I got lost! And when I noticed it, there I was in the middle of a kind of valley full of prickly brushwood that scratched my legs. Then I saw spiders as big as my hand. Black, with yellow stripes, and there was one that was twirling its moustache with its legs!'

'I've seen that done by a captain of hussars!' said her mother.

'Don't laugh, Mama! Those beasts were dreadful and I was frozen with fear! What's more, I was surrounded by snakes!'

'Did you see any?'

'No, but I heard them hiss in the thickets. Besides, they say that valley is full of snakes. It's well known.'

'Who told you that?'

'A young boy who rescued me and who's brought me back. May I introduce him to you?'

'With pleasure!'

*

She came running back, took me by the hand and led me on to the terrace, which I already knew because I had passed there with Lili when the house was still uninhabited.

This was a shaded platform in front of the long cottage, at the top of a steep slope; from here could be seen a vast landscape of low hills stippled with fields in between the pinewoods. A country lane, bordered with olive trees, ran down to the village, of which only the steeple was visible above some roofs.

Isabelle pulled me towards a lovely, fair-haired woman who was rocking herself in a hammock, an open book in her hand.

I had seen hammocks in the illustrations of Jules Verne's books; they were made of coarse canvas and hung on shipboard from iron hooks in the deck above. I had gathered that the inventor of those beds, which were gently rocked by the waves, had meant them to rock the little sailors to sleep so as to make them dream of their mothers.

The hammock I saw before my eyes was worthy of an admiral. It was a vast brown-coloured silk net, suspended from two polished wooden bars and furnished with bright red cushions. It was stretched between two acacias, in the blue shadow flecked with little freckles of sunshine that stirred in the wind.

The lady on that aerial couch was clad in a blue dressing-gown embroidered with gold thread, and she gracefully dangled a bare foot on which she just managed to keep, with the aid of the tip of her toe, a red leather slipper adorned with golden arabesques.

We advanced along the terrace, and Isabelle said, with a sweeping wave of her arm towards me:

'Here is my saviour! His hands are rather dirty but he is very brave. He only had a stick and yet he walked right into the thicket: he drove away at least ten snakes!'

'Young man,' said the lady, 'come closer. I congratulate you on your courage and on your gallantry.'

65

I bowed, rather vaingloriously. But she added suddenly:

'It's true that his hands are dirty, they're even very, very dirty! However, Babette, it wasn't for you to point it out to me.'

I blushed again and hid my hands behind my back. Then, with a piteous smile, I repeated my excuse:

'It's because I've been to fetch thyme for my mother . . . So, with pulling up the plants . . .'

'Well,' said the lady—and she nimbly jumped to the ground—'here's a charming boy, who goes to pick thyme for his mother, and turns the occasion to account to save a damsel in distress! Babette, go and fetch some grenadine, three big glasses, some water and a few straws. You'll find them all on the shelves in the "livigroub".'

I had never heard that strange word, but supposed that it referred to a cupboard, or rather a sideboard, of an Oriental type, like her slippers.

'Come and help me,' said Isabelle, 'because it's heavy.'

I followed her.

Behind the Provençal bead-curtain, which is supposed to stop the flies, there was a dark, narrow passage; a small door on the right opened on to a fairly large room. We walked in, and I was stunned with admiration.

I first saw a piano, which gleamed, deep black, near the window. Beside the fireplace, there was an extraordinary easy chair, for its back formed a very high niche. It looked like a sumptuous sentry-box. The framework of the chair was gilt, and it was upholstered in some pink material. Against the wall on the left there stood a big, varnished dresser, brand-new and with a fat, bulging belly; each drawer had two large gilt handles.

Above this monument there was a vast mirror in an enormous frame of carved fretwork that represented a kind of ivy.

In the tall fireplace were big fire-dogs, also gilt, and on the mantelpiece a tortoise-shell clock, as big as my little sister, entirely inlaid with gold. While I was admiring these luxuries, I noticed that I was walking on a very thick carpet, ten times larger than the rug by my bed and reaching right under the furniture!

Isabelle opened a very big cupboard, which I had not remarked since it was behind me. There were glass panes in its carved doors, and I could see regiments of cups and glasses, commanded by green and blue decanters, silver coffee-pots and bottles that weren't shaped like bottles.

I realized that this piece of furniture must be the 'livi-groub'.

From it she took a big, black, shiny tray, covered with gilt Chinamen in raised relief. She put this in my hands and loaded it with three glasses, syrup in a decanter encased in a silver lattice (even the stopper was made of glass and cut like a diamond), and a blue syphon such as one sees on the terraces of cafés.

We went and sat down at a green-painted table under the acacia, and I rubbed my hands hard on my trousers to lighten their colour.

We drank the cool grenadine and soda out of the big glasses by means of straws. The soda-water prickled like lemonade. That did not surprise me, for Mangiapan had told me it did.

Isabelle, sitting next to me with her chin raised, her eyes half closed and her hands pressed between her knees, seemed to be dreaming, while her mother was asking me questions.

She wanted to know where we lived.

'At the Bastide-Neuve,' I told her.

I saw with amazement that she was unaware of its existence and I had to specify its position.

And yet it was only two hundred yards from the village. But it was true that the olive and fig trees that surrounded it hid it from the passers-by unless they came down from the hills.

'Have you a sister?'

'Yes,' I said, 'but she is very small. She is three and a half.'

'That's a pity. She might have come and played with Isabelle and perhaps kept her from getting lost!'

'I won't get lost again!' cried Isabelle. 'And anyway, if I do, you'll only have to let him know and he'll find me at once!'

The lady seemed to hesitate, then she said:

'I'd gladly invite him to come and play with you if I were sure he didn't use any dirty words.'

'Mama, he didn't use a single one! He has dirty hands, that's true, but he doesn't use dirty words.'

'Is that quite certain?' asked the lady, looking at me.

I assumed a disgusted air and, keeping my hands under the table, declared:

'I may know some dirty words, but I never use them!'

'Never?' said the lady, a little doubtfully.

I made a concession.

'Perhaps at school, or when I pinch my finger in a trap . . .'

'A trap!' cried the lady. 'Do you set traps?'

It was not the thing to say in the home of a hunter of hunters.

But I immediately caught back the imprudent words, explaining:

'For rats! Just rat-traps, because the house is full of them!'

I realized at once that this confession of a house full of rats was going to discredit my family, and added precipitously:

'In the cellar! Rats sometimes get into the cellar.'

Finally, I reduced the number of rats:

'There are only two of them, but they are rather big, and they eat up our supplies. So when I pinch my fingers in a trap . . .'

She seemed relieved.

'That's not very serious,' Isabelle remarked. 'To use a dirty word when you are all by yourself in a cellar . . .'

She added, as an additional excuse:

'There's no one in a cellar, and besides it's dark!'

'Well, then, we try it. You look like a nice boy, and I suppost there *are* days when you have clean hands? . . .'

'Oh yes!' I said. 'Quite often!'

'Well then, on those days I authorize you to come and play with Isabelle.'

It occurred to me that in this family there was much talk of authorizations, but one didn't have to ask for them to obtain them.

I heard the angelus ring in the distance and promptly rose.

'I beg your pardon, madame. I think it's noon, and my mother is waiting for me . . .'

'Oh, you mustn't be late, and thank you again for your bravery! Babette, accompany your friend up to the road. Good-bye!'

When we got to the back of the cottage, she said to me:

'Will you come this afternoon?'

'If I can, because I have work to do at home. But as soon as I'm free, I'll come.'

'I'll invite you to tea,' she said. 'I have apricot jam and finger-biscuits. And then I'll show you my toys. I have heaps of them. I authorize you to kiss my hand.'

She presented me the back of her brown hand; there was a little pink dimple at the root of each finger. I took it and brought it to my lips.

'I was sure of it!' she cried. 'That isn't at all how it's done!'

'How is it, then?'

'You mustn't lift my hand: you must lower your head, as if you were bowing to me. Start again!'

I started again, a little hampered by my belt of thyme and my bundle of fennel.

'That's not too bad,' she said, 'but not quite right yet. Never mind, I'll teach you this afternoon!'

CHAPTER TWELVE

I HURRIED back to the Bastide-Neuve: I could see from afar that the whole family was at table on the terrace.

As soon as he saw me Paul got up and ran to meet me, to announce that the hunters had unearthed a badger, that is to say they had spent the morning extracting the animal from its burrow.

This trophy was hanging by its hindlegs from a low branch of the fig tree: it was a kind of small pig sewn into a bear's skin. It was ugly and stank horribly.

I loudly voiced my admiration for a moment, so as to obtain the hunters' indulgence for my lateness. Uncle Jules informed me with jaunty pride that he had 'corpsed it on the spot' with a charge of buckshot in its neck.

Aunt Rose, instead of congratulating him, declared that it was urgent to bury the corpse which was already attracting bluebottles and could serve no useful purpose. I then announced that François would eat it with great relish, and the useless murder was thus promptly justified to Uncle Jules' great satisfaction.

My mother praised the thyme I had brought her, but said:

'If I'd waited with the stew for you to come home . . .'

I answered as I sat down at the table:

'At Rapon I found a girl on a big boulder.'

Uncle assumed a look of terror and asked:

'Dead?'

'Oh no. She was lost.'

'That's an even more dangerous encounter!' said my uncle.

'On the contrary! She was scared of spiders, and I had to see her home, otherwise she'd have let herself die on the spot!'

'In short,' said my father, 'you saved her life!'

'I may have.'

'How old is she?' asked my mother.

'She's twelve. And as tall as me.'

'And where does she live?'

'At the long house at Les Bellons. I saw her mother: she's marvellous.'

'Is she now!' said Uncle Jules.

'And the girl?' asked Paul.

'She's very pretty. Only she screws up her mouth when she talks and she simpers a lot. But she has lovely round calves.'

'You noticed that?' asked my father.

'They show a lot because her face is so small. Her eyes take up all the room.'

'So you like her?' asked Aunt Rose.

'So-so. She addressed her mother as "*vous*".'

'Then she isn't her mother!' Paul declared dogmatically.

'Yes, she is, since she calls her "maman". You weren't there, I was. And what's more, her mother addresses her as "*vous*", too!'

At this announcement, Paul was seized with a fit of laughter in three such violent spasms that they misdirected a mouthful of sardines with tomato sauce, and I thought he was going to perish before our eyes. But a few slaps on the back enabled him to recover his breath.

'I bet,' said Uncle Jules, 'she's very dark-haired, that little girl of yours.'

'Oh yes, like a blackbird. And her mother is quite fair, and she lies in a hammock with a red slipper hanging from the tip of her foot!'

'Where did you see that?' asked my father.

'On their terrace, under the acacia.'

'Oh, then I know them,' said Uncle Jules. 'I've seen them at Mass in the village with the husband, whom I sometimes meet in the tram . . . The curé told me he's working on the *Petit Marseillais*.'

'That's right,' I said. 'And he's even more than the editor: he corrects the mistakes of all the others.'

'That is to say,' said my uncle, turning to my father, 'he's the proof-reader in the paper's printing-shop.'

'That means he corrects the printers' mistakes,' said Joseph, 'not those of the newspapermen.'

This seemed to me even more difficult and at any rate more glorious, and to give lustre to my new friend's family, I added:

'And what's more, he writes superb poetry, and in Paris everybody knows him.'

'Paris is a long way off. He hasn't made a name for himself here yet!'

I retorted:

'He's a nobleman anyway. He's called Loïs de Montmajour.'

'The devil he is!' cried my uncle. 'Did the girl tell you that?'

'Of course. Loïs de Montmajour. That's why they call each other "*vous*" in the family. Because they're noble.'

Uncle Jules smiled and said:

'That's obviously a *nom de guerre*.'

I concluded that the name must have been given to the family on account of some ancestor's exploits in war, and I answered:

'I shouldn't be surprised.'

Uncle Jules went on:

'Poets are never ones for modesty, but after all it harms no one!'

'Still,' said my father (who always feared he might underestimate strangers), 'don't let's be rash in our judgment. He *may* be a great poet!'

'That's not impossible,' said my uncle, 'for he twice got into the wrong tram.'

'I wouldn't trust a man like that,' said my mother; 'poets live in a never-never land and end up starving to death.'

'Not all of them,' Aunt Rose opined. 'Those who write songs manage very well. Lucienne's husband, the postman, writes songs for the Alcazar music hall, and they pay him quite a lot. And yet they're full of vulgar things. Only they rhyme.'

'You have quaint ideas about poetry,' remarked Uncle Jules.

'Well, I can tell you,' I cried with fervour, 'that her

father has a lot of money! I went into their house, and I saw furniture just like you see in the Longchamp Museum. *And* a piano!'

'A piano?' asked Aunt Rose. 'Now that would be the first time anyone saw a piano in these hills.'

'Well, I saw it! And all this is in a dining-room with a huge carpet on the floor. Besides, there's a terrific cupboard that's called a "livigroub"!'

'What's that?' Joseph asked, surprised.

'A livigroub.'

'Who told you that?' asked my mother.

'The lady did. She said: "The glasses are in the livigroub" . . . And they were.'

My father, with puckered brow, tried to understand. My mother, who did not know much but guessed everything, suggested shyly:

'Perhaps it is an English word.'

'I've got it!' cried Joseph. 'A living room! It wasn't the cupboard, but the room in which it was!'

'That must be it,' said Uncle Jules, 'and it's a great pity. Because a "livigroub" intrigued me, it was poetic. Whereas a living-room merely proves that the lady bust have a code id the dose, and that those people are a little snobbish.'

As I did not understand the last word, I made a concession:

'Now that may be. And also he must be a bad-tempered man, because his daughter told me he'd rather shoot at sportsmen than at birds!'

'That, I understand,' my uncle said, gravely, 'indeed I do! It's easier, because a sportsman is bigger and doesn't fly.'

'No, don't joke, Uncle. I assure you it's quite serious. Isabelle herself told me so.'

'Well!' said Paul, shaking his head in alarm.

'Has he killed many sportsmen yet?' my father inquired.

Since I could see they were pulling my leg, I shrugged.

'Of course not. Anyway, he said he would, and that proves he's bad-tempered.'

'Oh!' said Paul, philosophically, 'I sometimes say things and then don't do them! Perhaps, if he sees Papa and Uncle Jules in the hills and . . .'

73

'If he meets us,' Uncle Jules broke in with real ferocity, 'it'll be just too bad for him, because we'll have seen him first, and you'll find him hanging up in place of that badger . . .'

'A little higher,' said my father, 'because he must be bigger.'

But I wasn't listening to their jokes any more; I was devouring my food and thinking of the surprising Isabelle who had given me her hand to kiss, and who was waiting for me.

CHAPTER THIRTEEN

AFTER lunch everybody had a siesta on the chaises-longues or in their bedrooms, except Paul who had stolen embroidery scissors to cut the badger's bristles: he claimed he would turn them into hair-brushes for the ladies and into shaving-brushes for the gentlemen.

I decided it was time to pay a visit to our snares. I could make the round—at a fast trot—in less than an hour and a half. Lili would not get to the Bastide until five. I might thus, if I felt like it, go and play with Isabelle from three to five.

Obviously, it was a little ridiculous to spend two hours with a girl. To play at what? With a doll perhaps, or a skipping-rope? But since she had invited me I could not refuse without being rude. Courtesy above all—especially with nobles.

I went into the kitchen and soaked my hands in water for at least ten minutes. After that I soaped them three times over until they had become unrecognizable: the pads on my finger-tips were all flabby and crinkled, like those of washer-women. Then, with a matchstick sharpened to a point, I managed to extract the small dark crescents that were lodged under my finger nails. Finally, I discovered in a porcelain jar on a shelf a green, aromatic-smelling pomade, which was mentholated vaseline for colds in the head but which I mistook for a cosmetic. I plastered my hair with this and then smoothed it vigorously with a brush in the hope of flattening a cow-lick which obstinately reared up at the top of my skull, like the crests on certain parrots. My endeavour was only half successful: so I crammed my handsome blue linen cap right down over my ears to flatten out my strangely cool hair. Lastly, I went up to my room and chose a holland jacket, and emerged looking spick and span.

Paul, astonished by so much cleanliness, asked me:

'Where are you going?'

I answered truthfully:

'To have a look at the snares.'

So up I went towards the pine-woods. But when I reached the top of the hill of Petit-Oeil, which is just below Redouneou, I stopped for breath and, turning round, saw behind the roof of Isabelle's house the top of the acacias which were beckoning to me in the wind.

I suddenly had a feeling of guilt of the utmost delicacy, but which today seems to me rather suspect.

'I didn't go up to the snares this morning because I was obliged to rescue a girl. Now that wasn't my fault. But what's the use of my going up there now, since we'll be going back presently? If the animals have eaten the birds, what can I do about it? And if the Lame Man has passed by, the snares won't be there any more. So what am I going for? Just to make Lili believe that I went there this morning. Well, I think that's hypocritical. All I have to do is tell him the truth, and we'll make the rounds together at five. I've never yet lied to him: I'm not going to start today.'

Reassured of my own straightforwardness by these arguments, I changed my course and ran down to Les Bellons.

As I passed through an abandoned orchard, I climbed an old almond tree and filled my pockets with almonds that are called 'Princesses' because of their thin shell which can be broken between the thumb and the forefinger. Then, at a leisurely stroll, and stopping now and then as if to admire the scenery, I approached the nobleman's house.

When I reached the corner of the long, low building I ventured a glance. There was nobody on the terrace, but I heard the sound of a piano.

I thought her mother must be giving her a lesson, and advanced noiselessly towards the music, hugging the wall.

The window was open: another step, and I saw Isabelle's back. It was she who was playing, and with both hands at once! I was dumbfounded with surprise and admiration. The small brown fingers were running over the keys, a thin silver bracelet was dancing around her wrist. Sometimes she would lift her hand very high, it would remain poised in mid-air for a second, then swoop down with incredible speed on several notes at the same time, like a sparrow hawk on swallows.

I stood still as a statue, gazing at the movements of the frail shoulders and the small, pale nape between the two gleaming, silky braids; but the music suddenly stopped, and Isabelle turned her head towards me. She smiled and said:

'I saw you in the polished surface on the piano. Do you like this music?'

'Oh, yes!'

'It's a difficult piece. I don't know it very well yet but I'm practising it every day. I've got to play it for my father's birthday next month. I'll start it again for you. Come in! Mama isn't here. She's gone to meet the poet, because he's free this afternoon.'

I jumped onto the window sill, then down on the beautiful carpet.

She swiftly flicked the pages of a music album, then massaged her fingers and said:

'Come closer.'

To my great surprise, she made me sit on the floor, quite close to the side of the piano, and ordered me to put my ear to the black ebony panel: which I obediently did. I waited, already in ecstasy.

*

In those days, the gramophone was still a magical apparatus, reserved for millionaires alone, and wireless was non-existent.

To listen to real music one had to go to a concert or to the opera, and the price of a seat in those sacred places reached half a *louis d'or*.

Thus, up till then all the music I had heard was a military band on Sundays (its highlight was *Poet and Peasant*), the street-singers' guitars, the distant scales practised by some unknown neighbour, and the charming but reedy sounds of my father's little flute.

Utterly new to music and consumed with curiosity, I closed my eyes.

Suddenly I heard the mighty ringing of bronze bells. Spaced out at first, like the first drops of a summer shower, they grew closer and united in triple and quadruple chords which cascaded one on top of the other, then rippled and

77

widened in sheets of sound, unexpectedly torn by a hail-storm of fast-bouncing notes, while the thunder boomed far away in the dark bass, reverberating right inside my chest.

A sweet melody was roaming under the thunderstorm: now and then it soared up towards the sky and, climbing to the very top of the keyboard, made bright sparks of music quiver in the night.

I was dazed, then shaken, then intoxicated. With bursting head and throbbing heart, I was flying, with outstretched arms, above the green waters of a mysterious lake: I dropped into pockets of silence, from which I suddenly rose again on the breath of ample harmonies which carried me towards the crimson clouds of a sunset.

I do not know how long this enchantment lasted. Eventually, four chords on the edge of a cliff, one after the other, slowly spread their wings, flew away and disappeared in a golden haze, while the echoes in the ebony were endlessly dying away . . .

CHAPTER FOURTEEN

ISABELLE nudged me with the tip of her foot, and I woke with a shiver.

'That's all!' she said. 'Did you like it?'

I did not know what to answer: I was grinning in an embarrassed way, staring at those tiny hands which brought so much music to life, and I realized that she was a fairy who held the keys to another world.

I did not dare look into her eyes.

She suddenly got up, a little girl again, and laughed:

'Wake up! Come on! We'll play hopscotch!'

I was not displeased by this proposal, for we were coming back to my home ground. At school I no longer played hopscotch for lack of a worthy adversary: but on account of the music I decided to let her win the first match.

There was a big surprise in store for me. I noticed that I was hopping flat-footed, like a bear, pushing the pebble forward with the tip of my sole, with somewhat laborious skill. When her turn came, she began to dance like a wagtail: the bewitched pebble preceded her, skittering in front of her right into the middle of the next square.

I lost four matches and was hot with vexation. But she did not jeer at me. After a last pirouette which made her petticoat swirl round and gave me a glimpse of her pretty legs, she cried:

'I'm tired now. Let's play something else, with no running. Do you know the *Little Match Girl*?'

I was a little startled and answered:

'The one at the tobacconist's?'

She burst out laughing, then put her hand over her mouth, gave a prolonged 'Oh!' and stared at me with indignant surprise.

I was vexed and asked: 'What's the matter?'

'The matter is that it's the most beautiful story in the

world, but it isn't real life, it's a tale! And actually, you're lucky you don't know it, because I'm going to read it to you right away!'

She ran towards the house.

I did not have a very easy conscience. What would Lili say if he saw me here, gone all mushy with music and beaten at hopscotch by a girl? I briskly rose but stayed where I was, for she was already coming back with a book in her hand.

'Get into the hammock,' she said, 'and don't move.'

I had not yet had an opportunity to install myself in this sumptuous swing: at my first attempt, the treacherous net dodged away under me, and I fell heavily on my back.

She gave a peal of laughter, while I in my confusion was thinking of the *garçon manqué* who had fallen from a tree.

'Never mind,' she said kindly, 'get up. I'll help you.'

She held the edge of the hammock with both hands, and I managed to settle myself in it, with my head softly supported by a scented silk cushion.

Isabelle sat down on the edge of the table, dangling her legs. She opened her book and read to me the poignant tragedy of that little Northern girl.

I did not much care for sad stories and prevented myself from giving way to emotion, first by telling myself that 'all this wasn't true', then weakening its poetic power by means of practical considerations which, through the intervention of common sense, gave me time to overcome my sensibility. . . .

Right from the very first line of the story, it was cold and dark and snowing fast. These harsh atmospheric conditions did not concern me in any way, since I was swinging in the warm shade of an acacia, on the edge of the sunny *garrigue*.

At the fifth line, the unhappy child, already bare-headed, foolishly lost her old slippers and had to 'walk in the snow on her bare little feet which were red and blue with the cold'.

My first thought was that she didn't know how to manage, that her parents were criminals to let her go out in the snow by herself, and that the story teller was trying by every means to make me sad: I therefore refused to share her cold feet. But Isabelle took the thing very seriously, and went on reading with deep conviction as if it were written in a newspaper. She sounded as if she had several voices. Now cold and monotonous like the falling snow, now greedy and voluptuous to say : 'There was a delicious savour of roast goose in the street', then vibrant with indignation when the awful brat stole the innocent girl's second slipper . . . She must surely be top in reciting at school, for she read as well as my teacher, and perhaps even better . . . As the magical piano had already shaken my sensitivity, Isabelle's voice, pathetic as the story, gradually pierced my defences, and I felt her emotion taking hold of me.

It started when the little girl tried to warm 'her poor ice-cold hands' by burning 'her matches one by one': I was forced to feel sorry for the obvious inefficiency of such an inadequate heating arrangement, and as I saw her growing pale and blue, I felt the greatest alarm for the events to come.

*

The fairyland conjured up by the 'dazzling' flame of those matches (Swedish ones, without a doubt) comforted me for a moment, thanks to the sudden gaiety in Isabelle's voice which triumphantly described those wonderful visions; and the appearance of the grandmother reassured me, though it seemed to me inexplicable. When at last they both arrived at the Good Lord's, I was very glad he existed, so as to give them the happiness they deserved. But that wasn't the end!

The cruel story teller brought a dreadful revelation into the last lines. Isabelle read them out slowly, with tremulous emotion choking her voice, and when she came to: 'dead, frozen to death on the last night of the old year', she could not add a single word, and big tears were trickling down her pale cheeks.

I found it hard to contain a sob. At last she recovered her voice:

'New Year's Day rose above the little dead body sitting on the ground, among the burnt matches?' . . .

Then it seemed to me that the dead little girl was herself, I saw her quite white in the snow, and I jumped down from the hammock to run to her rescue.

She gently pushed me away, saying in a stifled voice:

'Wait!'

She read the last lines: 'No one knew of the sweet visions she had beheld, or how gloriously she and her grandmother were celebrating their New Year's festival.'

Those sweet visions did not console me. She was dead of cold, and that was that. The rest was sheer trickery, and since I was seeing Isabelle soaring up, airborne by the lifting power of a white-haired old lady, big tears kept rolling down my cheeks, and I clasped her to my heart to keep her earth-bound.

Still crying, she began to laugh.

'Big fathead!' she said. 'It's only a story, and none of it is true. You ought to be ashamed of crying like that!'

'But you're crying too!'

'Yes, but I'm a girl. And besides, I like to cry when it's for fun! Whereas a boy . . .'

She suddenly broke off and said:

'Here's my father!'

She pulled a little lace square from her pocket and wiped her eyes, while I blew into my checked handkerchief.

CHAPTER FIFTEEN

HER parents were coming up the hill that ended in the terrace on which we stood. I stared at them curiously, especially at the poet-nobleman, the dangerous hunter of hunters.

. He was not tall, and rather old: at least forty, like Uncle Jules. He was wearing a big black felt hat, a black jacket and a black string tie. He was leaning on his wife's arm and holding in his other hand a slender ebony cane which he used for gesturing as he walked.

His shoes were white with dust, and he seemed tired. When he came closer to me I saw that he resembled his daughter, but was much less pretty, because his cheeks were hollow and one could see a thousand blue dots on his chin, and in particular below his nose.

Isabelle walked up to them, stopped four steps away and dropped a pretty curtsy. The poet, in his turn, lifted his hat in a graceful greeting.

Isabelle approached, and her father, bare-headed, kissed her on the forehead. Then he turned towards me and said in a lyrical tone of voice:

Here comes the knight whom the viper can't daunt
Who combats the spider in its own woven haunt.

Isabelle looked at me with pride, and I opened my eyes wide with admiration: he was obviously a real poet. Without taking time to think, he went on:

Oh, pages of my castle, sound the bugle loud and wild
In honour of the hero who has saved my only child.

Isabelle triumphed, her mother smiled, and I marvelled.
'It's true,' said Isabelle, 'he was very brave; but still he cried when I read him the story of the *Little Match Girl*!'
'Did he?' asked the poet, looking at me.

I lowered my head in confusion, and Isabelle continued, mockingly:

83

'Yes, he did, and now he's blushing!'

'I'm charmed,' said the poet gravely, 'and I congratulate him! You're wrong to laugh, Isabelle. If it ever occurred to you to take for husband a man who felt no emotion when reading that masterpiece, I would undoubtedly refuse to give you my consent!'

This anticipated refusal of a possible rival seemed delightful to me, for I inferred from it that he found me worthy to become his son-in-law; and though my matrimonial projects were not yet very definite, this was a big step forward.

I therefore looked at Isabelle with the smug air of an accepted suitor, whereupon he handed his stick to his wife, placed one hand on my shoulder and the other on his daughter's, as if he were going to push us into each other's arms. But he did nothing of the sort, and said solemnly:

> For the poet, my children, you must not delay
> To bring green-eyed absinth on a golden tray . . .

I did not very well understand what he meant, but the enchantment of the rhymes was enough for me, and his heavily leaning hand was pushing me forward.

I noticed, however, that the long road had exhausted him, for even with the support of our two shoulders, his gait was a little uncertain, and the occasionally divergent movements of his feet made me think of Clémentine's eyes.

He pushed us like that towards the green table, let go of our shoulders and settled down in the wicker armchair.

Isabelle ran towards the house and disappeared.

The poet smiled at his wife and said, without taking any notice of my presence:

'Infanta, I am happy to announce to you that Princess Mélusine has plighted her troth to the knight in the presence of the druids and Merlin the Magician, under Brocéliande's leafy shade.'

Infanta—I thought that was her Christian name—seemed very moved, for she went and knelt down before him and, with her face raised, asked him shyly:

'When can I hear it?'

He pondered for a moment and shook his head several times, as if it were a very grave problem: at last, his eyes

84

staring vacantly into space, he gave his verdict in an under-tone:

'Perhaps tonight,' he said. 'Perhaps tomorrow . . .'

'Oh, Loïs!' she said, 'I should be so happy . . .'

'I know, my Infanta, I know. Thirty-two lines, perhaps the most beautiful ones of my whole work . . .'

She was gazing at him, quite illumined, as if she were about to cry with joy, and she kissed his hand.

I did not grasp much of this scene and stood waiting for Isabelle to return.

She reappeared, carrying a tray laden with glasses and bottles. It seemed to me rather heavy for her, and I ran to meet her. But as I was holding out my arms, she looked at me severely and slowly passed in front of me, her chin in the air.

The poet's eye suddenly gleamed.

Then, in deep silence, there began a kind of ceremony.

He set the glass—a very big one—before him after inspecting its cleanliness. Then he took the bottle, uncorked it, sniffed it, and poured out an amber-coloured liquid with green glints to it. He seemed to measure the dose with suspicious attention for, after a careful check and some reflection, he added a few drops.

He next took up from the tray a kind of small silver shovel, long and narrow, in which patterned perforations had been cut.

He placed this contrivance on the rim of the glass like a bridge, and loaded it with two lumps of sugar.

Then he turned towards his wife: she was already holding the handle of a 'guggler', that is to say a porous earthenware pitcher in the shape of a cock, and he said:

'Your turn, my Infanta!'

Placing one hand on her hip with a graceful curve of her arm, the Infanta lifted the pitcher rather high, then, with infallible skill, she let a very thin jet of cool water—that came out of the fowl's beak—fall on to the lumps of sugar which slowly began to disintegrate.

The poet, his chin almost touching the table between his two hands placed flat on it, was watching this operation very closely. The pouring Infanta was motionless as a fountain, and Isabelle did not breathe.

In the liquid, whose level was slowly rising, I could see a milky mist forming in swirls which eventually joined up, while a pungent smell of aniseed deliciously refreshed my nostrils.

Twice over, by raising his hand, the master of ceremonies interrupted the fall of the liquid, which he doubtless considered too brutal or too abundant: after examining the beverage with an uneasy manner that gave way to reassurance he signalled, by a mere look, for the operation to be resumed.

Suddenly he quivered and, with an imperative gesture, definitely stopped the flow of water, as if a single drop more might have instantly degraded the sacred potion.

The Infanta dropped her pose and lowered the pitcher; the poet delicately seized the glass, bore it to his lips, then tossing his head back, drank half of it without the least pause, his Adam's apple rising and falling under the bluish skin of his throat.

At last he put the glass down on the table and, with his mouth open, gave a long, voluptuous sigh.

I felt, however, a distinct alarm, for this drink, by its smell and colour, reminded me strangely of the terrible *Pernod* which had reduced our dear Bouzigue for several hours to the state of a wild-eyed, stupid, stuttering clown. But the perfect calm displayed by Isabelle and her mother reassured me. Besides, this was certainly not the first time that the poet had drunk this liquor, and besides he called it 'apsint'. So it couldn't be *Pernod* but was no doubt a poet's beverage. Moreover, he gave no sign of bewilderment and seemed, on the contrary, perfectly happy.

I watched him savour the rest of his nectar in small sips, before the marvelling eyes of the well-pleased Infanta. Then he said in a worried whisper:

'For four days now I have been trying to replace a rhyme that does not satisfy me. Forgive me for having hidden it from you. It is a brown stain on an alabaster statue, a thistle on a rose-bush. And yet the word isn't far away. It is fluttering around my lyre. If I have an hour's perfect silence I'm sure to capture it.'

Upon those words, he assumed a fierce expression and made a swift gesture as if catching a fly.

At last, he propped his elbow on the table, put his fore-head in his open hand and moved no more.

Infanta, with a finger to her lips, now approached me on tiptoe, took me by the shoulder and pulled me toward the house. Isabelle accompanied us.

When we were far enough away from the poet, Infanta said to me in a low voice:

'He's composing. The slightest noise can shatter his inspiration—so no more games for today. Isabelle will go to her room and do her holiday homework, but you can come back tomorrow morning at ten . . .'

I bade them good-bye in a whisper, and on my way home, rehearsed the proper tone to adopt for my explanations to Lili.

CHAPTER SIXTEEN

BEHIND the Bastide-Neuve, he was playing with Paul on the overgrown terraces of the abandoned olive groves.

Lili was holding in his hand a big cicada, into whose back they had stuck the twisted end of a little paper fan. Paul was striking a sulphur-match against a stone.

They obviously intended to set fire to this rudder before launching the insect into the air.

Paul explained to me that it would be a pretty sight to see a flying flame.

Lili, less poetically, was hoping that the cicada's speed might be greatly enhanced by the dire news it would receive from its backside as well as by the motive power of the fire, perhaps. This hope, though expressed in somewhat vague terms, foreshadowed more or less, in a modest way, the interstellar rocket.

Despite the interest of this experiment, I firmly opposed its execution. Not out of any misplaced sentimentality, for how could a perfectly dry insect, which doesn't contain a drop of blood and has neither father nor mother, be expected to suffer? It was just a small mechanism, a musical box reduced to two notes, a kind of toy which nature had put at our disposal during the holidays.

I did not, therefore, invoke the sufferings of the combustible songster, but pointed out that the eventual fall of a flaming insect might set alight the dry grass which would set fire to the olive trees, then to the pine-wood and finally to the house. When the experimenters envisaged themselves surrounded by flames they gave up their project, and Lili unplugged the cicada, which fled towards the woodland on a long note of protest . . .

Paul drew from his pocket his bread and chocolate, which he had not yet had time to eat. Lili, his hands in his pockets, was looking at me wordlessly, and I was not very much at ease: I therefore took matters in hand and began to question him. (Judges, being no fools, have always forbidden the accused to do so.)

'Why didn't you come this morning?'

'I was sorting potatoes.'

'And this afternoon?'

'I brushed the mule, and then I cleaned the chicken-run, and then I came here. And you?'

This question, short as it was, disconcerted me, and I said, with a false burst of laughter:

'Well, I had a funny thing happen to me, old boy.'

'I know. Paul told me.'

'What did he tell you?'

'That you went and had fun with a girl. A silly idiot who's afraid of spiders.'

I protested.

'She's not an idiot. It's true she's afraid of spiders—but that's natural for a girl: my aunt Rose is afraid of them, too, and so is my mother . . .'

'Maybe . . . But that girl gives herself airs . . .'

'Do you know her?'

'I've seen her.'

'Where?'

'She's been to our place twice to buy eggs, with her mother.'

'Why didn't you tell me?'

'It didn't seem worth while.'

'You don't think she's pretty?'

'Oh!' said Lili, 'she's like all the girls. Except that when she walks, she's like a bricklayer on a roof who's afraid of breaking the tiles!'

Paul burst out laughing: his bread in one hand, his chocolate in the other, he began to walk slowly with out-stretched arms, gingerly stepping in a straight line.

'That's just like it,' said Lili, 'only she doesn't stretch her arms out. And then she blinks all the time.'

He began to flutter his eyelids and gave me a sidelong glance.

I was vexed but did not want to show it, so I simply said:

'I wish you could hear her play the piano!'

'Can she play?' Paul marvelled.

'Oh, turning the handle isn't difficult,' said Lili. 'At the café I often wind it up myself!'

I scored:

'What handle? It's a real piano, a piano without a handle! Yes, sir! She plays it herself, with her fingers—all her fingers on both hands. She played me some terrific music, for an hour without stopping! And her mother is a piano *professor*!'

'She's a *caramentran*,' said Lili (he meant: a carnival dummy). 'She paints her mouth red and her eyes black. And when she talks, my mother can't understand her.'

'Because your mother doesn't know French well!'

He looked at me for a moment and I saw that I had hurt him. He said suddenly:

'Anyhow, I bet you didn't go up to the snares this morning.'

'Well, no, I didn't. I couldn't leave a lost girl all alone in the hills.'

He shook his head in consternation.

'Well! They must have had a field-day!'

I realized he was talking of the fox, the rats, the ants and the Lame Man.

So I said: 'Come on! Let's hurry!'

As Paul declined to accompany us I confiscated his matches: the vehemence of his protests proved this was a wise decision.

*

We climbed quickly towards Tête-Rouge, for it was already after six.

Lili was walking pensively in front of me, his hands in his pockets. I asked him:

'What have you got to do tomorrow morning?'

'The last almonds,' he said. 'Below Four-Neuf, on the edge of the Carriérade!'

'I'll come and help you. What time do you start?'

He suddenly stopped, turned round, and burst out:

'Besides, her father's a toper!'

'Who are you talking about?'

'You know very well.'

90

'Who told you he was a toper?'

'Everybody knows it, down in the village. He buys bottles of drinks all the time.'

'What does that prove? You know they're always talking ill of townspeople in the village!'

'And I know it too, because last week, coming back from Saint-Marcel with his cart, Baptistin was an hour late. And I'll tell you why: 'cos he found that gentleman going along the road on all fours, and he no longer knew what he was saying. So he loaded him on the cart and took him back to Les Bellons!'

I was crushed by this revelation at first, then answered:

'If it's true, then he must have been very ill, because he's very rich and learned, he's even a nobleman! Anybody can be taken ill.'

'That's what you think! Baptistin said he threw up a litre of *pernod*! Funny illness, that!'

The mention of *Pernod* troubled me, but I refused to admit such a horrible slander.

'The truth is,' I said, 'that your brother is a liar. Perhaps he's the one who got soused in a café and that's why he was late. So to make up an excuse, he invented just anything.'

I had spoken with warmth. Lili shrugged his shoulders lightly and left the path to have a look at a snare.

'We *had* caught a nuthatch,' he said. 'There are only the feathers left.'

They were spread out in circles—blue, yellow, buff, black —around a blood-stained beak. The rats had passed that way . . . Higher up a big skylark, caught the night before no doubt, was already half buried by small black insects which were feverishly digging out the earth below its body. They had already laid their eggs beneath the feathers of the corpse and were making preserves of it to ensure the food supply of their little ones, who would be born as orphans in the spring . . .

*

We continued our round, which had some more disappointments in store for us. Two snares had disappeared, and all that remained of three cross-bills were the beaks and legs. Lili accepted the fact without saying a word, but shaking his head. Nevertheless, we did collect some thrushes and a big rock-blackbird which in Provence is called a *Passe-Solitaire*—a 'Lone Passer'—for it is a migratory bird that always travels alone.

The last snare was set below the end of the cliff. There we rested for a moment under the slanting pine-tree with its fan of flat branches.

Above the mountain range of Allauch we could see the distant sea. It sparkled like a silver plate under an immense sunset which, as usual, made a terrific clamour of red and gold.

'Tomorrow, it'll be fine,' said Lili. 'If you come early we'll finish the almonds before noon, and we'll come and eat here. If my father doesn't want me to, I'll slip away all the same!'

To make his plan materialize, he set up a hearth between three fine, flat stones which he stuck into the ground and adjusted carefully. Then he built two seats, after locating the spot on which the shadow of the pine tree would fall at noon. Finally, I helped him prepare a small heap of dead wood.

When the sun touched on the sea we quickly trotted downhill.

Below, on the left, I could see Isabelle's house. The acacias were no bigger than sage-plants, and the surrounding olive trees were just like clumps of thyme ...

Lili was running in front of me, but he suddenly stopped and bounded away from the path to make a little detour in the *garrigue*. Then he turned round towards me and, with a terrified air, shouted:

'Look out! ...'

I stopped.

'What's the matter?'

He pointed at a cobweb across the path and screamed:

'A SPIDER! I'm scared of SPIDERS! Help!'

And, with mocking laughter, he took flight ...

CHAPTER SEVENTEEN

AT dinner that night the conversation was rather embarrassing. Paul began by pointing at me and declaring forcefully:

'He's a liar! A real liar!'

'Why?' asked my mother.

'Because he said he'd go to see the snares and then it wasn't true. He went to see the girl!'

'Oho!' said my uncle. 'The one of this morning?'

'Yeah!' said Paul. 'The one with the spiders! And he got himself up all bright and clean, because that girl is his fiancée!'

'If that's so,' said my father, looking at me, 'I think you're going a bit fast. . . What do you think, my dear Jules?'

'I absolutely agree with you. Before I could fix a date for our engagement I'd been wooing Rose for over seven months!'

'Seven months and twenty-one days!' cried Aunt Rose.

Then she suddenly blushed and lowered her eyes, as if she had said something rude.

Quite inexplicably Uncle Jules blushed too, put his big hand on his wife's, and immediately went on while looking at me:

'Anyway, you know better than anyone that our conversations in Borély Park went on for at least three seasons.'

'That's true,' I cried. 'I was there!'

Then, looking Paul straight in the face, I added vehemently:

'And I never said a word to anyone. Whereas you have to go and blab even when you don't know anything!'

'If the matter is serious,' said my mother, 'a lasting attachment, you'll have to introduce her to us, after all.'

'On that day,' said Uncle Jules, 'we'll hide our shotguns, for no doubt she'll come with the future father-in-law. Have you seen him?'

'Yes,' I said. 'He looks as if he thought a lot, but I don't

93

believe at all that he'd shoot at a sportsman. He must have said it for fun, and Isabelle believed him.'

'So she's called Isabelle?' asked my mother.

'Yes, but her mother calls her Babette.'

'Babette,' said Aunt Rose, 'is short for Elizabeth.'

'Yes,' said my mother. 'Isabelle generally becomes Bébelle.'

Uncle Jules declared that he preferred Babette.

'So do I,' I said. 'And it suits her very well. And it's true what she told me about her father being a poet. When he talks, it rhymes!'

'Did he recite poems to you?' my mother asked.

'No, he didn't recite them: he invented them. And he even made one up to say he wanted some apsint!'

'What?' cried my father. 'Did he drink some?'

'Of course,' I said. 'A big glass, filled to the brim. But mind you, it isn't *Pernod*—it's apsint!'

'That's even worse!' said Joseph. 'Absinth is the most violent poison.'

'That's probably,' said my uncle, 'because he wants to imitate Verlaine or Alfred de Musset!'

The thought that other writers had drunk it before him comforted me, but Joseph replied sarcastically:

'We know what it did to them! Unhappy wrteches!'

Those last words made me realize that things must have gone wrong with them.

'Anyway,' I said, 'he didn't seem to worry about that, and it smelled awfully good! And besides, I understood it helps him think, he does it for his work: afterwards he never said another word, because he was thinking.'

'If he's still able to entertain the least thought he ought to realize that this drug will ruin his intelligence, reduce his liver to the size of a lemon, and that he will write his last verses in a padded cell!'

'You mustn't exaggerate,' said Uncle Jules (who sometimes defended *apéritifs* in order to protect his vineyards). 'If you have a little absinth at night, in the country, in summer after a hot day's work . . .'

'A habit is soon acquired, for a habit starts with the very first time. After all, if the first time didn't count, the second time would be the first and thus wouldn't count either, and so it would go on until the word "habit" would finally have no meaning any more! I assure you, my dear Jules . . .'

But I was no longer listening to their conversation, heard a hundred times before, for the memory of Isabelle lost among the fennel below her wreath of poppies suddenly filled all my thoughts. I ate absentmindedly and heard again the all-pervading music, through which my father's voice pierced now and then, uttering mysterious and menacing words: dropsi, poplexi, sirosis, delirim tremendous . . .

As soon as I had gulped down the last mouthful of my dessert, I declared that I had to get up very early next morning to help Lili, and I went upstairs to bed. In actual fact, I ran to my nightly rendezvous with my daytime memories.

I made the discovery that today's meeting was an event of major importance; this did not, however, modify my opinions of girls in general, for it seemed obvious to me that this one was quite unlike the others, so that my admiration for her did not in any way benefit Clémentine. On the contrary, the latter seemed ridiculous in retrospect, for there's a great difference between a piano and a broom. As for her unmatched eyes which had sometimes troubled me, they now filled me only with generous pity.

I lived again through the whole of that day, hour by hour, and gradually fell asleep in the midst of wonderful dreams.

I was lying on a divan in their livigroub: I was clothed in a golden silk robe, and a red slipper was danging from the tip of my bare foot.

Isabelle was playing the piano: she was wearing a long black velvet dress which hid the piano-stool, and her train disappeared under the table. On her head sparkled a princess's crown—a gold one, of course—and on the tip of each spike was a big round pearl. Thousands of golden notes were issuing from the piano like a cloud of bees. From time to time, she would turn her face to me, smile at me tenderly and say! 'I permit you to address me as "*tu*" when my mother isn't there.'

But all of a sudden, I was in a street in which a great crowd was milling in front of a very beautiful house. Everybody was looking up. I did likewise, and saw long streamers of smoke emerging from the roof, followed by crackling flames. All the windows of the façade flew open at the same time, and people appeared in them, panic-stricken. Some of them were in their night-gowns, others wore top-hats, and they were shouting desperately: 'Go and fetch the fire brigade!'

But in the first row of the crowd I recognized the back of Uncle Jules' neck. He was shouting at them: 'As long as we have a Socialist mayor, there won't *be* any fire brigade! I've told Joseph so a hundred times!'

(And it was true, for he had said it one day on the terrace, as he was reading his paper.)

Thereupon the unfortunate people up at the windows, rendered desperate by Uncle Jules' statement, began to jump into the street . . . As they hit the pavement, their heads burst, and I could hear little 'pops' like bursting paper bags. Others up there were running along the edge of the roof, through the flames. At that moment the closed window on the top floor, right in the centre of the façade, opened by itself and Isabelle appeared. She was dressed all in white, like a bride. Behind her shone the red glow of fire. She was holding a sheaf of flowers in her arms. She showed no fear. On the contrary, she was smiling: she knew I was there.

I shot forward through the crowd. I ran towards the blazing entrance.

People were crying: 'He's mad! Hold him back!'

Uncle Jules' voice dominated all the others:

'Think of your father! Think of your mother!'

But nothing could overcome my dauntless determination. In a few prodigious jumps I bounded up to the top of the staircase which crumbled under my burning soles as I passed. I took Isabelle in my arms. Through the flames, which she did not see (for she was gazing into my eyes), I carried her away, as light as a feather; I kicked a secret door open, which opened into a church.

When we arrived on the church steps, we saw another crowd waiting for us: those thousands of people were shouting their enthusiasm, but they respectfully drew aside 'to let the hero pass with his precious burden'.

That was the first time I had rescued a girl and carried her off in my arms, to the applause of a crowd: that is why I did not understand the meaning of this heroic dream. I have since noticed that the nocturnal rescue of grateful young ladies has always heralded the birth of a *grande passion*.

Up to my *baccalauréat* I rescued a good dozen of them. I wrested them from cruel kidnappers, from raging storms at sea, from volcanic eruptions and even from earthquakes. These imaginary exploits proved the virile generosity of my feelings: their frequent change of object, however, seemed to show that my passions were neither eternal nor fatal, since the heroic rescuer would fairly soon take refuge in the next life-saving . . .

But of all this I was still unaware; that is why next morning, as I was dipping my buttered bread in my coffee-and-milk scented with the herbs of the hillside, I relived this first dream of glory and wondered if by any chance Isabelle had not had the same one.

Then I woke up completely and remembered that Lili was waiting for me.

CHAPTER EIGHTEEN

I THEREFORE took the path up to Le Collet which would lead me to him.

He must already be busy beating the leaves of the almond trees under a shower of dried almonds bouncing on his head. But at the crossing of the road to Les Bellons, instead of walking straight on to my goal, I turned to the left and, at a quick pace, walked towards Isabelle's house. It wasn't a very great detour and I had not the least intention of stopping there. I would pass at some distance from the house and if I saw her on the terrace would wave 'good morning!' to her from afar.

The hammock was empty, and there was nobody under the acacias.

I refused to admit that I was disappointed, and I thought:

'They must have gone down to the village to do some shopping. I'll probably meet them . . .'

I continued on my way, along the path that dropped down to Four-Neuf, and I was looking far ahead. I was telling myself sternly:

'So much the better! Lili has already been waiting for me two hours. I've no right to lose another minute and after what I did yesterday I oughtn't even to have passed this way!'

I began to run.

But suddenly a clear voice sang like a cuckoo, on two notes: 'Oo-hoo!'

I looked to my right.

At the far end of a small field of dry grass, under a very old olive tree, I saw her sitting in a swing. She was wearing a big white straw hat, whose brim was bent down to her cheeks by a wide blue ribbon.

As I had promised myself, I waved my hand to her, but I made the mistake of stopping. She cried:

'Where are you going?'

I cupped my hands before my mouth:

'To work with a friend!'

She did not answer. I added:

'I've got to help him pick almonds!'

As if she had not heard, she cried:

'Come and push me!'

I hesitated for a moment, then it seemed to me that two minutes more or less did not matter much and that, since I had rescued her from the flames, I might after all push her swing three or four times. Besides, I could—briefly—explain the situation to her.

I took a step forward, but suddenly I stopped: I could see Lili, all alone under the shower of almonds, glancing now and then towards the empty road . . .

Then she cried again, as loud as she could:

'Come and push me!'

I went.

*

Thus it was that my friend waited for me in vain near the spare pole he had brought for me, which remained lying in the grass while I was pushing, with outstretched hands, Isabelle's warm shoulders, and she screamed with fright and laughter whenever the wind, in her flight through the air, lifted her dress and stuck it against her face . . .

That is the way they part the staunchest friends, giggling on swings that swing no longer when the male stops pushing them on.

CHAPTER NINETEEN

THEREAFTER I spent all my days with Isabelle, and Lili no longer came to our house. I would still think of my friend at times, but with the feeling: so much the worse for him! . . . For whenever his face rose before my eyes, I was stabbed by remorse and ashamed of my treachery: but this honourable pain was something I held against *him*. I told myself, sometimes even speaking aloud:

'I'm very fond of him, and I'm his friend. But a friend is not a slave. Besides, why doesn't he come to see me any more? He's peeved because I don't do his work. But does *he* help me with my homework? I'm on holiday, after all, and I have the right to see anybody I like!'

And though he had never asked anything of me I found he was too exacting, and I reproached him for the grief that my absence was sure to cause him . . .

*

The poet took a liking to me because I looked up to him with evident admiration, and on the third day he asked me to lead the family on a pilgrimage to the place where I had wrested his daughter's life from the snakes.

Once more I beat the brushwood while the family stood back, and I slashed the spiders' webs with furious boldness. I realized that he was just as naïve as Isabelle, for he told us that the black-and-yellow spiders could jump at the faces of passers-by, and that their sting was often fatal—a thing he had probably read in the accounts of Brazilian explorers. As for snakes, he saw several of them, and the horrified Infanta clutched around her ankles the flounces of her dress which was trailing garlands of dead brambles.

Isabelle, who was walking close to my footsteps, encouraged and admired me.

At the bottom of the valley, on the boulder which the poet

named 'the Stone of the Encounter', the absinth ceremony was re-enacted. He had indeed brought with him, in a haversack, a phial of this poison (*dixerat pater*), a bottle of water and all the requisites.

Before drinking, he poured a few drops of the beverage on the stone, informing us that this was a 'libation of gratitude to the Sylvan Deities', then asked me if there were any wolves in those pine-woods. I coolly replied that they only came there in winter, but that I had repeatedly met wild boars.

He looked at me admiringly and said:

'You weren't frightened?'

I answered with a self-assurance that surprised even me:

'A boar is only a pig, after all.'

He said gravely to his wife:

'There's something of Bellerofon, perhaps even of Parsifle, about this child!'

I did not know those names, but I understood that they were famous heroes, added strength to my desire to show off. Isabelle was looking at me, and I could see that she was proud of her friend.

Together we went off to pilfer Niéni's grapes.

'Eat them without remorse,' the poet said, with a smile, 'for I shall indemnify him for his losses!'

While we were gaily searching for ripe grapes I saw that he was writing something on a sheet of paper, occasionally raising his eyes to the sky. At last, he tied the paper to a vine-stock with a thread he had pulled from the lining of his jacket, and declared:

'Now the poor man is repaid a hundredfold, for I'm leaving him four lines written in his own hand by Loïs de Montmajour, in payment of four bunches of grapes!'

He smiled, generous and benevolent. The Infanta gazed at him adoringly and said:

'Loïs, you're too kind!'

'One can never be too kind,' he answered.

'May I read it?' she asked, motioning to the precious paper.

'No,' he said gravely. 'It's an unpublished original, and it belongs to the vine-grower. A poet's gift must be entire.'

She said no more, and I promised myself I would let Niéni know of the value of this gift which, in his naïve ignorance he might otherwise fail to appreciate.

*

On our return at five o'clock, we had a lovely tea: jam, *brioches* and biscuits. I added two handfuls of Princess almonds, which I could easily supply at cost price—that is, some scratches on my calves.

Isabelle ate very daintily, with a cat's cleanness and grace. In the meantime, a fresh absinth-drinking ceremony took place at the next table. Then the poet and the Infanta, tenderly leaning on each other, slowly walked into the house.

As we were going down towards the swing, Isabelle gripped my elbow and said:

'Wait!'

She pricked up her ears. I heard the faint chords of piano-playing, interspersed with silences.

'Come!' she said. 'Don't make any noise.'

She pulled me towards the corner of the house, then we stealthily crept along the front. I could hear the murmur of a voice, and the chords seemed to follow it . . . She sneaked into the vestibule, pulling me by the hand, and we remained motionless, flattened against the wall, near the open door of the 'livigroub'.

The poet was reading verses and the Infanta was striking muffled chords . . .

It was all about a sort of horrible woman, who had claws and was called a 'gool'. She was flying in a 'silvan grove' and wanted to have a dig at the Knight's heart.

The reader's voice was jerky, the chords of the piano harsh and hurried. The valiant knight whirled his sword, which shot out blue sparks; but that was of no help to him, for every time he cut that gool in two the two pieces immediately came stuck again because of a spell cast by a wizard, who was called Merlin and who did not care for the knight. Suddenly the poet's voice became tremulous and desperate, for the generous young man had tripped over a clump of heather, and the gool flung herself on him to settle his hash.

Isabelle, who was chewing her handkerchief, nervously pressed my hand. But the piano suddenly sounded a fanfare, whereupon there appeared the fairy Mélusine, who was lovely as the day, and the voice became triumphant: the fairy only had to smile and the gool exploded in a cloud of sulphur, uttering a horrible scream which shook the window panes of the livigroub. Then Mélusine took the knight's hand and said wonderful words of love. The knight listened to her, pale with happiness, and the piano seemed as pleased as he . . . At last, they both sailed away in a magical boat on the waters of a blue pool covered with water-lilies, and all around the boat there were 'snowy' swans that escorted them towards happiness.

The piano struck three prolonged chords and stopped on the verge of a great silence. I was deeply moved, on account of the reciter's sonorous voice, on account of the music, and above all on account of Isabelle's hand which was still in mine. It was really a sublime moment.

The Infanta's voice—a little hoarse—suddenly moaned:

'Oh, Loïs! Loïs! You've never written anything finer!'

Isabelle, looking very pale, let go of my hand and ran to throw herself into her father's arms; his face was wet with tears, and she clasped him to her heart, sobbing, while the Infanta, who was weeping like a fountain, sat swaying on her piano-stool, wild-eyed and with drooping shoulders.

As for me, I remained on the threshold, not daring to step into so much sublimity and wondering why this great poet devoted his genius to composing verses that gave so much pain to all his family.

He saw me.

'Did you hear?'

I nodded, opening my eyes wide, and Isabelle cried:

'He did, father. It made him tremble.'

'That's a great sign!' he said, looking at his wife. 'A great sign!'

The Infanta, with a burst of energy, rose to her feet and cried:

'It's a bombshell! Yes, Loïs, this time it's a BOMBSHELL!'

I did not grasp this announcement at all. Loïs thoughtfully shook his head.

'Not so fast!' he said. 'Don't forget there's a coalition of publishers and a barrier of old *Pompiers*.'[1]

I realized that the presence of the *pompiers*—the firemen—had been rendered necessary by the explosion of the bombshell. But where, and when? As I was thinking over this question, he spoke again, as if out of a deep dream:

'No, I do not wish to reveal *Belphégor* before I have finished *Semiramis*; it is most important, on the contrary, to keep it absolutely secret!'

He turned to me.

'Will you swear not to mention to anyone that *Belphégor* is ready for publication? Raise your right hand and say: "I swear"!'

I stepped forward, raised my hand, and swore. I was quite proud to have given an oath in such an important matter.

'Later,' the poet went on, 'later you will be able to say: "I was present at the first private reading of the last hundred lines of *Belphégor*." Yes, you'll be able to say that.'

He remained silent for a moment, discreetly wiping away a half-dried tear.

'They probably won't believe you. So presently I'll give you an holograph certificate.

I had no idea what that was, but I was glad of it all the same.

[1] *Pompier* (= fireman) is colloquial French for conventional, academic art and for those who practise it.

CHAPTER TWENTY

In the days that followed I was admitted, or rather summoned, to two further confidential readings.

The poems were all of the same type. There were blind kings who wept at the feet of mad queens, lame dwarfs jeering and hopping on the battlements of keeps, magicians, ravens, toads, machicolations, posterns, drawbridges and always—fortunately—swans. There were far more of them than in the Zoo.

Isabelle had explained to me the bombshell, the publishers and the *pompiers*, always under the seal of secrecy; and as I was eleven years old, as I loved Isabelle and admired her parents, I stepped quite easily into the unreal world in which they themselves were living, a realm of mysterious words, vague music and pathetic dreams which I would find again in my own.

However, these poetic sessions were mere interludes, for our days were better occupied with all kinds of amusements and games on the large, shaded terrace or in the cicada-haunted pine wood.

Isabelle had a miniature race-course with little lead horses, set in motion by an invisible mechanism shut up in a box: you pressed the lever, and they all moved round. You could not tell which one would win. We each chose a horse beforehand, but we played for purely psychological stakes: the winner was proud, the loser cross. She also had a game of parcheesi and a backgammon-board. I never grasped the rules of one or the other; but I could gaze at the nape of her neck and her hands.

She also showed me her skill at diabolo. This was a kind of hollow spool, very narrow at the waist. By means of a cord tied to two sticks, she would make it spin at a whistling speed, then, suddenly spreading her arms, fling it up into the air; and the diabolo would fall bang onto the string with a perfectly diabolical precision.

She wanted to teach me this art. But when the whirring bobbin had fallen twice on my forehead and once on my nose I preferred to limit my collaboration to the rôle of spectator and admirer.

However, the games that require accessories, that is to say, more or less complicated objects that we call toys, cannot hold one's attention for long. When the object is not a pretext for satisfying an instinct (like a doll or a sabre), its spell is soon broken, as is the toy itself which ends its life in pieces. The diabolo and the mechanical performer on the trapeze were soon replaced by a game of Isabelle's own invention, which came straight out of her father's poems: it was the game of the Knight and the Queen.

The queen, obviously, was herself, and the knight was I. We began by making our own costumes, for like all girls she loved to dress up.

Out of an old curtain with a gold fringe she made a dress with a train, the holes in which were camouflaged by flowers. With a piece of cardboard, covered with the gilt paper wrapper of a block of chocolate, I managed to produce a really princely crown. The sceptre was made out of a long reed, around which coiled a spiral of red ribbon and which ended in a decanter stopper that must have been the work of a diamond-cutter, so dazzling was its sparkle. Finally, a contribution from the bead curtain outside the door provided us with a three-row necklace.

The knight's costume was obviously less elaborate. I had to be content with a fireman's helmet, rather on the small side (for it came from an old outfit of Paul's) but greatly embellished by a plume which had been a feather-duster in a doll's house. My rigout was completed by a cuirass of zinc, cut from the remains of a watering-can with the help of scissors that I had—discreetly—borrowed from Aunt Rose's sewing basket. She was really very unlucky: for just when I had succeeded in snipping off a last rough burr (actually a somewhat thick one) I heard a curious tinkle and half of one of the two blades gave a bounce and dropped off . . . Happily, I no longer needed this too fragile implement, and got rid of it by burying it unobtrusively at the foot of an olive tree.

Those preparations, which took up two entire days, were delightful—the second day above all.

We were sitting opposite each other, separated by a small table in the 'livigroub'. The room was dark, for a fine drizzle was patiently falling on the acacias, and the smell of damp earth was wafted in through the open window.

Isabelle was sewing attentively. I was sticking silver paper to the blade of a wooden sabre and looking at her from time to time. She was prettier than ever, for she was not 'pulling faces'. Her black locks hung over her needlework, the tiny thimble pushed the slender needle, sometimes she would raise her eyes to me and smile.

In the damp, warm silence, with the rain whispering in the pewter-coloured light, the clock's confidential tick-tock patiently wove the minutes we both shared, and I felt deep down the sweetness of being silent together. Then, without the slightest noise, she would rise and sit down at the piano, and her fingers released wisps of music that did not want to go out in the rain and kept fluttering in the shadows, all around the ceiling.

*

The result of our efforts was a great success. When I saw her appear with the crown on her head, the sceptre in her hand, girt with golden tassels and followed by a scarlet train, I was dazzled and really believed in her royalty: I promptly swore allegiance and faithfulness to her on my sword, and I declared myself ready to die for her, which she accepted without fuss.

The first orders she gave me put my strength and courage to the test.

She commanded me to fetch an abandoned nest from the highest fork of the acacia, overgrown with prickly spikes. Then she dropped a rose into the 'well' of Les Bellons (which was quite ten feet deep and in which nobody had ever seen any water) and 'authorized' me to climb down into that chasm to retrieve her flower.

I passed through an enormous (but untenanted) cobweb and brought back the precious rose which she authorized me to keep. Another day, she led me along the village road up to Felix's farm: this was a small shack by the roadside whose shutters were always closed because Felix, who was a stone-mason, never got home before nightfall; but in his absence his riches were guarded by a huge dog, so lean that it looked like a hairy skeleton, which would leap towards the passers-by, almost choking itself at the end of its chain whose thickness, fortunately, was proportionate to the beast's ferocity.

The queen declared that if I went and stroked the dog I should be appointed captain of the Palace Guards.

Without any apparent hesitation, I advanced towards the wild beast—relying on the well-known magnetism of the eyes of man, on the one hand, and on the solidness of the chain, on the other.

The sight of me seemed to drive the animal frantic: I cautiously stopped on the edge of the semi-circle traced by its comings and goings: it bounded out of the bottom of its kennel, but with such a prodigious leap that the ring of its collar broke. Isabelle gave a scream of terror. I jumped back —but too late! The long paws clutched my shoulders, I saw the gleam of four fangs as big and also as sharp as the fabulous tusks brought back by explorers . . . With all my might, I pushed back the hard-ribbed chest, but a long, soft tongue furiously licked my face, while the fierce animal let out long moans.

He was a misunderstood soul of tenderness, a pathetic lone wolf, a brute frantic with love, who grovelled at my feet to lick my calves and weep with joy . . . I had no end of trouble to get rid of him, for he crawled after me and would have followed me to the end of the world. Isabelle had fled: she came running back as I was fastening the beast's collar again. She simply said to me—from a fair distance: 'Knight, I am pleased with you.' This seemed to me somewhat lacking in warmth: but that very evening, when telling her father this episode, she asserted that I had laid low the ferocious beast. Perhaps she did believe it, too, for during my too easy victory she had been hiding her face in her hand. The Infanta said I was 'gloriously reckless', and the poet, pointing his forefinger at me, merely said: 'Bellerofon!'

Thus passed some ten days, days so short that I was always late coming home and only appeared there at meal-times. I admired, respected, adored Isabelle, and I no longer felt even the least remorse for abandoning Lili, for I had for-gotten his existence.

In the grass underneath the swing, I had found a green satin ribbon that had fallen from the hair of my beloved; I also owned a mother-of-pearl button from her dress, a gladi-olus she had given me, the stone of a plum she had eaten, a small crab-apple in which the imprints of her teeth could be seen, and one half of a small comb. I placed these treasures under my pillow at night; then, with the green ribbon tied around my neck and clasping in my fist the fruit deified by her bite, I would live again through the miraculous day be-hind closed eyes, and prepare the sentences that would tell her—tomorrow perhaps—of my undying love.

The queen, however, did not lose much time before abusing her authority. Today I realize that, after taking the measure of my boldness and bravery, she enjoyed humiliating those manly virtues before her girlish weakness: they adore a hero, for it is infinitely more thrilling to enslave a hero than, say, a devoted bookkeeper. And so it may happen that a frail young woman will marry a redoubtable wrestling champion for the mere pleasure of boxing his ears.

She began by ordering me to carry her train; then she pointed out that this was not a knight's task and, after show-ing me a coloured print on which the royal train was carried by two little blackamoors, she blackened my face and hands with a burnt cork. I had to fan her respectfully with the feather duster, while she pretended to sleep in the hammock, and, when she woke up, I had to dance the 'bamboula' to amuse her. Whereupon she would say, as a recompense: 'Open your mouth and shut your eyes!' and I had to bite into whatever delicacy she chose to put on my tongue: first it was a caramel, then a cherry, then a snail.

Happy and proud as I was to astonish her, I wallowed in this servitude and would tremble with emotion when, before I left, she herself would clean my face and neck with a swab of cottonwool soaked in eau-de-Cologne . . .

CHAPTER TWENTY-ONE

THIS exquisite scent attracted Paul's notice: as I approached, he screwed up his nostrils and ran towards the house, shouting:

'He's been to the barber!'

My mother came out on the doorstep, alarmed lest Joseph had fished up the clippers again. When she saw my un-harmed hair, she asked him:

'Why do you say that?'

'They put something good-smelling on him! I've sniffed him . . .'

I walked up casually and said:

'Isabelle's mother gave me something to put on my face. It's called eau-de-Cologne . . .'

She went back into the house, a little surprised but reassured.

*

My sudden transformation had naturally not escaped the sharp eyes of the rest of my family. My father would some-times look at me with an amused smile, and Uncle Jules, reading his paper after lunch, would occasionally deplore the recrudescence of *crimes passionnels* and express somewhat disturbing views, though couched in general terms, on the powerful delusions that commonly blind the love-sick. But Nobody asked me any questions. On the contrary, when young Paul asked me why I no longer went hunting with Lili, my mother answered in my place that Lili had no time to spare now but would soon be back again. But Paul persisted:

'And why doesn't he take me along to see his fiancée?'

Aunt Rose decreed: 'You don't go to see people who haven't invited you!'

'And why doesn't the girl come here? Three together have much more fun. She'd be an Indian woman and carry the parcels, and I'd pretend to beat her with my stick, and she'd pretend to cry, and—'

'And you eat up your soup,' said my mother. 'I'm sure she wouldn't care for your game. Besides, little girls don't go and see their friends without their mothers.'

'Well, her mother can come too. I bet you she'd come if you invited her!'

'Now that's a good idea!' cried Uncle Jules. 'I imagine those people must be very interesting since Marcel spends all his days with them. It would be very nice to know them. On Sunday at Mass, I'll talk to the poet, and he'll come and have his drink here!'

I was flabbergasted.

I dimly realized the cause of my alarm: Isabelle did not know the little boy I was in my family. And the character I was playing with her could not be shown to my people who wouldn't have known who he was . . . But I immediately found a solution to this problem! if she came to see us with her parents, I would pretend to have a painful toothache, and would remain sitting on my chair without uttering a single word.

However, the much-feared meeting—of my two characters which did not coincide in the least—occurred that very night.

*

That afternoon, the queen's demands were as numerous as they were varied: I was the faithful black slave who carried her train and fan, then a dancing contortionist; struck by a poisoned arrow I writhed in dreadful agony at the feet of my mistress, who uttered words of consolation and regret. I then impersonated the ferocious dog that runs barking and with foaming jaws around his mistress's palace, and I turned this to account by licking her hands; at last, encouraged by my blissful adoration, she dropped into my mouth a live grasshopper which I munched up to the moment when I realized what it was and, nauseated, rejected it.

The queen was good enough to forgive me for not swallowing it, washed my face thoroughly with eau-de-Cologne, then sat down on her throne—which was the piano stool placed under the acacia tree—and granted me an audience.

And while I was standing to attention, she announced to me a stunning piece of news.

'Knight,' she said, 'I am pleased with your valour and your faithful services . . . You have triumphantly passed the tests I was obliged to impose upon you. You will receive your reward.'

She looked deep into my eyes, with a thoughtful mien.

'The cares of her kingdom weigh heavily on a lonely queen. I've therefore decided to let you share my burden.'

I did not dare to understand. She went on:

'Her Majesty the Queen Mother is about to prepare a royal cloak for you. Our wedding will take place tomorrow, in the presence of all the princes in Christendom, and she herself will play the Wedding March.'

This was a sublime idea which definitely consecrated my triumph: I turned quite pink with pride, and bowed respectfully. She gave me her hand to kiss, then said:

'Now please to withdraw, for I see a famous poet approaching. A poet is more than a king, and I must go and serve him . . .'

Indeed, Loïs had just appeared, tottering, his mouth twitching, and visibly racked by inspiration.

I withdrew backwards, bowing at every step, and returned to the Bastide, dancing all the way.

*

The sportsmen had just come home. Uncle Jules was drinking quite shamelessly, under Joseph's nose, a big glass of undiluted white wine in which floated a lump of ice. My father was cleaning the barrels of his shotgun, now and then lifting them to his eye as if to inspect the sky, which was perfectly cloudless. Aunt Rose was knitting, with a nimbly darting forefinger. A single, rather hoarse cicada was sawing thin slices of music on the highest branch of the fig tree.

My uncle, glass in hand, looked at me as I approached.

'Oho!' he said, 'you seem in high spirits tonight.'

'Do I? I'm just as usual. Did Lili come?'

'He did,' said my father, continuing his exercises in astronomy. 'He actually came rather early, and when he saw you weren't here, went off with Paul.'

This was pleasant news: it relieved me of my qualms, since Paul was able to replace me. It was even a small breach of faith which could be deducted from mine, and I felt all the more justified in my own eyes.

I settled down in a chaise-longue to nibble a bar of chocolate. I had an open book on my knees and was pretending to read: in fact, I was thinking of my dear Isabelle and considered her decision to marry me the next day as a proper declaration of love. I decided to suggest, after the ceremony, that we should visit Our Kingdom: I would take her along to the pine-wood and there, on the pretext of consecrating our marriage, I would clasp her to my heart and kiss her passionately.

As I was rehearsing the dialogue that would lead up to this bold but decisive gesture, Paul and Lili appeared. Some fifty steps away they stopped, put their heads together in a whisper under the gnarled old almond tree, then advanced, swaggering slowly and exchanging inexplicable grins.

Their attitude seemed to me disturbing, I could not say why.

'Well, where have you come from?' my father asked them.

Lili, who was sucking a fennel-sprig, raised his right hand and silently pointed towards Isabelle's invisible house.

'We went for a walk down there,' said Paul, 'and we hid ourselves so as to have a little look at what you were doing with that girl. Well, we saw everything! Everything!'

I immediately felt my cheeks burn but did not utter a single word.

My father, greatly interested, asked:

'And what did you see?'

'They were having fun,' said Lili evasively.

'What games were they playing?'

Lili, who seemed a little embarrassed, answered:

'Oh, well, I couldn't quite make out.'

'But I could!' cried Paul. 'The girl smeared his face all over like a black man, and then he held the tail of her dress, and afterwards she made him run on all fours!'

'Barking,' Lili muttered, still keeping his eyes lowered.

'That's a surprising game,' said Uncle Jules.

'And perfectly pointless,' Joseph declared categorically. 'I've never in all my life let a girl make me run on all fours!'

'Nor have I!' cried Paul, emphatically. 'Never in all my life!'

'It's just a game we invented! The game of "the Queen's Knight".'

'Generally speaking,' said my father, 'knights don't run around on all fours!'

'And they never bark!' said my uncle.

I could well see that they weren't pleased. So I explained to them the rules of the game, stressing the elegance of chivalrous feelings and adding that in the poet's verses 'things like that always happened'. But Paul pointed an accusing forefinger at me.

'What about the grasshopper?' he cried. 'You haven't said anything about the grasshopper. She made him close his eyes and open his mouth, and then she popped a grasshopper into it!'

'Alive!' murmured Lili.

As I did not know what to say, I shrugged and burst into rather silly laughter.

'Come, come,' said Uncle Jules, and he sounded incredulous. 'How could you have seen what it was?'

'We were hiding in the gorse-shrubs,' Lili said in a low voice, 'and she came and caught it just in front of us.'

'And he ate it!' cried Paul. 'Yes, you did!'

In my turn, I shouted furiously:

'It isn't true! I spat it out! I did! I did spit it out!'

'It's a fact,' said Lili. 'I saw it.'

'Whether you spat it or ate it,' my father suddenly said, 'I think this sort of joke is perfectly inane. It's quite clear the girl takes you for a fool!'

*

He was obviously displeased and I did not know which way to look when I heard my mother's voice. She was standing in the doorway, her hands white with flour, and she was saying:

'If girls can make you swallow grasshoppers now, I wonder what they're going to make you swallow later!'

I was struck to the heart, because she had spoken in utter

earnest. But Lili came to my rescue. He had slowly backed away and now cried:

'There's just time left to have a look at the snares! I laid three dozen of them at Petit-Oeil.'

I jumped to the occasion.

'When?'

'At five this morning, before I went to work.'

I immediately put on a show of great interest.

'Have you made your rounds?'

'Well, no, I haven't yet. I wanted to go with you.'

'Now that's silly,' I said, 'because with that little *mistral* blowing this morning, the white-tails must have passed there! Let's go quickly!'

There had been no 'little mistral' and no one had ever seen white-tails at Petit-Oeil, but I had said just anything to cover up my flight: I dashed off along the road to the hills and ran so fast that Lili had a hard time keeping up with me.

I stopped, soon out of breath, and had to sit down on a boulder to wait for him.

'You know,' he said, 'I didn't want to talk. It was Paul.'

'I could see. But I don't think it's nice to hide yourself like a lot of German spies, and to see what I'm doing. It's no business of yours, anyway.'

'I know,' said Lili, 'I know. . . . I didn't feel like going. It was Paul. You see, it hurts him that you leave everybody for that girl. And then he was annoyed to see you play the fool to please that silly skirt. Who does she think she is, anyway, to order you about. Does she think you're a dog?'

I didn't know what to say. My hands under my seat, I was sitting on the big boulder, dangling my legs, and my heels were noiselessly striking against the smooth stone.

He looked at me for a moment with a dark scowl, then said roughly:

'And you! Do *you* think you're a dog?'

I shrugged my shoulders and smiled faintly. He thrust his hands into his pockets and paced up and down in silence, his eyes lowered to the thyme that hid his feet. His face was set and sombre. At last he stopped in front of me, looked me straight in the face and said forcefully:

'A kick in the pants, that's what some people need! A whacking kick in the pants!'

I tried to believe he was talking of *my* pants and, jumping down from my boulder, I said:

'If you like—but just now we must think of the snares. Come on!'

He followed me.

CHAPTER TWENTY-TWO

THAT night, under the hurricane lamp, I was striving to show perfect peace of mind by tucking into the bacon omelette and stuffed tomatoes with a healthy appetite. Then, as nobody spoke and the silence grew embarrassing—for I could feel they were all thinking of 'the Queen's Knight'— I deliberately began to talk and expounded, as if it were a vital question, on the temperamental differences of the three echoes of Passe-Temps.

The first echo to respond was the one from Petite-Baume, but it answered so quickly that it cut you short as if engaged in an argument, and it started again before it had finished, with the result that it sometimes stuttered. After that, the echo from the Pipits' Field would recite the whole sentence very politely but as if its mind were elsewhere. Finally, the last one (which was rather faraway, hiding in the ivy below the cliff of La Garette) took its time to reflect and then repeated every nuance accurately in a pretty voice that sounded hoarse but always friendly, even when you made it repeat rude words.

These interesting cogitations did not elicit any reply. My father's pensive gaze, Uncle Jules' ambiguous smile, and Paul's diabolical winks soon slowed down my eloquence, which I finally stifled with a big mouthful of rice pudding.

Then Joseph spoke up.

'I'm glad to see you're still interested in echoes, and therefore in the hills. This shows you'll come hunting with us again and go running about with Lili.'

'Running about on two legs,' remarked Uncle Jules, 'is indeed more dignified than going on four . . .'

'What's more,' my mother said briskly, 'a girl of twelve has more brains and craftiness than a boy of seventeen. So if your heart is so set on feminine company, you can play with your sister who is quite as smart as you are.'

I glanced at my little sister, who now had a boyish bob; she didn't grasp what was being said, for she was groggy with sleep, although she kept rubbing her eyelids with the backs of her hands. As smart as I was! How could my worshipped mother talk such extravagant rot?

Paul laughed impudently, with closed eyes and open mouth. I was about to give him a piece of my mind when my father spoke again, and this time peremptorily:

'Tomorrow morning you'll go and help Lili pick green olives, because your mother wants to pot stoned olives for the winter. You'll bring back ten pounds. And in the afternoon, I advise you to set your snares in the Gardener's Valley: Mond des Parpaillounds told us that a fresh flight of orioles will be passing.'

'Now that's interesting!' I said. 'Orioles are lovely—just like golden blackbirds!'

'The wind is blowing straight from the north-east,' said my uncle, 'the very one that brought us those passerines. There's no time to lose, for they'll only stay a week or so . . .'

'Where do they go afterwards?' my mother asked, as if this migration were her major care.

Uncle Jules began a little lecture on the habits and customs of those birds, and my father added some further particulars, freshly culled from the Larousse dictionary. But I realized that all this bird-lore had no other motive than their desire not to prolong my humiliation and to reduce the affair with Isabelle to the size of an incident which, though rather ridiculous, was definitely closed.

*

When the infamous Paul began to snore (while my father was concluding his description of the sicklebill oriole) I picked him up in my arms, carried him upstairs and put him to bed, still unconscious. Then I too undressed.

It seemed to me, however, that the conversation under the fig tree was in full swing. Very gently I opened the window and listened, but they were talking in an undertone and I could only catch snippets in passing:

'Pretty nasty turn of mind . . .' 'Already as stupid as a man . . .' 'silly simpers', 'scapegrace', 'histericle'.

Suddenly, my aunt's clear voice rose above the murmurs.

'I saw her at Mass with her parents. She's quite pretty, but looks conceited and rather sly!'

'That may be,' Uncle Jules said in his normal voice. 'Still, it's nothing to get all that excited about.'

'Of course not!' Joseph agreed. 'But I won't have my son clown about to amuse the daughter of an inveterate soak.'

Without waiting for more to come, I noiselessly closed the window again, slipped under my blankets, and proceeded to draw up my personal balance-sheet.

The situation was extremely serious, above all from a psychological point of view. The sudden hostility shown by my whole family filled me with despair, and I felt as abandoned as Robinson Crusoe. I did not, however, hold this against any of them.

Paul and Lili had betrayed me—but they'd been solely prompted by jealousy, that is to say, by their love for me. This, obviously, was forgivable.

Dear Uncle Jules had blamed me with an affectionate indulgence, marred by mockery, alas.

Aunt Rose had passed a cruel judgment on Isabelle but had said nothing against me.

My mother had been unjust and almost furious: that was simply out of motherly vanity. I was sure she'd have laughed with joy and pride had anyone told her that I had obliged Isabelle to munch live spiders or glow-worm fritters.

And finally, my father had shown all of a sudden the austere face he kept for great occasions and had pronounced his verdict in complete ignorance of the truth.

For that was the great point: where they had all gone wrong was in failing to understand the force of a sentiment that was unique in the world and which they had certainly never experienced themselves—since there was only one Isabelle, and they had not met her! So they just couldn't know that she was unlike everybody else. Aunt Rose had merely caught a glimpse of her from afar—and at Mass when you're not allowed to laugh—and Lili, who spoke of her so rudely, was just a peasant boy. If she had deigned to say a single word to him, he too would have run on all fours and crunched grasshoppers, or perhaps cockroaches. He would have let her blacken him from head to foot and would have fallen asleep with a smile, because of a green silk ribbon round his neck . . .

*

The tone in which Joseph had said his last words left me no hope: he had decided that I should not see her again. If I went there against his wish he would come and fetch me, and perhaps insult the poet whom he had called an inveterate soak! What was I to do?

Of course, I should have told them that the game was merely a series of 'ordeals', that this period was now over and that tomorrow I should be a prince, that is to say, the queen's husband.

In face of the concerted attack by my whole family, I had not had the courage to speak. But perhaps there was still time . . .

Thinking hard, I eventually hit upon a grand solution: I would go and see Isabelle tomorrow, in secret. After the wedding ceremony, and the resulting transfer of power to me, I would lead her to the Bastide-Neuve: with crowned heads, sceptre in hand, and draped in the royal mantles, we would nobly advance, hand in hand, through the daisies, and my family, moved and charmed, would offer us wedding-gifts and adopt Isabelle.

In the day-dreams that precede slumber, everything seems possible and even easy . . . I fell asleep in such perfect bliss that it brought tears to my eyes.

*

When I woke up, it was raining! I opened the window and stared at the hard-falling but transparent drizzle. I looked up to see which way the clouds were moving. There was only one motionless cloud, its brim resting on the semi-circle of the hills. The leaves of the olive trees moved no more than in a picture.

I murmured under my breath:

'The *mistral* will start blowing. It can't stay like this! There's always sunshine after rain.'

Without even opening his eyes, Paul asked:

'Are you talking to me?'

I answered sternly: 'I don't talk to spies. I'm talking to Nature.'

He turned towards the wall, mumbling:

'You're going crazy!'

I did not deign to reply.

*

In the kitchen, my mother was pouring a dribble of boiling water into the filter of the coffee pot.

While I was washing in front of the copper tap, I asked: 'Is Papa still asleep?'

'Oh no,' she said. 'They went shooting early.'

'Was it already raining?'

'Yes, but Uncle Jules said it wouldn't last.'

This was disturbing, for as he applied to Provençal meteorology the knowledge he had acquired in Roussillon, he was fairly frequently mistaken. As my plans required radiant sunshine, however, I accepted his weather forecast without demur.

I washed and brushed myself with great care—a real wedding rub-down.

This diligence roused my mother's distrust; she suddenly eyed me suspiciously.

'You haven't forgotten what your father told you last night, have you? He's forbidden you to go there again.'

'I know,' I said, 'I'm going to see Lili.'

'That'll please everybody, and him above all. When he came and brought the milk every evening and never found you in, I could well see he felt like crying.'

This information left me quite unmoved. In the first place, there is no pity for spies. Moreover, since he now played with Paul, he no longer had need of me. And finally, as Isabelle was now going to take a place in our lives, he would soon get to know her, she would come up into the hills with us, and we'd all be very happy in the end.

I dawdled over my bread and butter, then set out, under my hooded cape, hopping and jumping to avoid the grey puddles that the rain was pricking with a thousand little pecks.

CHAPTER TWENTY-THREE

I was impatient to see the royal mantle which the Infanta, now the Queen Mother, had made for me, and I was preparing the little speech with which I would ask for her authorization to present my Queen to my parents . . .

I arrived at the back of the house, passed round the corner, and listened: a great silence, hardly disturbed by the light rustle of the rain. I ventured a glance: nobody.

I advanced noiselessly, my back brushing against the wall to avoid the dripping of the gutterless tiles. I reached the bead-curtain; I lifted it. The door was open. There was no one in the narrow vestibule. I heard footsteps on the upper floor. Rather diffidently, I knocked at the door. The Infanta's voice cried:

'What is it?'

Then the window opened and she saw me.

'Do come in!' she told me. 'Isabelle is downstairs.'

It seemed to me that neither the look on her face nor the tone of her voice was worthy of a Queen Mother receiving a princely suitor. I walked in.

I stepped forward on tiptoe, to catch my beloved unawares. She was not in the livigroub, in which reigned a certain disorder. I walked along the corridor without making a sound. Above the ceiling, the Queen Mother was striding up and down, opening and closing complaining wardrobe doors.

I reached the kitchen: nobody. Where then was Isabelle? Probably in her room, busy sewing the royal cloak she had promised me? As I was walking back along the dark corridor, I suddenly heard a thundering noise, and a grey door opened in the bulging wall: it was the door of the lavatory.

*

Ever since my earliest childhood I have found it hard to tolerate our enslavement to animal needs that mock our high human estate.

As I ate a chop it would cross my mind that I was chewing a slice of a beast that had been dead for several days, impregnating with sticky spittle a small chunk of a corpse, and I was sickened by the thought that this repulsive action was only the prelude to an abominable ending.

The family ceremony of the pot, which my aunt and mother organized in honour of my little cousin, was always followed by a scrutiny that gave rise to expert opinions: sometimes anxious ones, more often flattering. I would quietly leave the room, sick at heart and holding my breath.

That is why when I saw Isabelle emerge from that cubbyhole of infamy, to the accompaniment of the mighty hiss of the purifying flush, I stood dazed, as if paralysed, and I could feel my heart inside my breast making a little grimace.

She seemed in no way embarrassed and immediately cried:

'You've arrived in the middle of a catastrophe! Come!'

She went towards the livigroub and I followed her, already in despair. She said as she walked:

'First of all, I've caught a cold, I was feverish all night, and now I'm ill. Still, that isn't the worst, because it's happened before . . . But the crowning misfortune . . .'

She had just entered the livigroub, and suddenly broke off to sniff the air:

'Don't you smell something?'

My nose all at once filled with an abominable stench which immediately invaded my whole head.

She ran to open the window and said:

'It's that awful cat again—Felix's cat! He sneaks into the kitchen to steal and then leaves nasty things in the corners!'

While I was wondering whether the mysterious feline was really the one to blame, she picked up the copper shovel in the hearth, and bent down low to look under every piece of furniture, while going on talking.

'And the crowning misfortune, I'll tell you what it is . . .'

Alas! I already knew what it was . . . The crowning misfortune was that my princess, my fairy simply had a stomachache and that her violet-blue eyes were sweeping the ground under the rickety divan in the hope of coming across a cat's droppings . . .

Happily she found it and left, in a reinforced stench, carrying the shovel at arm's length.

I was really very miserable, I went over to the table and saw on it a little pile of exercise-books. On the cover of the top one I read:

LYCÉE MONTGRAND
Exercise-Book
belonging to
Isabelle CASSIGNOL, Form 5A

This name was repeated on each exercise-book. I was wondering who that Isabelle was, when I discovered an envelope addressed to Monsieur Adolphe CASSIGNOL, proof-reader, 'Le Petit Marseillais', Quai du Canal, MARSEILLES.

I was completely bewildered.

She came in saying:

'And now I tell you the worst. My father has had an argument with the director of *Le Petit Marseillais*, who is an idiot and jealous of him, and he's going to another paper where his position will be even more important, but he'll have to stay at the printing plant till midnight! So we're going back to town this afternoon. A cab will come and fetch us at four. So there! There's a catastrophe for you!'

If this news had been announced to me the day before, I should no doubt have burst into tears. But my thoughts were in such a tumult that I simply answered:

'That's a pity . . .'

'Is that all the effect it has on you?'

I opened my arms with a stricken air and shook my head repeatedly. She seemed annoyed.

'I thought you were going to cry!'

I said under my breath, for I was talking to myself:

'So did I.'

'Well,' she said bitterly, 'I know that *I'll* be awfully sad when the cab comes. And yet I have friends in town and am going to start at the Conservatory which is full of artists. And nevertheless I'm sure I won't be able to help crying. And you ought to know why.'

She was very pale, there were rings round her eyes, her face was drawn and her black curls dishevelled: but I had not yet reached the age of heavenly tenderness, and I was quite simply disappointed.

After a pause I asked:

'Are these your exercise-books?'

'Of course,' she said. 'But I won't need them any more at the Conservatory.'

'Well, I shall start on my homework, for the holidays will be over soon and, besides, it'll keep me from thinking of other things.'

'I'll play a farewell piece for you, anyway. I hope that's going to make you cry!'

She really was set on it. I therefore got ready to make a little effort to be pathetic.

But just as she was going to sit down at the piano, she suddenly opened her eyes wide with alarm, and said:

'Wait. I'll be back.'

And she ran out.

Up on the first floor, groaning furniture was being pulled about. Mme Cassignol was putting the house in order before leaving. And Loïs de Montmajour was Adolphe Cassignol, who had assumed a false name, as escaped convicts do. Now I noticed on the cracked marble of the mantelpiece a chipped cup in which undissolved sugar had left sticky marks. There was a hand missing on the tortoiseshell clock, the large Venetian mirror reflected a yellowish mist, flecked with black stars. The precious table-cover was a vast tattered rag, studded with frayed rents, and the queen's name was Isabelle Cassignol . . .

I felt I was ruined, and the lavatory flush rumbled again.

I jumped out of the window and fled through the rain.

CHAPTER TWENTY-FOUR

In my bewilderment I ran to Lili.

As I arrived in the barnyard, a shaft of sunlight brutally stabbed the clouds and struck the peak of Tête-Rouge like an arrow. The vast flock of misty clouds tore itself to pieces against this golden bar, then receded on either side of an azure triangle which widened as you watched it.

On the stone threshold, with a carpet beater, Lili was softening up a salted codfish for his mother's 'aïoli'.[1]

The face he raised towards me was grave but gradually lit up with a lovely smile.

'Do you need something?' he asked me.

'No, I've come to see you because my father told me that the orioles have come . . .'

'I know. I caught three this morning, down below in Gustave's olive groves. If you had the time, it would be the right moment to set snares below the Taoumé.'

He looked me straight in the face and repeated:

'If you had the time.'

'Now I do have the time.'

*

He gave another three strokes to the mummified cod which was beginning to crumble, and asked:

'Is it on account of what they said to you last night?'

'Perhaps. At any rate, I've decided not to go there any more, and I've been to tell her so.'

'Maybe you've told her, but you may go back all the same.'

'Oh no, I won't!'

'How did she take it?'

'She cried, and I think she'll be going away.'

[1] Mayonnaise with pounded garlic—a Provençal speciality.

I was lying out of vanity, but without any qualms, because she had told me that she would be leaving in tears.

'Is she leaving because you aren't going there any more?'

'That's possible. It wouldn't surprise me.'

'That's well done!' he said. 'Shall we go for the snares?'

'This afternoon, because this morning my mother wants us to pick a small basket full of green olives for potting.'

He jumped up, abandoned the cod on the window-sill, and put his hand on my shoulder.

'Come on, *zou*! We'll go right away. I knew she'd want some: I left more than half of them on purpose on the olive tree by Peru's fountain. It's an old tree and a small one, but it gives fruit as big as walnuts!'

CHAPTER TWENTY-FIVE

I BROUGHT our pickings home, and everybody admired them. My father turned them to account to teach us that the olive is a 'drupe' like the plum or the peach. This seemed to me a sad and harsh word, but I was delighted with *olivaison* which is the French name of the olive season.

During lunch, I took care not to inform my family of Isabelle's departure, but I spoke enthusiastically of the thrush-catching plans I had hatched with Lili. As I was praising the marvellous liveliness of the red winged ants— the *aludes*—which he had been feeding with coarse brown paper suitably moistened with lukewarm water twice a day, Uncle Jules said:

'These *aludes* are indeed an excellent bait and attract all the birds. But for thrushes, at this time of year, I recommend this!'

And he pointed to a saucer full of black olives, which my mother had bought at the grocer's.

'We must take advantage of the time while ours are still green, like those you've brought home . . . These here are already quite ripe because they come from Tunisia or perhaps from Greece. So they'll seem a choice rarity to the greedy thrushes and they'll fight to be the first to get strangled.'

My mother—charmed by my return to a healthy frame of mind—promptly said:

'I've got two pounds, and I'll give you half of them.'

*

I was meanwhile thinking of Isabelle and, with the vanity of a little male, I was suddenly afraid that Adolphe Cassignol's daughter might come right here for a tear-drenched farewell and sob in front of my family. As I dreaded pathetic scenes and useless emotions, I decided to escâpe into the hills before Lili's arrival.

I therefore announced that I would set out for the Taoumé all by myself in order to watch the passage of birds and choose the best spots for our snares, and I instructed my mother to tell Lili, when he came at four o'clock, that I would be waiting for him at the charcoal burner's hut at the foot of Mt. Taoumé's spur.

I filled my haversack with snares and put in a paper bag crammed with Tunisian olives. Then, under the watchful eye of my father who wanted to make sure of which way I was going, I took the path into the hills and now and then climbed on a rock to reassure the suspicious Joseph.

On the way I pondered over my adventure.

I saw the grey door again, the dishevelled curls, the horizontal shovel on which the cat's delinquency fumed like smouldering embers . . . She was neither a fairy, nor a queen, nor noble. She was Mademoiselle Cassignol, a little girl like all the others, who had enjoyed humiliating me by making me run on all fours. Paul and Lili had been quite right to sneer at me and to blush at my weakness. And it was a fact that the poet never stopped drinking absinth, and that he would eventually die raving mad and making horrible grimaces, like the plain Adolphe Cassignol he was . . .

However, I had been 'madly in love'. It was an interesting experience and one which I would never forget. I saw Isabelle again under her wreath of poppies, then the little blue petticoat opening like a butterfly in the breeze on the swing. It wasn't her fault, after all, if she'd caught a cold in her tummy. Besides, everybody went to that place, even one's parents. And anyhow, if you tried not to go there, it would be even more disgusting, and you would be dead in no time. Life is like that, and there's nothing you can do about it . . .

As I reached the first plateau, that of Redouneou, I stopped and turned, and lay down in the shadow of a cade . . . I noticed that I could see her house . . . Lying on my side, my elbow propped on the *baouco* grass, my cheek resting on my hand, I looked at the distant acacias which had seen my enslavement and my love . . . The air was calm and the sky clear around the hazy sun. Above Isabelle's roof I could see a stretch of the road that sloped down from Les Bellons to La Treille. It ran, perfectly white, between two rows of olive trees, then disappeared behind a bend.

And suddenly, emerging from under the roof, a carriage appeared. Its black paint gleamed and sparkled, and two black horses were trotting before it. Behind the coachman's back I saw a big hat, the Infanta's. Next to the hat Isabelle was standing, her face turned towards Les Bellons, and her little raised hand was waving a white handkerchief.

I was certain that it was meant for me . . . I jumped up and, without a moment's thought, raced down the stony slope: big tears were rolling down my face and despair choked me . . . But the cab was moving away all the time, with the fast trot of the abducting horses . . . It vanished round the bend . . .

Out of breath I leaned my cheek against the trunk of an olive tree, and wept like a lost child.

On the pebbles of the road fast footsteps were approaching. Lili was climbing ahead of time towards our rendezvous. He saw me, came closer, looked at my face and said:

'What's the matter?'

I dropped my head and murmured:

'She's gone.'

He approached, put his arm around my neck, on my shoulders. And as I was still crying, he said softly:

'Come on, zou, don't be a bloody fool . . . don't be a bloody fool . . . don't be a bloody fool . . .'

He kept repeating his exhortation at least a dozen times, and when he saw that it did not comfort me, he said:

'There now! You'll find her again, in town . . .'

I stammered:

'I don't know her address."

'Did you mention your school to her?'

'Yes.'

'Well then, if she loves you, she'll write to you. And if she doesn't, she isn't worth talking about. Come on, zou, don't be a bloody fool!'

I went on being one for some more minutes, with drooping head, while my tears fell perpendicularly. At last he pulled me towards him gently and dragged me away to the hills. The weight of his arm was still on my shoulders.

CHAPTER TWENTY-SIX

To my great shame I must say that my despair, though sincere, was cut short by an event of great importance.

We had reached the plateau of Baptiste's Pen, and Lili was leading me to the cliff edge, along which he intended to set our snares. As I was still hanging my head I did not see the landscape, but my glance happened to pass beyond the edge of the sheer drop and plunged right down into the valley. Across the tree-tops of the lower pine-wood I suddenly saw, in an empty space amid the dry pine needles, a long green and yellow thing that was quite round and as thick as my thigh, and slow ripples were sliding along it. I opened my eyes so wide that my dried tears tautened the skin over my cheek-bones ... The thing was as long as a man and yet, on my right, I could not see its end, for it emerged from a thick undergrowth. On the left, however, I distinguished through the branches two long horizontal ears on either side of the yellowish triangle that was lying on the ground.

I thought I must be dreaming and strongly squeezed Lili's arm.

'Look! What's that?'

After a moment, he whispered:

'A snake!'

'It can't be, it's got ears!'

'They aren't his. He's about to swallow a hare!'

At that moment something stirred in the undergrowth, two yards away from the big, flat head ... We saw a yellow flash ... This was not another snake: it was its tail!

Lili recoiled three steps; he was quite pale and pulled me by the arm.

'Oh, good Mother of God!' he said. 'It's Pétugue's snake!'

*

Pétugue had a thick, ruddy moustache, and a tuft of ginger hair had earned him his nickname, which is the Provençal name of the hoopoe.

He cultivated in the hills a fairly large vineyard of Jacquez vines: their grapes, tightly clustered, small and blue give a wine of exceptional potency. Pétugue, who was content with an onion in the morning, a few tomatoes at midday, and half a loaf of bread rubbed with garlic at night, completed this diet with five or six litres of this nectar with the result that, to his indignation, he was regarded as the village drunkard.

One afternoon he was seen arriving on the village square, pale, shaking and knock-kneed. Bending over the basin of the fountain, he had drunk like a mule, and this surprising spectacle aroused the curiosity of the butcher and the baker and of Monsieur Vincent, who was just passing by.

Then, still trembling and stuttering, he told of his adventure.

He had spent the morning in his vineyard, then, after a siesta under the big pine tree, had gone down towards the village, as usual, carrying his shotgun under his arm and preceded by his dog, which was called Suffering but did not yet know why.

As he was passing through the bottom of Escaouprès valley, Suffering came to a beautiful point, his four legs stiff and his muzzle pointing, in front of a thicket of needle gorse, over which a holm oak spread from several trunks. Pétugue approached noiselessly: when he was well within range, he shouldered and cried as usual: 'Snap! Snap!'

To his great surprise, Suffering, instead of jumping into the cover, made a prodigious bound backward: but he could not dodge the attack of a huge, yawning, reddish mouth that gripped him in mid-air, threw him to the ground, and pulled him into the thicket, which was immediately shaken by a furious saraband.

Pétugue confessed that he had shrunk back some thirty steps to give himself time to reload his gun with buckshot. During this operation, he had heard Suffering's cries of suffering, then a kind of cracking 'like when you break a faggot of well-dried vine-stocks'. He had flung a big stone into the thicket: then the horrible head had reared into the

132

sky at the top of a huge mattress-spring, thick as a man's calf . . .

'Bang! Bang! I fire one shot after another. Well, my friends, that buckshot made no more impression on it than a handful of chick-peas! It hissed and swayed as it looked at me. I realized that it was trying to make my blood curdle: I took fright, dropped my gun and took advantage of the downward slope of the valley to save my skin. Maybe, if five or six of us went there, with bullets, we might get it!'

*

They went there the next morning, preceded by half a dozen dogs; they found Pétugue's shotgun, but no trace of Suffering or of the monstrous snake. Baptistin T'Other (for there were two in the village) set up a stalking-post in a tree, some twenty-five yards from a black hen tied to a long string: but he never saw the slightest sign of a snake, and while he was rolling himself a cigarette, a fox carried off the hen under his very nose.

After a week it was finally concluded that Pétugue had perhaps seen a big grass snake, that Suffering had followed the track of some bitch with spring fever, and that all the rest was due to the hallucinatory qualities of Jacquez wine.

But Pétugue had always stuck to his story. Gun in hand, he would spend most of his days searching for the monster, and on Sundays, in the village square or at the café, he would tell his tale all over again, even giving up a chance to play bowls in order to be able to gesture.

In the early stages, the snake 'easily' reached a length of four yards; but when the hilarious listeners exchanged knowing winks or openly burst out laughing, Pétugue promptly lengthened the beast by two feet in order to terrorize them.

Then, solemnly calling heaven to witness, he summoned the Good Lord to strike him dead on the spot if he had lied by more than half an inch. With crossed arms and raised eyes, beaming with trust and defiance, he would wait for thirty seconds. The Good Lord—who has other fish to fry— did not strike him dead; so, triumphing bitterly, he would walk away towards the esplanade, in search of other listeners. But at the end of five years, he no longer found anyone

133

patient enough to listen: except the children who would ask him to 'tell about the snake' and would yell with laughter at every word. Sometimes, too, day-trippers would stop; the wag of the party would introduce himself as the special envoy of the Natural History Museum and, with a straight face, ask precise questions about the size of the monster's head, the number of its teeth, and beg him to imitate its hissing: then Pétugue would produce a long, threatening hiss, to the delight of his audience. In short, he had become the village idiot, and his family was ashamed of him.

*

And here was the monster stretching out before our eyes!

We were going to bear witness on behalf of Pétugue and, giving the solemn oath of 'wooden cross, iron cross' on the village square, we would be able to rehabilitate this martyr to the *galéjade*—the Southerners' yarn-spinning propensity—who would clasp us to his heart, with tears in his eyes.

Then, all the hunters of the region would make a *battue* (as happens in Indo-China where there is a warning of a 'man-eating tiger') and we would have the honour of leading them!

*

At the sight of such a beast many men would have beaten a retreat, and every sensible woman would have taken to flight. But my hobnobbing with Redskins, and the boldness of my favourite heroes (who never withdraw before a herd of wild elephants, but rather rejoiced in such splendid luck) had forged me an heroic soul which was fortified by boyhood's natural tendency for showing off, and by the certainty that this kind of adventure could only have a happy ending—at least for the 'nice' characters.

Although the size of the reptile was enhanced by my own littleness, I took a step towards the cliff edge. The terrorized Lili wanted to hold me back, because he had not read my books.

'Don't! If he as much as looks at you, your blood will turn as thin as water!'

I pushed him away without a word and crawled to the very edge of the precipice.

The monster was still there—motionless and horrible.

Slow undulations deformed its neck with a series of sliding bumps that signified the inner hare whose ears, sticking out sideways, had shortened by half.

Lili had joined me without making a sound; and he communicated his impressions to me by pinching my arm. I replied by pulling a variety of faces that expressed my amazement and my admiration.

I motioned him to withdraw, and we took counsel with each other under our breath.

'Do you see that big boulder on the edge of the cliff? It's just above him: if we pushed it, it would drop!'

'You're mad!' he said. 'We're sure to miss him, and afterwards he'd want to harm us.'

'With the hare in his gullet, he can't get up here . . . Come on!'

I crawled again towards my vantage point. He followed me.

I pointed to a rock pillar: it looked as if it would fall exactly on the horrible flat head. We pushed it with our four hands. It did not budge any more than a milestone. Then Lili lay down on his back, and I did likewise. With our shoulders jammed against a rise in the ground, our clenched hands caught tight in cracks, we pushed the rock away with our heels, with all the strength of our grasshopper thighs. It weighed much more than we did and it refused to topple over, but it lifted very slightly, showing a black chink at its base.

With stiffened legs and swollen neck, Lili murmured:

'Hold tight!'

With his right hand, he scratched the soil and picked up a few pebbles which he flung into the chink. While I was arching myself desperately, he repeated this manœuvre several times and at last said:

'Let go gently.'

The pillar moved back: but it could not resume its position, because of the pebbles jammed beneath its base, and it remained leaning forward.

Three times we repeated this operation, and the weighty pillar gradually inclined towards the valley. We took a last pause for rest.

Lili whispered:

'Rub your legs well and breathe as hard as you can. Four times!'

I massaged my calves, then inhaled four times as prescribed.

'Get your back well propped! It'll go off this time. I'll count up to three!'

He counted in a low voice.

I made such a violent effort that my whole body rose up on my heels and shoulders: the tip of the rock slowly moved away, wavered for a second, and vanished.

I heard a dull detonation, followed by a stony rumble that made the ground shake under my back . . . Lili's eyes opened wide with alarm, and we approached on all fours.

I had miscalculated the trajectory of the drop: but Providence, which often takes care of little boys, had rectified my mistake.

Our boulder had fallen on a kind of small balcony of crumbling rock, and a big slab of bluish limestone, loosened from the side of the steep drop, had collapsed on the monster. We could no longer see its head, hidden under some gravel: but its tail was whipping the cades and the rosemary with such violence that we were seized with panic; and we hurtled down the slopes, like hares chased by dogs, all the way to the Bastide-Neuve.

*

Uncle Jules and my father were just coming out of it, their guns on the sling, to have a go at the wood-pigeons at bedtime, under the big pine tree of Tête-Ronde.

They stopped in the middle of the road, surprised by our bounding arrival.

Breathless and gasping for air between words (to make myself interesting) I gave a brief account of our exploit, and sat down on a stone, panting.

Uncle Jules turned incredulously towards Lili.

'Oho!' he said, 'is that snake really so long?'

'As long as from here to the olive tree!' Lili replied, pointing to a tree ten steps away.

I immediately added:

'And it's as thick as my thigh!'

136

'I think you must be exaggerating just a little!' my father said, laughingly. 'Nobody in Provence has ever seen a snake more than a couple of yards long!'

'Excuse me!' cried Lili. 'Poor old Pétugue has been telling about this fellow some fifty years, and everybody thought he was a liar!'

'Besides,' I said, 'there's no point in arguing: come and see it, because by now it must be dead!'

'You go ahead!' Lili said. 'I'll go and fetch a rope to tow it.'

*

It was indeed dead. In its spasms of agony it had managed to extract its half-crushed head from the scree. It was really almost as thick as a stove-pipe, and on its yellow scales there ran a pattern of green arabesques.

One could not clearly judge its length because its body meandered in the undergrowth, but what one could see of it was already stupendous.

The two sportsmen confessed their surprise and advanced, their guns at the ready. I jumped ahead of them with three bounds, and seized the beast by its tail.

'Lili!' I cried, 'try and get the hare out!'

He pulled with both his hands at the sticky ears of the engulfed rodent: he managed to pull out a hairy sausage of amazing length, and flung it into the brushwood. Then I took the rope and passed a noose behind the protuberant jaws of the monster.

I could see that my father was proud of my courage, for he smiled as he looked at me, and said:

'Those crazy kids! Who'd have believed it? And to think that that little goose made him walk on all fours! You ought to go back and see her and drag this reptile right up to her terrace!'

Without displaying the least emotion, and pulling the noose tight, I answered:

'She's gone.'

'Where to?' Uncle Jules asked.

'Back to town.'

'That's a pity,' said Joseph.

Well, yes, it was a pity that she had not been present at

this triumph, which would at last have opened her eyes to the true worth of her knight ... But already Lili was helping me pull at the rope, and the monster was lengthening behind us in all its glory ...

Followed by the sportsmen, who had decided to forget about the wood-pigeons, we towed it home.

Its black, varnished-looking belly slid effortlessly along the sloping path, and we marched ahead, keeping in step. But on a steeper descent the beast gained on us with such a brisk and sudden sprint that I thought it was attacking us. We let go of the rope to jump sideways: the long yellow ribbon passed like a flash between us, but a big stone changed the direction of its slide which it continued on its back before coming to a halt against the trunk of a pine tree. The sportsmen burst out laughing, and I was obliged to laugh louder than they, for it had sent a cold shiver down my back!

Our arrival overjoyed young Paul, who executed a scalp dance around the interminable corpse, while François, who had come to bring us milk, kept repeating:

'*Peuchère* Pétugue! *Peuchère* Pétugue! Lili, fetch him quickly! *Peuchère* Pétugue!'[1]

My father, armed with his yardstick, measured the snake, which I held by its tail while Uncle Jules pulled at the rope in order to give it its full glorious length.

In the meantime, our dear women, leaning out of the window, emitted cries of horror and disgust, and my mother kept rubbing her arm to remove the goose-flesh.

'Three yards, eight inches!' my father announced.

'You'd think it was a python that had escaped from a circus!' said Uncle Jules.

I was, however, a trifle disappointed by this metrical operation, for it fixed a limit beyond which the monster could no longer grow in the telling of my tale.

'*Peuchère* Pétugue!' François was saying.

We set out in a procession towards the village.

[1] *Peuchreè*, a Provençal exclamation of many meanings, here stands roughly for: poor dear.

CHAPTER TWENTY-SEVEN

On the little square, near the fountain, there was a circle of children at first; the women arrived next, then the farmers. Cries of surprise, of horror, of admiration, surrounded me; as Lili had gone to fetch Pétugue, who was up in his vineyard, I was alone next to the reptile, in the middle of the circle, and I answered a thousand questions, assuming the impassive face of a Slayer of Serpents.

The women were saying:

'*Bou Diou*, what a monster!'—'Just looking at him gives me goose-pimples!'—'What a brave boy!'—'He's the real monster!'

The girls were looking at me with visible admiration, and I could not help swelling my chest. So great was my glory that young Paul slipped through the crowd and placed himself next to me, holding my hand, so as to have his little share of it . . .

Mond des Parpaillouns arrived with long strides. He took the snake by the neck, opened its jaw and, despite the dreadful stench, closely scrutinized its teeth, without apparently feeling any ill effects. Then he spoke.

His vocabulary was no vaster than François's, but it was quite sufficient to express his thoughts and feelings. He communicated them to us by saying:

'What a son of a bitch! Now that's a fine son of a bitch!'

He repeated this opinion some ten times, chuckling complacently. Then he suddenly pointed his forefinger at me and expressed his admiration in the following terms:

'And he too is a son of a bitch! A hell of a son of a bitch!'

Thereupon *Monsieur le Curé* arrived, followed by Monsieur Vincent.

Monsieur Vincent admired and loudly congratulated me, while the Curé, who was carrying his photographic apparatus slung over his shoulder, examined the beast in silence but with a scholarly air. At last he said to Joseph (who was smiling at him in a friendly way):

'This animal obviously belongs to the species of Colubridae.'

'Without a doubt,' said my father, 'for it has no poison fangs.'

'That's well observed,' said Monsieur le Curé. 'But,' he added, raising his forefinger, 'it is not at all a *colubra gigantea*, as you might be led to believe . . .'

Despite the presence of those Latin words, Joseph faintly motioned 'no' with his head, to indicate that he was not misled.

'For,' the Curé went on, 'despite its name, the *gigantea* is never gigantic.'

Joseph approved, with a pitying smile for the pretentious *gigantea*.

'What, then, is it?' asked Uncle Jules.

'To my mind,' said the Curé, 'according to its colouring, it would seem to be a *viridiflavus*, which means green and yellow . . . But I want to fix the brute and its victor at once on the sensitive plate!'

He took me by the shoulder, led me towards the animal's head, and placed in my hand the stick borrowed from Mond des Parpaillouns.

'Stick this lance into the monster's skull and rest your foot on its neck.'

I adopted the pose with much conceit. Young Paul had dropped my hand, but regretfully: he only waited for a sign to come and stand next to me. But glory spoils the heart of man, and I never made the sign.

Monsieur le Curé stepped back and said, as he fiddled with his camera:

'Bellerofon slaying the dragon!'

My heart gave a little twinge . . . Isabelle, my dear Isabelle . . . I thought of making inquiries about this Bellerofon, whose spelling I did not even know, but to whom I bore such a terrific resemblance, since the poet already had told me so . . . Then I saw again the glistening cab that had carried my love away to the city . . . But the Curé suddenly cried:

'Look at me!...Smile! Good. We mustn't move now! One, two, three! Thank you.'

He pulled a sort of glass pane from his camera, took another one just like it from a black bag, and inserted it in the former's place.

Meanwhile, Lili had appeared panting at the far end of the square. He shouted:

'Pétugue's coming!'

And he went to stand modestly behind Monsieur Vincent, with his head lowered and his hands in his pockets, noiselessly scraping the gravel with the tip of his shoe. I cried:

'Please, Monsieur le Curé, wait a second! I wasn't the only one to kill him. Lili, come on!'

Without looking at me, he shook his head.

'Come on,' my father urged him. 'Hurry up! You're going to be photographed . . .'

He mumbled, blushing all over:

'Don't bother, really! I wouldn't know how, anyway, 'cos it's never been done to me before!'

Everybody laughed, and Uncle Jules intervened:

'Hurry up, fathead! All you have to do is keep still while Monsieur le Curé is counting!'

He gripped him by the shoulder and pushed him forward.

Beaming with pleasure, Lili reached my side in three bounds, slipped his arm into mine and proudly raised his head.

'Look out!' Monsieur le Curé cried again.

Young Paul, unable to restrain himself any longer, had slipped behind us, he suddenly squeezed his head between our hips and gave a lovely smile in the direction of the camera. I did not have the heart to push him away, and the Curé operated for the second time in a religious silence.

Then Mond cried:

'Here's Pétugue!'

He had got here at last, on his drunkard's legs, followed by a fresh swarm of children.

This was the second stage of our glory and, no doubt, its apotheosis. I was going to tell him the story of our exploit, restore his honour, and confound all those who had hitherto accused him of lying: it would be a solemn moment.

141

In a deep, respectful silence, eloquent of the remorse of the whole village, the circle of bystanders opened wide to let him pass.

But he did not condescend to approach the reptile.

Stopping ten steps away, he looked at it for a moment, burst into sarcastic laughter, and cried with insulting contempt:

'Is that your serpent? Oh, Good Mother of God! Well, I can tell you that MINE, MINE is twice as thick and three times longer! It has a head like a calf, mine has, and it could make a mouthful of five or six little turds like you!'

He turned on his heel and tottered away, limping and jeering. After ten steps he turned round and cried:

'Next to MINE, this one is a piece of STRING!'

The indignant company responded by booing, but were quickly appeased by Monsieur le Curé.

'We must be charitable,' he said. 'For I'm sure the poor man is quite sincere.'

'*Monsieur le Curé* is right,' said Joseph. 'What we mustn't forget is that he downs five or six litres a day, and that his snake has for a long time now fed on the vapours of Jacquez wine. So it's gradually invaded all the available intellectual space—which can't have been very vast in the first place—and that's why he no longer recognizes it!'

'Sure enough,' said Mond, 'that must be it!'

He turned to François, who looked perplexed.

'Do you get it? It means that he's had that snake in his noddle for ten years . . . And by and by it's swollen his brain. So it squelches the roots of his eyes, and that's why he sees it much littler.'

CHAPTER TWENTY-EIGHT

I CONFESS that this epic and romantic event absorbed all my thoughts for two days. The need of facing first danger, then to glory, had forced me to lay aside my treasury of grief, regret and hope. On the second night, before falling asleep, I called upon my memories: but the image of the young face was almost at once replaced by the photograph which Monsieur le Curé had promised me: I decided to send it to Isabelle, with a letter signed Bellerofon as soon as I had checked the spelling of this glorious name in the dictionary.

The letter would contain the account of that grand adventure, a suitably edited account. It seemed to me that—in everybody's interest—I should say nothing of the murderous stone-fall. It was preferable to have killed the monster by hurling at it a single sharp stone with a steady hand, at the very moment when its huge head was swaying in the air, ready to pounce on me. On the other hand, it might not, perhaps, be necessary to mention Lili and give him a share of the glory which he did not care about and which, therefore, would be wasted.

This version was also intended for the use of aunts, cousins, and even of my future classmates at the *lycée*, its credibility being assured by the irrefutable photograph.

After copying from the *Petit Larousse* the hazardous spelling of Bellerophon, I started drafting this epic when Uncle Jules, returning from Mass, brought me a sad piece of news: by some inexplicable deviltry, the Catholic camera hadn't worked and all the chemistry of Monsieur le Curé had been unable to conjure up the slightest picture from the bedevilled plates . . . As bad luck would have it, my aunt and my mother had forced us to bury the corpse on the pretext that its decomposition was threatening us with a serpentine plague, and with cries of horror they set their faces against an exhumation which would have enabled us to pose for fresh photographs ...

Monsieur le Curé's failure was therefore beyond repair, for without substantiating evidence my song of victory had a good chance of being taken for a *galéjade*, and Bellerophon for another Pétugue ... I therefore renounced writing my letter and took refuge in my renewed friendship with Lili.

*

We were in mid-September, the month of blue sloes, berried ivy, red arbutus-berries, sun-gilt stones. The first snow in the Alps sent us heavy thrushes, which Baptistin bought from us at a franc apiece, because he resold them for two. That is how I was able to replace surreptitiously the scissors borrowed from Aunt Rose, who found them in the very place where she had looked for them a dozen times, and this perturbed her all the more as their inaction seemed to have made them new and lengthened their blades a little. But the only conclusions she drew from this was to blame her failing memory.

Further, I was rich enough to buy a scarf of Pyrenees wool from the pedlar, and this filled my mother with more joy and pride than a diamond necklace. I must say that it had cost me seven francs, the price of fourteen bags of marbles at the general store in the Chemin des Chartreux. For no woman have I ever made so great a sacrifice in proportion to my wealth.

We spent all our days up in the hills, and we had nine dozen snares. To make the rounds twice a day, we had to walk for six hours: the last round, at night, took us all along the hill-crests up to the plateau of Baume-Sourne.

A huge red sun would be setting far away in a sulphurous sea, our shadows would already be long: their feet sticking to our soles, they would slide on our right over the surface of the kermes oaks, be slashed in two, in passing, by a pine tree trunk and suddenly loom vertical against a golden rock face. The first hardly perceptible evening breeze flowed towards us from the hilltops. In the sky, a black flight of starlings dived and soared again, changing in size and shape along unexpected curves, like an ant-hill carried away by the wind,

144

and then, amid the resinous silence of the pine-woods, a few lost notes of the angelus of Allauch would evangelize the echoes of the cliffs.

I had not forgotten my love, but my grief took on the tinge of the season: it was a wistful regret, a tender melancholy which recomposed my memories. I had obliterated the humiliating ordeals, the poet on all fours on the road and the devastating last appearance of the Cassignol family. I saw two violet-blue eyes across a sheaf of irises, a bunch of blue grapes before half-open lips, and, on the singing swing, the brown nape of a little girl who was pointing her white sandals towards the quivering boughs of an olive tree . . . Then, in my dreams at night, I would hear distant music and the little red queen would glide away, infinitely sad and lonely, under the gloomy arches of the forests of long ago.

CHAPTER TWENTY-NINE

I WAS quite happy now and thought that the real holidays were beginning. I should have understood, however, the warning of the short showers and noticed that the hurricane lamp was no longer swinging under the branch of the fig tree: we had our evening meal in the dining-room, under a modern hanging-lamp of fretted brass, whose opaline half-globe had a fringe of blue crystal drops.

While I was admiring Uncle Jules's virtuosity in elegantly carving a partridge, my father said to me without any preamble, and as if it were the most natural thing in the world:

'So tomorrow at ten sharp, we'll start reviewing.'

Paul underlined this announcement with a burst of mocking laughter.

As I manifested indignant surprise and my eyes searched for the Post Office calendar, Joseph continued:

'I can quite understand that you have lost all notion of time, because you've had some very interesting occupations this year.'

'Yes, indeed,' my uncle chimed. 'Hunting, trapping, nature, high society . . .'

'The fiancée!' cried Paul. 'He went there all the time! And they didn't want me!'

'Shut up!' said my mother. 'Since it's over, we don't talk of it any more.'

'But I—' Paul started.

He could not finish his sentence, for she had just pulled the knot of his napkin tight round his neck, and she added:

'Eat up your soup, you can talk later.'

'At any rate,' Joseph went on, 'a period of your life has just come to an end: today is the 18th of September, and you'll make your entrance into Secondary Education on Monday, October 3rd, that is, in a fortnight.'

'Yes, of course . . .' I agreed. 'But one can still have lots of fun in a fortnight!'

'You can have fun till ten in the morning,' said my father. 'But the rest of the day will henceforward be devoted to reviewing. It's essential that your beginnings at the *lycée* should be brilliant so as to do honour to our elementary schools, which those gentlemen of the Secondary sometimes seem to despise . . .'

And out of the corner of his eye, he glanced at Uncle Jules who, his blue eyes bulging over the white part of the partridge, was straining to extract the number six shots which he himself had grafted into the flesh of the unfortunate fowl.

My uncle suddenly interrupted his surgical investigations, pointed his knife tip towards the ceiling, and cried:

'No, no, my dear Joseph, no! Nobody despises elementary education. It's the only praiseworthy result produced by your Revolution. But it is true that we can reproach those who have never gone further for thinking they know everything and have exhausted the sum of human knowledge when they leave school with their Higher Certificate. I'm not saying that of you, who on the contrary are modest to a fault. But you must admit that there are some of them who overdo it.'

My mother became quite pink, there was a pinched look about her nose, and she said abruptly:

'There are pretentious people everywhere, and perhaps even at the Prefecture!'

'Oh! there's no lack of them!' said Aunt Rose.

'But we know of simple schoolmasters,' Augustine continued (and she was speaking more and more quickly), 'who have become High School professors or inspectors of the *Académie*, and even doctors, and even members of Parliament!'

Uncle Jules realized that he had sat down on an ant-heap; and as, moreover, he was very fond of his little sister-in-law, he replied with great conviction:

'You're right, my dear Augustine: there are ministers, high magistrates, great lawyers, who are former schoolmasters. But allow me to add that those were the very people

147

who completed their elementary tuition with several years' hard work in Higher education and at the Universities!'

'Obviously,' said Joseph, 'that's normal.'

'Besides,' Uncle Jules added, 'I admit and proclaim that up to School Certificate, the common elementary school is much superior to the prep. school at the *lycées*!'

My mother now gave him a lovely smile, while Joseph confirmed this semi-official declaration by an official testimony:

'I've heard our school superintendent say so himself, and I hope that Marcel will prove it once more this year.'

He turned to me and said gravely:

'You owe a debt to the Republic, the daughter of the Revolution. She has granted you a Scholarship: that is to say, she will give you sound instruction free of charge, will pay for your lunches and will lend you every year all the books required for your studies until your second *baccalauréat*. We must show ourselves worthy of such great generosity and, without the least regret, consent to sacrificing a few days of our holidays. We'll start reviewing tomorrow morning.'

'Can't you leave him another two days?' my mother asked.

'My dear,' said Uncle Jules sternly, 'if it had been my son, I'd have put him to work the day after August 15th.'

I looked at cousin Pierre. Perched on his high chair, he was shaking his rattle from time to time and had no misgivings of what was in store for him.

While my aunt, already alarmed, was carrying him off to his cot, my uncle talked at length about the *lycée*: he had spent six years at the one in Perpignan, and another four years at Marseilles.

He began by describing to us the punishment cell of the *lycée* at Marseilles: it was, he said, a real dungeon, almost subterranean, for it was below the staircase and only received scant light, through a small, square grille, from an echoing corridor which was almost always deserted.

Paul gripped my hand and pressed it with feeling. My mother looked pale and expressed her indignation that one should treat children 'like criminals'. My father at once set her mind at rest: staring fixedly at Uncle Jules, he declared that those reactionary methods, a dreadful legacy of a clerical past, had most certainly been abolished for a very long time.

Uncle Jules replied with spirit that he was not born in the days of King Herod and that he had, nevertheless, been locked up once in this prison; that this ordeal had left him with the dreadful memory of a long battle in the twilight with a fierce rat which had stolen his crust of bread, and that he owed his success in his subsequent life to the fear of a second encounter with that frantic rodent.

His conclusion was aggressive:

'It is, however, possible that this punishment is no longer in use. This would explain the mediocrity of present-day graduates, just as the destruction of the Bastille explains the anarchy in which we're living.'

Joseph, with flaring nostrils, was certainly going to talk of St. Bartholomew's Massacre and the crimes of the Inquisition, when Aunt Rose gave a cry of pain: by extraordinary chance, a wasp—or perhaps a spider (one never knows)—had just cruelly stung her in the calf, and Uncle Jules rushed into the kitchen to fetch a bottle of ammonia, of which my mother shouted a description ('a red label, on the second shelf to the right'), but which he could not find.

This did not surprise me, for nobody had ever seen it there or anywhere else for that matter.

*

Next morning, as we set out under the last waning stars, I announced the sad news to Lili. He comforted me as best he could, and declared it was nice enough, to be able to go poaching from five to nine. Anyhow, he himself would be requisitioned for picking the 'love-apples' for winter and for the first autumn ploughing . . .

I came home towards ten, laden with game which I ostentatiously spread out on the dining-room table in the hope of obtaining permission to go and set snares again in the evening. But my father pushed the thrushes away without a word, and made me take a long dictation which related in vain the misfortunes of an idiotic king called Boabdil.

In the afternoon, after a festival of logical analyses and a short recess, I had to adjust the flow of three water-taps that

149

were filling a basin, then calculate the speeds of a cyclist who was trying—I don't know why—to catch up with a horseman, whose mount stopped every now and then to have a drink. After which Paul was summoned to listen to a reading, which I had to do aloud, of the mishaps of Vercingetorix . . .

At last, at five o'clock, Uncle Jules came back from the shoot, with a partridge in each hand. He threw them on my thrushes and administered to me 'Rosa the Rose', first declension. Joseph listened with naïve interest.

I asked him:

'Why do you want me to learn a language that you don't know yourself? What good will it do me?'

He answered:

'If one has learnt nothing but French, one doesn't know French well. You'll realize that later.'

I was appalled by this reply, by which he stood himself condemned.

Moreover, the twelve 'cases' of this rose were rather an odd surprise. I asked Uncle Jules:

'What's the use of twelve names for the same flower?'

He was only too eager to unfold the mystery to us. The explanation was passably terrifying: the Latin words changed face continuously according to their function, which enabled you to place them anywhere! I concluded from this that I would never know Latin: but to please Joseph, I learnt the twelve cases of 'Rosa the Rose', like a parrot.

These lessons only lasted for six days, anyway, for we had to go back to town—for good—to complete our preparations.

*

On the last evening, I went to say good-bye to Lili whom I had not seen all day.

In his parents' vast barn, a ray of the setting sun entering through the skylight illuminated a bar of gold dust.

He was sitting on a stool, in front of a big heap of small love-apples, which looked like red plums. Each one had a green stalk which he inserted between the two strands of a double string, then tied a knot, before placing the next one. He thus plaited long braids of brilliant red, which he hung from the beams of the timbered roof.

For a moment I watched him work in silence. At last he raised his head and said:

'At heart you must be pleased to go back to town.'

'Why?'

'Because there you'll see HER again, perhaps.'

'First of all, I don't know her address. And then, I won't have time.'

He carefully tightened twice the end knot of a plait, and said without looking at me:

'We've had fun this year—but we might have had more. It's a pity . . .'

I made no answer to these regrets. He probably would have liked to hear me disown Isabelle: I refused without saying a word, but he understood and changed the subject.

'What's it like, that new school you're going?'

I promptly described to him the *lycée*—which I did not know—as a temple of knowledge. I dwelled particularly on Latin, then on the punishment cell where Uncle Jules had all but perished. He urgently advised me always to have a small rat-trap on me, then he got up, went to rummage in a sack and put into my pocket a handful of poisoned corn . . .

Meanwhile, I was looking at the long plaits of red fruit and wondering whether it would not have been more sensible to tie up tomatoes all my life rather than learning—without the slightest hope—the twelve cases of 'Rosa the Rose' . . .

CHAPTER THIRTY

In town, my mother, with the help of the sewing-machine, finished a black schoolboy smock, cut out of crackling sateen which shone with all the gloss of its dressing: this I was no longer to wear in the street, but only at the *lycée*, where it was to remain henceforward. For outdoor wear I was given a wide-collared sailor-suit which included not only knee-breeches, but a pair of long trousers—'just in case'. On the ribbon of my cap, the name of Surcouf gleamed in gold lettering. My mother bought me a pair of 'hand-sewn' shoes with nailed soles, and we went to the 'Belle Jardinière' to choose a little half-belted overcoat which I could admire on my person in a three-sided mirror and of which I was as proud as of an Academician's cape.

Moreover, I discovered my profile that day: I had never yet seen it and was delighted with this free gift. Paul meanwhile asked the loquacious salesman why this lovely gardener —'La Belle Jardinière'—spent her time making suits instead of looking after her garden.

On the night preceding the great day, there was a dinner at Aunt Rose's.

She first presented me with a pencil-box of glazed cardboard: on the lid one could see Napoleon at St. Helena: one hand on his stomach, the other shielding his forehead, he was gazing at the sea. It was very beautiful. If you pressed a button, the lid opened by itself: I then discovered three new pen-holders, nibs of all shapes (there was one with a duck's bill), several coloured pencils and, above all, an india-rubber so soft and velvety that I was dying to eat it right away.

My uncle made me a present of a box of compasses and dividers, which had cost 2 Fr. 95 (it was marked on the label), a blotter bound in real leather, and six exercise-books with stiff covers on which he had written my name in fine roundhand: it looked as if it had been printed.

These presents filled me with joy, but I was a little worried on account of Paul's jealous admiration: Aunt Rose, however, had foreseen everything, and when he lifted his napkin, he discovered a very pretty pocket-knife with four blades: they were half-open at different angles, one could count them straightaway, just as in a shop-window. He then kissed everybody, and his happiness was complete when I declared that I would gladly give my pencil-box to have such a beautiful pocket knife.

During dinner my father gave me final detailed recommendations.

He first confirmed that, as was to be expected, the Republic had abolished the sinister punishment cell, for he had made inquiries. We were all well pleased to hear it, especially young Paul who had been trembling for me. But, he added, one must not believe that a lycée was a carnival for all that, and he particularly dwelt on the sanction of being 'kept in', which is something like being sentenced to hard labour and brings the blush of shame to the brow of a family.

Uncle Jules, during the dessert, described the supreme punishment: a summons to appear before the Disciplinary Council, from which one of his fellow-pupils had emerged alive, but disgraced.

At last, when we got home—it was past nine o'clock at night—all the parts of my equipment were laid out in my room: the clothes on a chair, the new socks in the new shoes, and on the chest of drawers a knapsack, made of imitation leather, bulging with my exercise-books, pencil-box, and carefully folded smock.

In short, this new departure in life was prepared with as much care as the placing of a sputnik on its orbit, and I was soon to discover that I was indeed entering into a new universe.

*

On Monday, October 3rd, at six in the morning, the great call to action. sounded. Washed, scrubbed, scoured (I almost pierced my ear-drums) and filled to the brim with bread and butter, I put on my sailor-suit. Paul was wearing a brand-new grey blouse and a handsome white turn-down collar, from which emerged a pretty sky-blue silk bow. As for Joseph, he seemed a little choked by his starched collar (it was always like that after the holidays) but he nevertheless looked very stylish in his light grey suit, brilliantly set off by a socialist tie of red silk.

My mother had warned us that she would not be able to accompany us, because my little sister had no suitable dress for the occasion. I was glad of it, for I feared the ridicule of entering the *lycée* at the head of a family procession, like the corpse at a funeral.

So we left, three strong, towards half past seven. I was walking on Joseph's right, while Paul clung to his left hand.

My knapsack, pulling my shoulders back, stuck out my chest to advantage, and my new heels clicked against the pavement which was still cluttered up with the dust-bins of early morning.

My father pointed out to me in passing the names of the streets, so as to put me in a position to find my way home again. My mother was to fetch me from school that evening, but thereafter I would have to navigate unaided between the *lycée* and our home, which frightened me a little.

After a quarter of an hour's walk we arrived at one end of the Rue de la Bibliothèque: Joseph pointed out that this street was noteworthy for the fact that it contained no library of any kind, and that I must not be led astray by this false appellation.

It issued onto the top of a steep slope, which we walked down at a fast stride.

Near the bottom of this descent, my father pointed to an enormous building on our right.

'That's the *lycée*,' he told me.

In the middle of the vast façade, under some very old plane trees standing on the edge of the pavement, I saw a crowd of boys and young men, carrying brief cases under their arms or knapsacks on their backs. A double door, like a cathedral doorway, stood ajar. People were walking in and out of it, but the groups of schoolboys who were chatting in circles on the pavement seemed in no hurry to slake their thirst at the fountain-head of all knowledge.

'This door,' said my father, 'is that of the day-school, that's to say the building where the classrooms are. You have to go in by the door of the boarding-school, on the other side of the building.'

We passed through the groups, from which surged bursts of laughter or which greeted the arrival of fellow-pupils with loud acclaim.

We went on walking down the slope and, after we had gone some hundred steps, I was amazed to find the building was still following us.

At the moment when the boulevard swerved off to the right, a bronze hullabaloo fell about our heads: on the edge of the roof—which rose to a stupendous height—I saw in a kind of little house with a triangular pediment the face of a clock as big as a cartwheel.

'Half past seven!' said Joseph.

'It chimed at least four times!'

'Eight chimes for the half hour!' he went on. 'It's a *carillon*. Four chimes for the quarter hour, eight for the half hour, twelve for a quarter to, sixteen for the full hour and, of course, it also strikes the hours on another bell. So that at noon, for instance, it rings twenty-eight times!'

'I can read the time quite well on the clock in our room,' said Paul, 'but I wouldn't be able to count this one!'

I was already surprised by this resounding novelty, and it seemed to me that in this school time itself was being very closely supervised.

We walked for another few minutes, then turned to the right into a small street.

'The Rue du Lycée,' my father said. 'You'll remember, won't you? You first go down the Boulevard du Musée, then take the Rue du Lycée . . .'

It led us to a small square, which was also called the Place du Lycée . . . Always that *Lycée*!

It made the gigantic school of the Chemin des Chartreux lose its capital letters, for it now seemed shrunk to the size of a little private boarding-school.

At the top of a flight of at least fifteen steps there was another double door, a little smaller than the first, but flanked by two high windows, whose iron bars proved the presence of captives.

This door was closed, but at the far end of the square

there was another, smaller one, and this one stood wide open on a rectangular entrance-hall.

There, behind a glass screen, sat a doorkeeper, or rather an officer of the Doorkeepers' Corps, for he wore a tunic with gold buttons.

This man obviously did not know whom he was dealing with, for he stared at us through the glass for half a minute before opening the glass of a kind of ticket window.

To my great surprise, my father did not make himself known. He merely asked where the day-boarders of the 6th form A2 were to assemble.

The other answered with the most surprising indifference:

'Pass through the small yard, the corridor on the right. *Monsieur le Surveillant général* will tell you.'

Whereupon he closed his window, without bestowing on us the slightest smile of welcome.

My father was weak enough, however, to say 'thank you'.

'Is that the headmaster?' asked Paul.

'No,' said my father. 'That's the doorkeeper.'

I asked: 'Why didn't you tell him your name?'

'Because he wouldn't know it.'

This reply perturbed me. The doorkeeper of our school called him Monsieur Joseph, with a most respectful familiarity; he often asked for news of my mother's health and would sometimes say: 'It's quite unfair that you have not yet got the *palmes académiques*, Monsieur Joseph. I consider that you deserve them quite as much as the Head.' Whereas this monkey, shut up in his glass cage, looked as sad and also as insolent as the animals in the zoo.

It seemed to me that this was 'a bad start'; my father had to drag Paul along who, with his head screwed back to front, was making sure the door had not closed on his liberty.

We passed through a small yard, paved like a sidewalk, and we walked into the building through a low door which seemed all the narrower for being cut through a three-foot-thick wall.

At the end of this tunnel, we came out into a corridor as high as a church.

On the black and white flagstones that stretched out as far as the eye could see, schoolboys of all ages milled around.

The youngest ones were accompanied by gentlemen or ladies in rich clothes, all of whom had the looks of pupils' parents. At the intersection of two corridors, we found *Monsieur le Surveillant général* at the door of his office.

He was a stocky little man with a goatee below a thick pepper-and-salt moustache. He wore quivering *pince-nez*, tied to his buttonhole with a black cord. On his head sat a grey velvet skull-cap, of the same colour as his jacket.

Besieged by a semi-circle of children and parents, he cast a glance at the sheets of paper held out to him and directed the pupils; but beyond this fatal spot the parents were not entitled to follow them. There was a great deal of kissing; I even saw one little fair-haired chap crying and refusing to let go of his mother's hand.

'That's probably a boarder,' said my father. 'He won't see his parents again till Christmas.'

This seemed such a cruel thought to Paul that it brought tears to his eyes.

Joseph meanwhile had handed my paper to the *Surveillant général*. He glanced at it and said without a moment's hesitation:

'Third door to the left. Pass through the prep room, leave your things there and go and wait in the Junior courtyard.'

It was *me* that he was addressing as *'vous'*!

I could see that my father would have liked to talk to him: but other sheets were already before his eyes, and he continued to distribute schoolboys in all directions, like someone dealing cards.

'Well,' said my father, 'we too have a beginning of term, and we mustn't be late.'

He kissed me, and I kissed Paul who could not keep back his tears.

'Don't cry,' I told him. 'I won't be here till Christmas! I'll be back at home tonight.'

'You'll tell me everything?'

'Everything!'

'And if they put you in the dungeon?'

'Papa told you: it isn't done any more on account of the Revolution . . .'

'Come on!' said Joseph. 'Let's go. It's a quarter to eight!'

He dragged him off while I was walking away . . .

I got to the third door. I turned round. Through the bustle of schoolboys I could see them both, stopping before the tunnel on the way out: they were looking at me, and Paul was waving good-bye to me with his raised hand.

*

To reach the recreation yard I had to pass through what the *Surveillant général* had called the 'prep room'. This was a classroom in which three columns of desks, each seating two, advanced towards a table set up on a rostrum which seemed to me of abnormal height. Along the walls, at the level of my head, ran a long row of small lockers.

Seeing that there were schoolboys' briefcases and bundles of books tied with straps on the desks, I unbuckled my knapsack, took my smock out of it and put it on over my suit. As I was buttoning it up I noticed that on the big blackboard which was fastened to the wall above the rostrum, an anonymous hand had traced, in capitals, the famous word of General Cambronne. The solitary five-letter word, without comma or full-stop, had no doubt spent the two holiday months staring at the empty desks amid silence and indifference, and I had the impression that it was dead: but suddenly I was afraid that a supervisor's entrance might revive its insolence, and I ran for safety to the Junior yard.

Under the very old plane trees, yellowed by autumn, there were already some thirty boys.

I immediately noticed five or six Chinese (actually they were Annamites), a Negro and a swarthy boy with frizzy hair. I was to learn later that he was the son of a mighty Algerian Arab chief. The others were ordinary schoolboys.

Some were wearing brand-new outdoor clothes, but almost all of them had black smocks, limp with long use, studded with patched rents and fastened all awry, for lack of buttons.

My own smock, too well pressed, fell in stiff pleats and gleamed with all its lustre while my new shoes, which were a little tight around my ankles, were saying, 'wheat, wheat, wheat', at every step.

I was afraid this outfit might advertise my newness; but the boys—several of them a year or two older than I—had already organized games that claimed all their attention.

There were games of marbles and leap-frog going on. Right in the middle of the yard, a knights' tournament assembled some twenty participants.

The big boys—the black boy among them—served as mounts. They lined up in two rows facing each other at a distance of ten yards. Then, at a given signal, they rushed forward with wild shouts and the neighing of palfreys. The horsemen grabbed at one another's hair in an aerial fight and tried hard to dismount the adversary, while the horses attacked one another with vicious kicks. At every moment some combatant would tumble down and the fierce winner would immediately veer to attack some other victim.

This seemed to me a beautiful game, but at the Chemin des Chartreux school the masters would never have tolerated it. My eyes cast around for the teacher, who would probably let fly a volley of dishonouring punishments. I saw a young man walking up and down, his hands clasped behind his back. He was skinny and crowned with a big black felt hat. He was thinking. Whenever he passed close to the tournament he raised his eyes towards the combatants with blank indifference, and I got the impression that he had resolved to stop his walk only in the event of an ascertainable death.

More schoolboys were arriving all the time. The older ones, very much at home, would rush into the yard at a gallop, sometimes with loud yells, and promptly throw themselves into the lists. I was glad to see some new smocks that, like myself, did not venture to advance too far and did not speak to anyone. One of these newcomers, watching the skirmish, came to stand next to me. After a moment he asked me: 'Are you a new boy?'

'Yes, and you?'

'So am I.'

He was small, almost diminutive. His curly, gleaming black hair brought out the pallor of his skin. His eyes shone like anthracite, and thin blue veins could be seen on his temple.

'Where are you from?'

'The elementary school in the Rue de Lodi.'

'I come from the one in the Chemin des Chartreux.'

We were friends straightaway.

'Which form are you in?'

'Sixth B 1.'

'I'm in the Sixth A 2.'

'Then we won't be in the same class, but we're both in prep 7.'

'What's your name?'

'Oliva.'

I gave a start.

'Were you the one who passed out First in the Scholarship exams?'

He blushed just a little.

'Yes. Who told you?'

'I came second.'

He smiled, amazed.

'Now, that's extraordinary!'

I too considered that our meeting was due to a fantastic chance, a caprice of fate. Yet it was obvious that two boys who had got their scholarships for the sixth form in the same year would necessarily find themselves together at the beginning of term. But so far we had been no more than a competitor's name to each other, and this sudden materialization seemed to us as surprising as the apparition of Tom Thumb or Captain Nemo in the flesh. That is why we gazed at each other, alarmed and delighted.

'I was stumped by the problems in arithmetic,' I said at once. 'Whereas you got it!'

'It was a fluke,' he said. 'I got three solutions and didn't know which was the right one. I chose one at random and just struck lucky.'

I liked this confession. This scrawny chicken-neck was a '*chic type*'—a good sport. I was sorry to have tried to give him a bad name as a counterfeiter's son and—mentally—apologized to him.

Just then, the *lycée* came crashing down on our heads.

I gave a big jump forward, then turned round and saw a little man with a thick moustache furiously beating a drum. This instrument—of yellow brass between two blue wooden hoops—looked enormous, and I was wondering why this virtuoso gave us such an ear-splitting concert when the stampeding crowd swept me towards the door of the prep room: everybody lined up in two rows, in front of the drummer, who was still drumming away fit to make my head burst, while the clock was striking like several churches.

At last the racket stopped, the moustachioed fellow turned on his heels and withdrew by way of the prep room. His departure disclosed a very distinguished gentleman, who was standing motionless like a statue. He was very tall; an opulent, fawn-coloured overcoat was thrown over his shoulders; he carried his head high, and his black eyes gleamed like glass. He took a step towards us, and leaning on a rubber-tipped black stick, said in a voice of command that had a resonant, coppery ring:

'Sixth and Fifth Form boarders into the prep room next door, the eighth prep. I said: the boarders.'

There was a great bustle in the column which broke up for the departure of those prisoners.

The gentleman waited until our ranks had re-formed, then said in a deep voice:

'Day-boarders of the Sixth and Fifth Forms A and B! Go in.'

We went in.

No sooner had we passed through the door than there was a general rush to settle in the most favoured places. I noticed with surprise that they were the ones farthest from the rostrum.

As I was about to sit down at the desk on which I had left my things, the stampede swept me forward to the first row and I only just had time to clutch my precious satchel. Oliva, pushed forward by the 'big boys' of the Fifth Form, landed on a bench at the far side of the room. There were loud wrangles, insults, shouts.

Our master, impassive as a rock amidst a heaving sea, was watching events. At last he shouted a sentence which I was to hear every day for the next two years:

'How slow you are, gentlemen, how slow!'

It was a kind of melancholy bellow, a threatening plaint tinged with surprise and regret.

He remained silent for a minute, and the tumult gradually died down.

Then he cried in a thunderous voice:

'Silence!'

And silence there was.

I had been carried right to the front of the class by the scramble for places and found myself sitting next to a dark-haired, round-cheeked boy, who seemed appalled at having been shoved to the fore.

The gentleman slowly walked up to the blackboard, dragging his right leg a little. Then he looked the whole company full in the face, and with a hardly perceptible smile said in a voice that brooked no reply:

'Gentlemen, the pupils who most require supervision have a natural tendency to try and elude it. Since I do not yet know any of you, I have left you free to choose your places: in this way, the ill-intentioned ones have, by their desperate efforts to be seated far from the rostrum, advertised their own intentions. Boys in the last row, stand up!'

They rose, surprised.

'Take your things and change places with those in the first row.'

I saw my neighbour's face light up with joy, while the dispossessed ones came forward in dismay.

We went and settled down in the very last row, in the right-hand corner facing the master's desk.

'Now,' said our teacher, 'each one of you will take possession of the locker nearest to his place.'

Everybody got up, and the hubbub started all over again. Many of the boys produced a padlock from their pockets to ensure the inviolability of this classroom safe.

No padlock had been foreseen in my equipment, but it crossed my mind that my father had one: the château-keeper's padlock, which Bouzigue had triumphantly brought us. I promised myself that I would ask Joseph for it that very night. It was hanging in the kitchen, with its key. No one ever touched it and I had the feeling that it still scared everybody: I was sure they would gladly let me have it.

Our master suddenly broke into his lament:

'How slow you are, gentlemen, how slow!'

He waited for almost a minute, then commanded in an officer's tone of voice:

'Take your seats!'

In a deep silence he walked up to his desk, sat down in his chair, and I thought that he was going to start the lesson: I was mistaken.

'Gentlemen,' he said, 'we are going to spend a whole school year together, and I hope that you will spare me the pain of having to give you nought for behaviour, keeping you in or curtailing your days of leisure. You no longer are children since you are in the Sixth and Fifth Forms respectively. You will therefore understand the need for work, order and discipline. Now, to start your school year, I am going to distribute your schedules.'

From a corner of his desk he took a sheaf of papers and walked round the room, giving us each a copy.

In this way I learnt that our days started at a quarter to eight with fifteen minutes' prep, followed by two lessons of an hour each. At ten, after fifteen minutes' break, there was another hour's lesson, and forty-five minutes' prep before going down to the dining-hall in the basement of the boarders' house.

After the midday meal a whole hour's recess preceded a half-hour's prep which was followed—*ex abrupto*—by two hours' lessons.

At four o'clock another break, and then, from five to seven, the long and peaceful evening prep.

In short, we remained at school eleven hours a day, except Thursdays, when the morning was occupied by four hours' prep: it was a sixty-hour week, which could be further lengthened by being 'gated' another half-day on Thursday or an entire day on Sundays.

While I was pondering over this, I heard a whisper saying:

'Which lot are you in?'

At first I did not know that it was my neighbour speaking, for his face remained perfectly motionless, his eyes fixed on his schedule.

But I suddenly saw the corner of his mouth move almost imperceptibly, and he repeated his question.

I admired his technique and, trying to imitate it, answered:
'Sixth A 2.'

'Fine!' he said. 'Me too . . . Do you come from the Junior *Lycée*?'

'No. I was at the Chemin des Chartreux school.'

'I've always been at the *lycée*. On account of Latin, I'm "redoubling" the Sixth.'[1]

I did not understand this term and thought he meant that he intended to redouble his efforts. He went on:

'Are you a good scholar?'

'I don't know. Anyway, I was second in the scholarship exams.'

'Oh, grand!' he said, joyfully. 'I'm a real wash-out! You'll let me crib from you.'

'Crib what?'

'Your exercises, of course! So it won't show I'll put in a few mistakes, and then . . .'

He rubbed his hands with glee.

I was amazed. To crib from a neighbour was a disgraceful action. And he talked of resorting to it, not in a desperate emergency but as a daily routine! If Joseph or Uncle Jules had heard him they would certainly have forbidden me his acquaintance. Moreover, it's always dangerous to let a neighbour copy. When two exercises are alike, the master cannot know which of the two is an imposture, and the overgenerous accomplice is often the one to get nabbed.

I planned to expose my fears to my cynical neighbour during the break and was preparing my arguments when, to my great surprise, the thunder-clap of the drum broke out in the corridor, and the entire class rose. We went and lined up in front of the door: it opened by itself, and the playtime monitor appeared and simply said: 'Go!'

We followed him.

'Where do we go?' I asked my neighbour.

'To the classroom. Up at day-school.'

We walked along a solemn corridor, dimly lit by very high-placed windows under heavy Romanesque vaults that were as full of echoes as a cathedral.

They worked especially well with the drum that marked

[1] 'Redoubler' in French means: staying another year in the same form.

the rhythm of life at the *lycée*. Its tattoos rolled through them like a rumbling hurricane: projected from the vaulting to the floor, then ricocheting against the lateral echoes, they sped away swishing against the ancient walls and the rattling window panes . . .

We arrived at the foot of a staircase, for on account of the sloping ground on which the *lycée* was built the playgrounds of the day-school and the classrooms were situated on the floor above.

My neighbour pointed out to me, under the staircase, a black door furnished with a barred peep-hole; it was the door of the punishment cell, and I saluted in passing the shade of Uncle Jules dancing in the night with his rat.

The staircase led to a covered gallery with rectangular pillars, which surrounded the vast courtyard of the day-school on three sides: the fourth side was closed by a very long, grey wall, scarcely enlivened by a dozen lavatories with their alignment of shoulder-high doors.

Our row of boys immediately got lost in an innumerable throng of pupils who filled the gallery. Almost all of them were older than we. There were even some who wore little moustaches: I mistook them for masters and was surprised at their number. My companion corrected my misapprehension:

'Those,' he told me, 'are pupils of "*filo*" and "*matélem*".'[1]

A mysterious reply, which would have deserved an explanation; but I was much too busy, in the general scramble, keeping in touch with my guide: perfectly at home, he jauntily squeezed through the crowd, exchanging greetings or insults in passing with boys of our age.

Our progress was soon slowed down: a small circle of big boys, moored like an island in the middle of the gallery, parted the stream of schoolboys into two arms. They were deep in conversation and, from the look of them, perfectly indifferent to the churning eddies they were causing, though visibly satisfied at thus proving their importance. One of them was holding behind his back, with both his hands, some stiff-covered notebooks and a fat volume. My friend, with a deft flick of his fingers, made the whole parcel clatter to the

[1] *Philo* (philosophy) and *math' élem* (elementary maths) are colloquial French school slang for the two top classes before the *baccalauréat*.

ground in passing and kept right on going without looking back.

Luckily, a fifteen-year-old boy, with a crown of ginger hair, had just slipped between us, and he was the one who received a kick in his backside, which abruptly speeded up his course. I gave a wide berth to the big chap who was picking up his books, while the recipient of the kick was carried away by the stream: but his face, turned backward to his assailant, fired furious glances and an explosive volley of abuse.

I was able to join up with my guide. He had stopped a little further away, his back to the wall, and was listening with an expert's appreciation to the shameful slanders and ignominious advice freely lavished by the voice of outraged innocence. I was myself amazed by the wealth of the Secondary vocabulary: but the drum brutally drowned this vengeful lyricism. So we plunged back into the stream, and my pilot towed me, through whirlpools and counter-currents, towards the place of our labours.

*

It was a very large room. The wall at the back had four windows, through which one could see the branches of the plane trees of the boarders' house. On the left, very long desks with benches for seven or eight rose in wooden tiers. On the right, starting from the door, there was a stove, then a big blackboard above a platform; at last, on a somewhat higher rostrum, a desk, and at the desk sat the master—the *professeur*.

He was a very voluminous man. On heavy shoulders there sat a fat, rosy face, which was lengthened by a fine, fair, vaguely curly beard. In his buttonhole I saw the gleam of a violet ribbon. The *palmes académiques*! The hope and dream of my father, who counted on receiving them on the day he would retire. This very same ribbon was the glory of the Headmaster of the Chemin des Chartreux school. I was proud, but a little alarmed, to have a teacher who wore a headmaster's decoration.

Quite a number of pupils had got there before us, and I was surprised to see that this lot was silently squabbling for the seats in the first rows.

'They're the day-boys,' my friend told me. 'They must always show off. Come quickly!'

He pulled me towards two still vacant seats at the far end of the uppermost row but one, next to another window looking out into the gallery.

We settled down, with a modest and submissive air. On the last bench, behind us, there were already two strangers, who seemed to me pretty big for the Sixth Form. They welcomed my friend with grins and sly winks.

'You here too?' the bigger one asked in a low voice.

'Yes, on account of Latin.'

He spoke to me once more out of the corner of his mouth:

'They too are "redoubling".'

'What does that mean?'

He looked amazed, almost incredulous. Then, in a tone of pity:

'It means that we start the Sixth all over again, because they wouldn't have us in the Fifth!'

I was very sorry to learn that my friend was a dunce but it did not surprise me, for I already knew that he intended to copy my homework.

While I was getting out my exercise books and pens, I cast a glance at our Latin master who was examining his flock with perfect serenity.

I asked under my breath:

'Do you know him?'

'No,' he said, 'last year I was in A 1, with Bergeret. I know that this one is called Socrates.'

We could not go on talking, because Mr. Socrates was looking at us. But the name intrigued me: I knew that there had already been a Socrates, a Greek poet, who used to stroll with his friends under plane trees and who had ended up committing suicide by drinking a brew of hemlock. Perhaps it was because ours was a relative of that one that he had been given the *palmes académiques*?

There was a deep silence, because we didn't know him; on that first day we were almost all of us a little lost and lonely: the class had not formed yet.

Mr. Socrates began by dictating to us the list of books we would need. It filled a whole page, and the collection looked like costing a good deal. But I was not worried for Joseph's exchequer because, thanks to my scholarship, the *lycée* had to supply them free of charge.

When this dictation was over, Mr. Socrates went to the blackboard and wrote, in a beautiful hand, the declension of 'Rosa the Rose', telling us that this would be our lesson for the next day.

While he was calligraphing the word 'ablative', my cynical neighbour asked:

'What's your name?'

I showed him my name on the cover of my exercise-books.

He looked at it for a second, winked an eye, and said astutely:

'*Est-ce Pagnol?*'[1]

I was charmed by this flash of wit, which was still new to me. I asked in my turn:

'And yours?'

His only answer was a little quavering bleat. But he had underestimated his transmitting power: the sound pierced the veil of whispers and the whole class heard it. Socrates spun round in a murmur of stifled laughter, and the culprit's confusion gave him away:

'You, over there, what's your name?'

My neighbour rose and said in a clear voice:

'Lagneau.'[2]

There was some suppressed titters, but Mr. Socrates tamed them with a single glance and snapped: 'What?'

'Lagneau,' my neighbour repeated, 'Jacques Lagneau.'

Mr. Socrates looked at him for a second, then said sarcastically:

'And is it because you're called Lagneau that you bleat in class?'

This time, the entire classroom burst into unrestrained laughter.

Mr. Socrates did not seem displeased by the hilarity that greeted his witty question, and he himself was smiling when Lagneau (who had not grasped that certain questions had

[1] In French, 'Is it Pagnol?' puns with 'Spanish?'.
[2] L'agneau in French means 'the lamb'.

168

better remain unanswered) got up, crossed his arms, and said humbly:

'Yes, sir.'

He had spoken quite truthfully; for it was really to tell me that his name was Lagneau that he had bleated too loudly.

The class redoubled its laughter; but Socrates did not appreciate a comedy effect which he had not provoked himself, and he took this admission for an impertinence. That is why he struck the laughers dumb with a stern glance, then turned to Lagneau and said:

'*Monsieur*, I do not wish to sadden the first Latin lesson by inflicting on you the punishment that your insolence deserves. But I am warning you: this leniency will not recur, and at your next prank, the *Lamb*, instead of frisking in the happy Thursday *meadows*, will remain confined, under the *shepherd's crook*, in the gloomy *fold* of the boarders' quarters with the *flock* of other detainees! Sit down.'

These brilliant metaphors had a great success. The reprieved Lagneau had the wisdom to join discreetly in the laughter, and Socrates, rather pleased with himself and his public, could not help smiling broadly as he smoothed his fine beard. At last he pacified the flattering laughter with his hand, and said:

'This little incident reminds me that I must call the roll.'

He walked up to his desk, opened a notebook, and asked us to reply 'Here', with our hand raised.

Because of the pleasant jests he had just indulged in and as if trying to draw the enemy, the class attempted a form of impertinence that was quite new to me; its astuteness scared yet delighted me.

Socrates first called 'Alban'. This was a flaxen-haired youngster who answered 'Here!' in a piping, rather shrill voice.

The next one was 'Arnaud', whose 'Here' rang out in a much deeper register, while Aubert's rose to the high notes again.

At this moment Lagneau nudged me with his elbow, gave me a wink, and I realized that something was happening. And indeed, Barbier sank again into bass, while Berlaudier (a big, red-faced fellow) squeaked a girlish 'Here!'

'They're giving him the "yodel",' Lagneau whispered.

I thought that such an impertinence would never have been tolerated by the teachers of the Chemin des Chartreux, and that Monsieur Besson, for instance, would have put a stop to it with a single glance. But Socrates went on with his roll call without any sign of impatience, so much so that the yodellers' boldness grew and their answers became ever more discordant without his apparently noticing it. This was an admirable game, and I was mustering my courage to play my part when Galliano's turn came: he was one of the two dunces behind me, who had been kept back in the Sixth Form. To uphold his reputation and his rank, no doubt, he gave his reply in a beautifully cavernous voice, but at the cost of a visible effort.

Socrates looked at him with interest and said:

'Again, please.'

Intimidated, Galliano again said 'Here', but in a perfectly normal voice.

Then Socrates remarked in an almost friendly manner though with masterly firmness:

'No, Monsieur Galliano, no. I can admit all voices in nature, for nature has its quirks, but I cannot stand for a change of voice, for that would be proof of impertinence . . . So will you repeat "Here" in that premature baritone which is your natural voice and which will delight us throughout the year.'

One could hear some stifled titters.

Galliano blushed crimson, lowered his eyes pitifully, coughed and kept silent, while casting glances in all directions as if hoping for a helpful miracle.

'I am waiting,' said Socrates.

There was a rather long silence. At last the poor fellow made a great effort, swelled his chest and managed to say—in a ludicrous bass: 'Here.'

'Excellent.'

The whole class burst out laughing; but not at Socrates who gave a slight smile and again smoothed his beard before calling: 'Galubert, Grenier, Guigues . . .' who all replied very modestly, trying to keep to the same pitch.

Lagneau seemed hurt by this prompt surrender; he

shrugged his shoulders in the direction of Galliano (who hung his head with shame) and said to me in a cross whisper:

'You'll see!'

I wondered—with some alarm—what he was up to, when Socrates' voice called:

'Lagneau!'

Then, with breathtaking courage, my friend got up, crossed his arms, closed his eyes, and answered:

'Baa-a-a . . .'

A roar of laughter shook the classroom, and Galliano (redeeming his weakness) took advantage of it to give a quick tattoo with his feet on the sounding-board of the wooden steps, without the slightest quiver of his chest and shoulders (which reflected some serious training), and produced a magnificently rumbling thunder.

At the same time, Berlaudier gave a long bellow with closed lips, and a swarthy little chap right behind me, who seemed far in advance of his age, stuffed two fingers into his mouth and emitted a brief but powerful whistle.

Socrates' face had flushed, his nostrils flared, his shoulders hunched up, his beard stuck out horizontally. He knew that the peace and quiet of his whole school year were at stake; he thumped his desk violently with the flat palm of his hand and shouted in a ringing voice:

'Silence!'

The pandemonium stopped dead, and Lagneau remained upright and motionless amid a silence that heralded the end of the world. He was not trembling, but his neck had shortened and his volume had shrunk by at least one-third.

Then, in a grave, solemn voice, clearly articulating every syllable and pausing after every group of words, Socrates spoke thus to the Sacrificial Lamb:

'*Monsieur*, we are not at the circus . . . and your buffooneries . . . overstep the permitted bounds . . . You force me . . . to inflict upon you . . . two hours' detention . . . to teach you . . . that there are certain limits . . . which it is dangerous to transgress.'

Then, in one breath and with pointing forefinger:

'Go and stand in the corner, by the door, with folded arms. If you thought that my kindness was a camouflage for weakness, you were strangely mistaken, and if you persist in your error, I shall be regretfully compelled to send you before the Disciplinary Council.'

Pale and mute, Lagneau went to put himself in the pillory, with lowered head and hunched back, while Socrates, in a still threatening voice, went on with the roll-call.

I was overwhelmed by the misfortune that had struck my new friend. To be kept in! I was trembling at the thought that the lightning had fallen so close to me.

In the meantime, my classmates continued to answer the roll-call without any vocal acrobatics, and when my turn had come at last, my 'Here' was clear, without malice or pretension and equally without humility.

At last Socrates pronounced the name of Zacharias, who was at the bottom of the list (and remained there for the whole year, even when the order wasn't alphabetical), and at the same moment the liberating drum roll rang out in the yard.

Galliano rose instantly and reached the door in three bounds. But Socrates shouted:

'Where are you going? Back to your place!'

The fugitive returned to his seat; then, by the sole power of his eyes, our tyrant paralysed the entire class until the last beat of the drum-stick. At last, when the rush from the neighbouring class could be heard along the gallery, he said with sovereign authority:

'You may go!'

The class rose noiselessly and Galliano walked out on tiptoe, with a perfectly imitated look of contrition.

Lagneau left the pillory, came over to our desk to pick up his books, and we went out.

CHAPTER THIRTY-ONE

In the corridor he simply said:

'He looks a nice fellow, but he's a swine.'

He did not seem very affected by his punishment.

I asked him: 'What's your father going to say?'

Instead of blenching at the thought, he sneered.

'Don't you worry about my father. Come on. Let's look for the English class.'

'Is it a different one?'

'Of course.'

'Have we several classrooms?'

'Yes.'

'Why?'

'Because some of the boys do German, and others English. So we're going to be mixed with the English of the Sixth Form A 1.'

I was a little bewildered.

'So it won't be Socrates?'

'What an idea!' said Lagneau scornfully. 'He's got enough to do knowing Latin!'

*

We found another master sitting on the rostrum.

He was much less impressive: small, square, dark, with a pleasant voice. He called our names all over again and dictated another list of books. I was eyeing with curiosity the faces of the 'English' of the Sixth A 1, and found them very much like those of the Sixth A 2.

I learnt that our teacher's name was Monsieur Pitzu: a rather odd name. But Lagneau explained it to me by saying that he was a genuine Englishman, which seemed to me confirmed by the fact that he spoke French with an accent unlike ours.

He taught us, 'This is the door, this is the desk, this is a chair, this is a book,' and it seemed to me an admirable language because there were no declensions.

After this lesson, there was a semblance of recess: that is to say, we went to spend ten minutes in the vast schoolyard, where several hundred boys of all ages, some at a trot, others at a gallop, were running towards the lavatories while the masters, with heavy briefcases under their arms, were roving through the gallery.

There was neither time nor room to organize any games, and one could only just finish in a hurry some quarrel started in the schoolroom. There were two battles of big boys; I could not see anything of them, on account of a circle of other big boys who had taken the best places, but I was able to hear the crack of a mighty swipe in the face and to see a black eye.

We then went to our mathematics class. The word had frightened me, but it turned out to be quite simply a lesson in doing sums.

The teacher was quite small, with a black moustache, thick but short, and he rolled his R's after the fashion of Uncle Jules.

He again had a funny name: Monsieur Petunia. He questioned us, one after the other: Alban (a well-groomed day-boy) and N'Guyen, an Annamite boarder, seemed to me rather eminent. But I was the one who gave the best answers, and this made Lagneau's mouth water at the thought that he would crib my exercises. Petunia congratulated me and gave me top marks: I knew at this sign that he was a good teacher.

We then went down to the prep room and once more I heard the long, modulated complaint: 'How slow you are, gentlemen, how slow!'

I copied out 'Rosa the Rose' in my Latin exercise book, then 'this is the door' and the rest in my English copybook.

Lagneau admired my handwriting but did nothing to show me his: he was reading an illustrated book behind a pile of exercise books.

'What are you reading?' I whispered.

'Victor Hugo.'

'Which one?'

'The Soilers of the Tea,' he answered, without smiling or lifting his eyes.

I burst out laughing; Monsieur Payre looked at me severely and would certainly have called me to account: luckily, there was the drum-roll, which broke the spell of compulsory silence ... The stern look faded, and we dashed into the basement, where I discovered the dining-hall.

This was a vast room, brightly lit by a translucent glass roof.

We went and sat down on benches fixed to the floor, around marble tables as long as sidewalks. I was sitting between Lagneau and Berlaudier. Opposite us sat little Oliva, between Schmidt and Vigilanti.

Lagneau informed us that the long tables were divided into 'squares' of six pupils, so that we formed a kind of unit, and that the dishes which the waiters brought us contained six portions each. The bottle, similarly, contained six rations of wine: at the news that neither Oliva nor I drank any, our four partners loudly congratulated themselves on our presence.

The meal was like a party for me. I had never dined with boys of my age with no grown-up about to impose silence on us ('Children don't talk at table!') or force us to swallow tasteless food ('Eat up your soup!'—'Finish your chicory!'). The conversation, too, was enlightening, and I savoured the pleasure, quite new to me, of using bad language while having a meal.

The menu was extraordinary. Instead of soup, we were first given hard sausage, butter, and black olives, then a slice of a leg of mutton with potato-chips. I thought that was the end. Not at all. They next brought—guess what?—macaroni covered with a lace-work of melted cheese! And then, a beautiful orange for each. Vigilanti couldn't believe his eyes, Oliva tucked in like an ogre, and I myself was dazed by such opulence.

'Is it like that every day?' I asked Lagneau.

'More or less,' he said. 'Only there's never a change. You haven't stopped seeing cold mutton. And then beans, and then little cracking stones mixed in with the lentils.'

'I love lentils,' I declared. 'I'll throw the stones away but I'll guzzle the lentils!'

'After three months,' said Berlaudier, 'you'll do like the rest. Have a look where the lentils are!'

He showed me some lightly-coloured murals on the wall: all the figures on them, however, seemed to have suffered from chicken-pox. A more attentive scrutiny revealed that the small holes that pitted their faces were actually tiny bumps made by boiled lentils which, on the eve of the holidays, the boarders had thrown at them by the handful with such vigour that they had remained stuck.

*

We walked, always in line, up to our courtyard for the long break, which lasted for an hour.

Schmidt and Vigilanti, who were football champions, left us to try and form a team. Berlaudier, detecting a fight taking shape in a corner of the yard, strode off with ready fists in the hope of joining in . . .

I went for a stroll with Lagneau, under the plane trees that were dropping a flutter of dead leaves.

A blond boy came and joined us. I had already noticed him in our home room. He wore a smock as new as mine and said to me point-blank: 'You come from an elementary school.'

'That's right,' I said. 'The Chemin des Chartreux one.'

He was an expert, for he nodded his head by way of admiration, and added modestly: 'I come from the one at Saint-Barnabé.'

'Are you in B?' Lagneau asked.

'Yes. Sixth B 1.'

'You're a lucky dog,' said Lagneau. 'At least you don't have to swot Latin. What's your name?'

'Nelps.'

The strange name surprised me.

'How do you spell it?'

'As it's pronounced.'

He was taller than I, with fine, copper-coloured hair, big blue eyes and a ready smile.

We naturally talked of our beginnings at the *lycée*. Lagneau, who played the part of an 'old boy', announced that 'you haven't had your bellyful yet', which gave us food for thought. Then, with a swagger, he told of his 'Baa', which Nelps judged premature: in his opinion, to be gated on the first day dangerously affected the future.

Lagneau was content to shrug and declared that being kept in did not frighten him, which further enhanced my admiration for his heroism. Then, as the rowdy players kept knocking into us, we went and sat down on the thick wooden bench that ran along the back wall of the covered walk.

There Nelps told us about his form, we told him about ours and about the hardship of having to learn that God-awful Latin under Socrates' rule. Whereupon Nelps, who had never seen or even heard of him, declared quite coolly that he certainly was not called Socrates, and that this must be his nickname.

We argued hotly, and I asked him—in a sarcastic tone of voice—how a boy straight from Saint-Barnabé could know more about OUR teacher than we—who didn't know anything about him, anyway.

Like all silly squabbles, this one would have gone on for ever. We had got to the stage of making bets, when a big, dark-haired boy, who was sitting not far from us, broke in to say:

'Socrates is called Lepelletier.'

He got up and I saw he was wearing a triple-soled boot, supported on each side by a pair of nickel braces. He came towards us with a deep limp, and added:

'I had him in the Sixth Form, two years ago . . . He's a wealthy bloke: one Thursday I saw him in the Prado, in a real automobile, wearing a bearskin overcoat. He could do without being a schoolmaster if he wanted to, but he enjoys making a nuisance of himself.'

'He's already had a go at me,' said Lagneau. 'He's keeping me in on Thursday.'

'Don't be surprised,' said the other, 'it'll probably happen a number of times . . .'

He told us that his name was Carrère, that he was fourteen years old and that he was in the Fourth A.

'Then why,' I asked him, 'do you come into this courtyard?'

He smiled, slapped his thigh with his hand.

177

'On account of that hoof of mine,' he said. 'This one wouldn't grow at the same time as the other. It's not an illness, I'm sure it'll make up its mind to grow some day. But my mother worries herself sick about it and she's asked the Principal to let me stay in the Junior yard because she thinks it's less dangerous. So, to please her . . .'

He had a beautiful face, a skin as pale and soft as a girl's, curly hair and large black eyes. I liked him at once, because of those handsome looks that were so cruelly let down by the stunted leg.

He was, moreover, a fount of knowledge.

After throwing light on the case of Socrates he informed us that Pitzu was not called Pitzu but Ferronnet. He then insisted that he was 'a really good sort' and that 'he taught you English without your knowing it.'

As for Monsieur Petunia, his name was Monsieur Gros. It was fun ragging him, because he flew into dreadful tempers, handed out a dozen detentions and then cancelled them all at the end of the lesson.

I asked him if he knew our prep master. He disclosed to us that he was called Monsieur Payre, and that he dragged his leg a little because he was a former general of the hussars, who had been seriously wounded by a poisoned arrow during the conquest of Madagascar. He was unfamiliar with Latin (like all generals) but terrific in maths, a science indispensable to high officers who must be able to calculate (without paper or pencil) the number of men, rations, cartridges, kilometres, enemies, prisoners, dressings, decorations and even coffins, that may be required at any moment by the hazards of war.

Finally, he told us that the *lycée* had been founded by Napoleon I, and that this was engraved on a big marble plate in the corridor leading to the Middle School yard. That is why the school drums had come down, in a straight line, from the Imperial Guards. Ours, the boarders' drum (he knew because the doorkeeper had confided it to him) was the very one that had beaten the last charge at the Battle of Waterloo.

This moving revelation—which reduced to insignificance the commonplace bell of the Chemin des Chartreux—was promptly confirmed by a grandiose drum-roll, which set the

178

giant cuirassiers of the Imperial Guard careering through the courtyard and made us repair to our prep room, while the handsome lame boy made for the Middle School yard.

At two o'clock, there was another change of teachers, for we were taken up to the fourth floor, to the drawing lesson.

Our teacher did not look at all like a schoolmaster. He had a beautiful, fair beard and long hair like an artist.

'Grand!' said Lagneau as soon as we walked in. 'It's Shaggy! We'll have fun!'

On the strength of Carrère's revelations, I realized that this was a nickname, and one which he owed to his mop of hair. Shaggy was as deaf as a dormouse and wonderfully easygoing as a consequence. As long as you satisfied his eyesight, all the pleasures of the ear—shouts, mews, bellows, songs and whistling—were freely granted.

In this fairground atmosphere Shaggy, very earnestly, taught us how to sharpen pencils and showed us how to use sandpaper to whittle charcoal to a point. He then proceeded to place a big earthenware jar on a wooden tripod, and we tried to draw it. We had to take the measurements from a distance, by closing one eye and holding the pencil upright in our outstretched arm. It is difficult to explain, but it is a wonderful trick. Nobody knows who invented it.

At three, the drum of the Imperial Guard put an end to our artistic endeavours Zacharias had disguised himself as a Negro with charcoal dust, and he could not manage to regain his natural colouring. That is why the history master, who was waiting for us in our classroom, turned him out with humiliating comments and ordered him to wash his face at the infirmary. He did not return from this expedition for he was intercepted by the day-school *Surveillant général*, who put him in the pillory in a corner of his study and scrubbed his face clean with two hours' detention, for poor Zacharias' copious tears soon restored his natural hue, except for two black rings round his eyes which made him look like a sick owl.

The geography master, who was called Monsieur Michel, had no nickname. He was rather short and stocky, with chubby, tightly stretched cheeks, and a thick, black moustache.

He talked to us about the universe, then about the solar system, then about the Earth. The Earth was so small that it made you wonder how Marseilles could be contained on that speck of dust. In the end, there was the mystery of the Australians, who walk head downward without even noticing it. Monsieur Michel told us that this was an attraction which derived from an English law. All this seemed hard to believe and, on the way out, I asked Lagneau what he thought of it.

'Maybe,' he answered, 'that's why the kangaroos jump so far. Anyhow, I couldn't care less.'

During the four o'clock break, in the boarders' school-yard, a boy came to call us, in groups of five or six, to fetch our school books from the library. How many staircases, how many corridors! It was as vast as the Longchamp Museum.

The librarian, a man in his thirties, was slim, fair and had blue eyes that gave us a friendly glance through his spectacles. He handed me two big parcels of books of all sizes. There were two enormous ones: they were the Latin dictionaries. I was amazed by their weight and disheartened at the thought that I would have to stuff my head with those eight or ten pounds of Latin, for which there wouldn't have been room in my cap.

The day ended with two hours' prep. This was devoted to putting some order into our lockers, then to our homework for the next day.

I 'swotted' 'Rosa the Rose', then the multiplication table which I knew up to thirteen times thirteen.

Next to me, Lagneau was studying the Franco-Latin dictionary with the keenest interest.

I asked him for the reason for this diligence. He whispered: 'In my father's dictionary there are all the dirty words. But this one jumps from arrow straight on to arsenal . . .'

'Perhaps the Romans were a fighting lot,' I said, 'and went to war all the time.'

'That may be,' Lagneau agreed, 'but I bet you that once in a while they must have sat down on their—'

But a stern look from Monsieur Payre cut the conversation short.

CHAPTER THIRTY-TWO

On leaving school at seven, I got the surprise I had been hoping for. My mother and Paul were waiting for me on the little Place du Lycée. They rushed up to me and kissed me, as much moved as if I were coming back from America. Then my mother inspected me under a lamp post to find out how I had stood the ordeal.

I answered their questions gaily and, on the way, arranged the version of the day's report for Joseph's ears.

As we were laying the table, Paul suddenly stopped still, with the salt cellar in his hand, and cried in the height of anguish:

'He's forgotten his book bag!'

I shrugged and said condescendingly:

'At the *lycée* we have lockers and put all our things there.'

'Are they locked?'

'Mine isn't yet. But Papa will give me the padlock from the château! Won't you, Papa?'

'Wouldn't you rather I bought you another?'

'No,' I said. 'I'd rather have this one, because it scared us. Even now I can see the way you look at it. Whereas if I'm going to put it to work every day, it'll become just as silly as any old padlock.'

During dinner, I related my day in detail, and my family listened to my account with the greatest interest.

When I disclosed that our teachers had addressed me as '*vous*' and had called me 'Monsieur', Paul looked at me with deep admiration and my father declared: 'I didn't think they were so strict.'

I talked of Socrates, stressing his headmasterly decoration, then of Pitzu, and announced in English, before the marvelling Paul:

'*Zis iz ze taybol. Zis iz a chair. Zis iz ze dor.*'

I described the rough-house of the drawing lesson, and my father informed me that this was a tradition, justified by the fact that silence was not necessary for drawing; at last I spoke at length of Monsieur Payre, whom I liked a lot, but Joseph emitted some doubts about his having been a general of the hussars.

'First of all,' he said, 'there's no such rank. Moreover, I've never heard that the hussars were sent out to Madagascar. And lastly, if he is as tall as you say, he certainly didn't serve in the hussars which are part of the light cavalry.'

When he saw that I was a little disappointed, he added:

'Now, in the dragoons that might be possible, or even in the cuirassiers . . . At all events, if his pupils were the ones who invented this pretty story it shows that they're fond of him and that he is a good teacher. Try to be worthy of his friendship!'

*

During the first two months I felt a complete stranger and, despite the interest of so many novelties, I would occasionally regret my dear Chemin des Chartreux school, of which Paul brought me news every night.

To begin with, in these Secondary barracks I was no longer Joseph's son, the little boy whom all the masters addressed with the familiar '*tu*' and who would play in the empty schoolyard on Thursdays and Sundays. Here I was no longer at home, but a stranger.

I no longer had 'my' classroom and 'my' desk. We changed rooms all the time and the desks were not ours, for they were also used by others, of whom we knew little except sometimes their names which emerged (at the rate of one letter a week), deeply carved with a knife, on the thick hardwood top.

Instead of one schoolmaster, I had five or six 'professors' who weren't only mine but also taught other forms; not only did they not call me Marcel, they would sometimes forget my surname! What's more, they did not watch over us during recess. One only saw them from the waist up behind their desks, like centaurs forever on horseback, or lady cashiers in the big stores . . .

Finally, I was hemmed in by a great number of personalities, who were all quite different from one another but who all coalesced against me to push me along the road to knowledge. In addition to our professors and our form-master, there were, first, the *pions* or monitors who did duty as our police at recess, watched over the dining-room, were in charge of Thursday morning prep and escorted our movements.

The one who shepherded our flock between the boarders' house and day-school was Blue Ginger. He was so called because he was red-haired and had big, transparent blue eyes. He was very tall and lean, and I imagined that his navel was stuck like a barnacle to the inner side of his backbone.

Invariably at his post, he never spoke to us except to say: 'Go!' or 'Stop!' in a voice rendered hoarse by too long silences. Carrère told me that he was studying for a degree in mathematics and that his vacant eyes no longer took in reality: their inward gaze was turned towards an ant-hill of figures that were teeming in the tunnels of his ravaged brain.

The Thursday morning monitor was called Piquoiseau—Birdpeck. His black, curly hair, bulging eyes and flat nose made him look like a sturdy peasant, but Carrère revealed to me that he was a philosopher. He proved it, anyhow, by his pensive indifference. After ensuring silence at prep by stuffing two little cottonwool balls into his ears, he would write dozens of pages without stopping; but he could not have been imbued with a very strong belief in philosophy, for he would sometimes burst out laughing without even raising his head. However this may be, he was considered 'a good sort' because he deliberately ignored our little games and chattering.

These monitors, who were easy-going on the whole, were under the orders of two *Surveillants généraux*, who prodded them to a display of zeal.

The one in charge of the boarders' house was continually cruising round the corridors in his grey skull-cap, like a gunboat on a colonial river, but he had a habit of emerging in the courtyard at the very moment when his presence there was least desirable.

The other, in charge of the day-school, had a long, waxed

moustache with ends as sharp as needles, two glassy eyes, an icy voice and ankle-boots with gleaming buttons.

He must already have invented radar in those days, for he infallibly spotted boys who had been sent out of classrooms and who, to avoid him, would turn round a pillar of the gallery as squirrels do at the sight of a hunter.

He was nicknamed the Bird of Ill Omen because his appearance, which was always unexpected, would herald some scholastic catastrophe.

Above those sergeant-majors, there towered two awe-inspiring persons—the *Censeurs*, or proctors.

The *Censeur* of the day-school had neither name nor nick-name. He was very tall and thin, wedged into a pearl-grey jacket, with white spats over shoes that were as tan as his long, drooping moustache which looked just like that of some distinguished old Gaul. You caught a fleeting glimpse of him entering or leaving his study, in elegant conversation with boys' mothers. He did not condescend to look at us. We feared him all the more as he had never punished any-body, but we supposed that a sentence falling from such exalted heights would undoubtedly crush the culprit.

The *Censeur* of the boarders' house was more familiar to us. He wore no spats, and he was small. Moreover, during the midday break, he was the one who summoned to his study those who had received bad marks for behaviour, gave them a homily and drew the penitentiary consequences of the regrettable incident. One evening he paid a visit to our prep room, that is to say, leaning over a pupil's shoulder he watched him do his homework for a moment and gave him some advice in a low voice. As I had never yet had nought for behaviour, I found him rather nice.

Finally, above everybody else, there ruled *Monsieur. le Proviseur*, who only rarely showed himself.

The first time I saw him, he was accompanying the day-school *Censeur*, who had come into our classroom to notify us of the results of our maths paper. His entrance made a great impression.

He was a huge man, wore a silk hat, a white waistcoat and a long, gleaming black frock coat. He had a big, brown beard, and a magnifying glass squeezed into one eye.

The moment he appeared in the doorway the whole class rose, with their arms folded on their chests. He then seized the brim of his gigantic silk hat, gave a sweeping greeting in a black flash, walked up to the master's desk and, without a word, shook the hand of Petunia, who had respectfully gone to meet him.

The *Censeur*, who walked in behind him, then read out the results. *Monsieur le Proviseur* still kept silent, but in a very grand manner.

The *Censeur* did not confine himself to proclaiming the results of the maths paper only. After disclosing the marks obtained by each, he reeled off an arpeggio of three figures which expressed, in absolute values, 'conduct, homework, lessons'.

I was third, after Gillis and Picot who tied for first place. I was quite satisfied, for I have a natural tendency to be content with anything. Lagneau had cribbed my solutions, craftily adding some mistakes; but he had overdone it and had to wait at least two minutes before at last he heard his name proclaimed: he was twenty-second, but quite unaffected by this result anyhow. From that place onward the *Censeur's* voice became tinged with gradual melancholy, then with regret, and then with blame. At last he announced slowly, in a tone of deep consternation:

'Thirty-first and last, Berlaudier, $1\frac{1}{2}$, 4 and Nought.'[1]

Thereupon the *Proviseur* repeated in a black voice, while not the slightest quiver shook his beard:

'Nought.'

Monsieur le Censeur marked a little cross on the sheet and said automatically:

'Kept in Thursday.'

Thus, without deigning to pronounce sentence, *Monsieur le Provissur* could make it fall with a single word, as the mere echo of a breath may sometimes be enough to release an avalanche . . .

*

The members of this organization frightened me. They were really too numerous, you could not understand them,

[1] The marks in French schools range from a maximum of twenty to a minimum of nought.

nor love them nor charm them. I mourned for Monsieur Besson, who wasn't handsome but knew everything; this was proved by the fact that he taught us the lot—French, sums, natural history or geography. He had no decoration and he would sometimes give you a clout, but there was always a smile on his face . . .

*

What's more, the school population was not homogeneous. There were boarders, semi-boarders, and the day-boys who really constituted a very different species from ours.

When Paul asked me what the day-boys were like, I simply said:

'They're chaps who put on their Sunday best every day!'

'That must cost a lot!' observed Paul, full of admiration.

'Their fathers have pots of money. There's one, called Picot, who's so rich that he butters his sandwiches on both sides every morning.'

Paul gave a long whistle, overwhelmed by such lavishness.

And it was a fact that the day-boys were too dazzling.

They would arrive in the morning in all their glory. They wore low-cut shoes of fawn or tan leather, and their shoe-laces, wide as ribbons, were bound with an edging that made them look like bow ties. There were even some whose heels were fitted with a thick rubber disc held in place by a metal cross which was fixed with a nickel-plated screw. This was 'the revolving heel', the acme of modern luxury. It left a sort of medal imprinted in the dust, with the raised cross in the middle. That's why one could detect the passing of a day-boy as easily as an old trapper identifies the track of an ostrich or a rhinoceros.

They had pockets full of marbles, they sucked soft butter-scotch (of the 'Jumping Dog' brand) or violet-scented liquorice drops; in the ten o'clock break they bought from the doorkeeper golden-brown *croissants* or pale crisp biscuits which cost five *sous* apiece, and that is why it was traditionally affirmed that the doorkeeper had long ago joined the ranks of millionaires.

But in the schoolroom their luxury became really over-powering.

They would open the nickel-plated clasps of their fawn leather briefcases—sometimes they were blue morocco—and, before sitting down, pull from them a small rectangular cover, often as glossy as silk, which they carefully placed on the bench in order to protect their precious behinds which could not have borne the contact of the hard wood. This precaution seemed to justify the claims of the princess in the story who had woken up, bruised all over, because of the brutal presence of a chick-pea underneath four feather mattresses.

After this preliminary installation they took out lacquered pencil-boxes, the contents of which they spread out before them: there were india-rubbers as big as cakes of toilet-soap, pencil sharpeners of shiny metal with a conical hole, enormous pencils of various colours; Auphan, who sat in the row before us, even showed me one that was not made of wood! The thick lead-pencil was surrounded by a narrow strip of paper which coiled around it in a clever spiral. When the lead broke you only had to strip off a bit from the coil, and there was the pencil all ready! There also were pen-holders of onyx or jet—or some precious substance—with nibs of gold, and mother-of-pearl pen-knives that cut like razors.

Next to such riches my own cut a sorry figure, and I confess that I was a little ashamed of them in the early days; but I spontaneously invented the philosophical solution that has been comforting the poor for centuries and rescued them from cruel envy: I resolved to despise the fortune of others, to consider material advantages as altogether secondary, and decided that objects of luxury were a credit to their manufacturers rather than to their owners. In this way I could painlessly admire Auphan's wrist-watch with its gold bracelet. I could learn the time from it just as well as he could. But the responsibility for it being his, he was unable to join in any fight for fear of a shock that might break it.

However, a boy called Bernier, of Sixth Form A 1, who was my left-hand neighbour in English, almost overcame my wisdom, and I must confess that my serenity gave way—for a few minutes—to a painful and contemptible jealousy.

His father was said to be an '*armateur*', which meant that he chartered ships but which made me believe for a long time that he manufactured revolvers, rifles and perhaps even cannon, for Bernier's wealth stuck out all over his person: he had a beautiful watch, leather gloves, shoes that were always new, and he was a substantial buyer of *croissants*.

One morning, while Pitzu was revealing to us that in English the adjective is invariable, Bernier distracted my attention from this agreeable news by lightly nudging my elbow. He winked at me and pulled from his breast-pocket a silver tube whose cap he proceeded to unscrew. Then he turned the metal disc that enclosed the other end of the tube, and I saw a gleaming nib slowly emerge.

'It's gold!' he whispered. 'It's written on it!'

This luxury seemed to me insolently useless at first sight, and I asked coldly:

'Can one write with it?'

He winked at me again and simply said: 'Look!'

Then, without dipping the pen into the inkwell, he wrote his name before my very eyes!

I thought at first that it was a kind of pencil. He enlightened me. This gadget wrote with blue ink that was contained in the tube and which reached the gold nib by its own volition!

It was then that I thought bitterly of the unfair distribution of wealth, for Bernier scrawled like a cat, and my heart felt a nasty twinge.

He explained that this gadget was called a 'fountain pen' which his father had brought him back from England, and that it enabled you to write for a week without stopping; and when at last it was empty, you could fill it again by pulling at a kind of piston.

He wanted to show me how it worked: but he was not yet very skilful at handling this English mechanism and only succeeded in spurting a sudden jet of indelible ink onto his splendid new exercise book.

I felt such intense pleasure that I promptly forgave him for owning a wonder that he would never know how to handle.

The worst defect of the day-boys was that they were tattle-tales; it sometimes happened that they complained to the authorities and denounced a friend for some innocent joke, such as tripping them up successfully or propelling a paper bullet (soaked in ink, of course) by means of a blow-pipe on to a beautiful page of handwriting. What's more they did not always understand our language, whose manly roughness was beyond them. Their own was distressingly refined: they even talked of giving 'a kick in the *back*'! And one day Picot, at the height of his rage, had even shouted at Berlaudier: 'You're only a fool!' Such poverty of expression made us smile with pity—'us' meaning the boarders.

For our homeland was the prep room, ruled over every day by Monsieur Payre (How slow you are, gentlemen, how slow!). That was the place where our smocks were hung up every night, below the padlocked lockers in which we kept our belongings and sometimes even our secrets. Berlaudier tried to rear a white mouse there: it died after a week, but not before having devoured four good marks, the only ones he had ever had and which he treasured all the more for having obtained them by shamelessly copying the description of a sunset from the *Petit Echo de la Mode*.

The composition of the prep room did not vary like that of the classrooms. Every day we spent seven hours together, now at our desks, now in the yard and, above all, there was the intimacy of the dining-hall; the day-boys seemed strangers to us because we had never met them round the table . . .

By the end of the term I was acclimatized, and I felt at home in my prep room where I always sat down with pleasure among those of my tribe.

I spent all that year in the Sixth Form next to Lagneau, on the last bench of the first row, and I only had to get up to reach my locker.

In the beginning, there was Berlaudier in front us, next to Sicard. This was a curse, for he continuously attracted Monsieur Payre's attention by divers noises: he would cough, clear his throat, blow his nose like a trumpet, and his belches were not what irked us most. As he was sly and crafty, he would retch with lowered head: Monsieur Payre could not catch him in the act, with the result that dark suspicions hovered over our corner.

Luckily, after a month the sound-producing Berlaudier had an unfortunate idea.

He brought to school a very small musical instrument. It was a metal disc with a hole in its centre over which a thin rubber band was strung. With the disc placed under your tongue and your mouth almost closed, it was possible to draw sounds of charming melodiousness from it, without anyone being able to tell where they came from.

Berlaudier must have been training at home, for his debut in the drawing lesson was that of a virtuoso. There was no great danger, for Shaggy could not hear anything: the musician practised his scales for twenty minutes, just to warm up, then seeing that he was running no risk, gave up in discouragement.

In the Latin class, his solo lasted only five seconds; Socrates expelled Zacharias, indignant but loyal, for the latter did not denounce the culprit and, raising his eyes to heaven, nobly marched out. Whereupon the dastardly Berlaudier refrained from continuing his little concert, and the perfect silence that followed the execution confirmed the guilt of the innocent victim.

In the English lesson the gods smiled on the musician, for in the very first minute Pitzu wrote on the blackboard, in English: 'The little bird is singing in the tree', translating the sentence as he went along.

Berlaudier promptly corroborated this statement by a prolonged trill. Our good master, quite charmed, went over to the window, opened it wide and tried to glimpse amid the branches the sparrow that was giving such a well-timed twitter.

He must have seen one sparrow, for he pointed to the yellow autumn leaves and announced in English:

'This is the little bird that is singing in the tree!'

Berlaudier was carefully writing down this sentence with his head over his copybook, meanwhile illustrating it with a delightful *roulade* which prompted a general outburst of laughter. Amazed to hear the bird behind him, Pitzu abruptly turned to face us, and his eyes swept over the benches. He saw thirty faces expressing the most deferential attention and Berlaudier, with his pen in mid-air, looked up to him with innocent eyes.

Pitzu closed the window and without taking his eyes off

us, slowly returned to his desk. But as he turned his back to step on to the rostrum, the bird gaily called him by his name:

'Pitzu! Pitzu!'

He spun round, his eyes flashed ominously as they roved over us, and he said:

'Who is the jackass that mimics a bird?'

A deep silence answered him.

'Very well,' he said fiercely. 'I observe that this bird's virtuosity is only equalled by his cowardice. I said, his COWARDICE!'

He had repeated the word with a grimace of contempt. But Berlaudier, hardened in crime, experienced no other emotion than a violent urge to laugh, which he disguised by a sneeze, and Pitzu had just wasted his breath.

That afternoon, in maths, Petunia elaborated for us on the blackboard a few variations on the art of reducing fractions to the same denominator, a feat he always pulled off with success. He soon noticed that each of his triumphs was greeted by the discreet warble of a nightingale. This intrigued him for quite a while until he caught sight of young Vernet in the third row. Vernet was a day-boy, and as good as gold: but whenever he applied himself to writing well he pursed his lips into a marked pout without realizing it: from a distance one might have thought he was whistling. Petunia did think so. That is why he congratulated Vernet on his 'charming drawing-room talent' and put him in the pillory next to the stove, with the promise of keeping him in. Berlaudier feared for a moment that the day-boy would give him away. But Vernet, who was shy to a fault, dared not say a single word and stayed in the corner of infamy till the end of the lesson, with his arms obediently folded on his resigned chest so that he provided a model of what an innocent boy in the pillory should look like, and the very perfection of his attitude advertised his innocence.

Berlaudier was touched by so much humility, and when the drum had released us, in the scramble preceding our departure, he pretended to be tying his shoe-lace and, while doing so, emitted a beautiful flourish so as to proclaim the innocence of the still motionless martyr. Stern but just, Petunia unhesitatingly admitted his mistake.

'Monsieur Vernet,' he said; 'I am afraid you have been unjustly punished. I shall therefore give you an official expression of commendation to recompense the dignity of your conduct and your respect for discipline. I congratulate you, Monsieur Vernet.'

And while Monsieur Vernet, flushed with pride, was going back to his form to pick up his briefcase, Petunia added in a deep silence:

'As for the wicked bird which let an innocent be punished, I believe that his shame at committing such a misdeed, aggravated by the contempt of his school-fellows, will be sufficient punishment for him—at least for today. Go!'

Berlaudier immediately manifested his remorse by a light, but infinitely sad whistle. In the stampede on the way out, Petunia pretended not to have heard it, so as not to be forced to make a scene and hold an inquest which probably would have been inconclusive. But I saw a hard look come into his eyes which seemed to me to bode rather ill for the bird's future.

*

It was at prep that evening that Monsieur Payre cut its throat.

At half past five, in the studious silence, while our master was reading his newspaper at his desk, a timid trill was heard, like a kind of prelude from a nightingale limbering up its throat.

The whole room was suddenly gripped with conspicuous zeal. Bénézech and Gambier, who were playing chequers on their form, hid the papier-mâché chessboard under the desk and opened their school books at random. Lagneau abandoned Buffalo Bill—tied though he was to the torture stake—and I feverishly flicked the pages of my Latin-French dictionary.

But Berlaudier himself beat everyone for earnestness. Surrounded by coloured pencils, the india-rubber in one hand, dividers in the other, he was copying out the map of France from a wide-open atlas, with an attentiveness that seemed strained to the breaking point.

Monsieur Payre had not even lifted his eyes.

Then, while Berlaudier, his head down and his elbow up in the air, was drawing a black line along the ruler, a long trill rose, swelled, then faded *diminuendo*. All the heads ducked between shrinking shoulders. Monsieur Payre, looking perfectly indifferent and without even a glance in our direction, rose, stepped down from the rostrum, casually strolled over to Lambert and bent over his homework; he turned his back to us and made some remarks in an undertone. One heard the bird twitter, then burst into a song powerful enough to shame four-and-twenty blackbirds, baked or not. Monsieur Payre did not even turn round, and I thought he might be deaf, but had so far hidden the fact from us, which saddened me a little.

The bird stopped. Monsieur Payre walked to the far end of the room, but along the opposite side to ours, and took a keen interest in the mathematical problems of Galubert, a scientist of the Fifth Form B 1.

The bird had recovered its breath and suddenly began to warble like a nightingale. Monsieur Payre still presented his back to us: he was talking to Galubert, who was listening to him, with his raised face displaying absorbed attention but also obvious strain, for the bird-song was upsetting him.

But Monsieur Payre still did not hear it. This indifference began to get on Berlaudier's nerves; he stared at Monsieur Payre's back and shook his head by way of protest, as if reproaching him for not playing the game and shirking his obligations.

Then he suddenly produced three vocal flourishes, one after the other, on a note of defiance and followed them up with a long, sad lament . . . Monsieur Payre left Galubert, gave him an encouraging little pat on the back, then slowly and thoughtfully directed his steps towards us.

He passed along the lockers, turned into our aisle, and suddenly bent over Berlaudier's map.

'What map is this?' he asked him.

Berlaudier showed him the atlas, without uttering a word, as if he deemed, like Napoleon, that a small sketch was worth more than a long speech.

Monsieur Payre persisted:

'Who gave you this homework?'

Berlaudier opened his eyes wide and, in dumb show, mimicked stupidly blank ignorance.

'What!' cried Monsieur Payre. 'Don't you know the name of your geography master? What's he called?'

Lagneau cut in with helpful promptitude:

'Monsieur Michel, sir.'

'I wasn't talking to you!' said Monsieur Payre.

He addressed himself again to the cartographer and, looking him straight in the eye, said sharply:

'What is the name of your teacher?'

Berlaudier could no longer back out and, making a desperate effort, he said:

'Mifter Mifel.'

'Very well,' said Monsieur Payre. 'Spit out what you have in your mouth!'

I feared for a second that Berlaudier would choke himself by trying to swallow the bird—he had turned crimson. The whole room was looking at him, and the dunces in the first row had half risen, the better to see his execution.

'Hurry up!' thundered Monsieur Payre, 'or I'll send for Monsieur le Censeur!'

Berlaudier, panic-stricken, stuffed his thumb and forefinger into his mouth, extracted from it the disc gleaming with spittle and put it on the desk.

Monsieur Payre looked at it for a moment, and said (as if he were giving a lecture on musical instruments):

'This contraption is remarkable, but it isn't as modern as one might believe. I owned one myself when I was a Fifth-form pupil at the college of Arles . . . Unfortunately, it was confiscated by my form-master, whose name was Monsieur Grimaud. And do you know what Monsieur Grimaud did?'

Saying this, he stared fixedly at the poor Berlaudier as if waiting for an answer.

'You don't know,' Monsieur Payre went on, 'but you might have an inkling. Well, Monsieur Grimaud not only confiscated the precious instrument but he inflicted upon me a full detention, a whole Sunday's detention. Out of respect for the memory of that honest man, I find myself obliged to treat you as he treated me. You will therefore spend the whole of next Sunday at school, and it's not impossible that Monsieur le Censeur, of his own initiative, will extend you a supplementary invitation for the following Thursday—for he is not fond of music. Now take your things and sit down in the second row, just in front of my desk, in Bigot's place, who will move here instead. But before doing so, wipe this slimy disc and put it next to my ink-stand. I presume that *Monsieur le Surveillant général* will exhibit it in a good place in his little museum of criminal instruments.'

This is how we were delivered of Berlaudier's dangerous presence; his exile was a double blessing for not only did he no longer attract Monsieur Payre's distrust towards us, he actually turned it away and fixed it on a different region of the room: our freedom was thus assured.

As for Bigot's arrival, it greatly enriched our corner. He was in Fifth Form A 1, and a scholar capable of reading at sight the *Epitome Historia Graecae*! My marks in Latin translation showed a sudden improvement.

Sitting next to Bigot was Rémusat, a pupil of the Sixth B. He was fair-haired and thin and his fine handwriting was famous, at least in our prep room. His father was a confectioner: every morning he produced a small white paper bag from his pocket and shared out among us toffees and sometimes even chocolates filled with strong liqueurs.

In front of Bigot and Rémusat sat Schmidt and Vigilanti. Schmidt was Swiss, big and fleshy like all Swiss, and quick to laughter. This caused him no end of trouble, for every time a hoaxer in his class started a 'rag', he could not help bursting into laughter, and he was the one who would be sent out. He played football admirably and he taught me with infinite patience the fine points of the 'spin shot'. I remain eternally grateful to him for it, although this precious gift has not been of much use to me, at least up till now.

His neighbour, Vigilanti, came from Corte, that is to say the mountains of Corsica. He had much thicker bones than I, a heavy chin, black hair and big blue eyes. He spoke in a funny way, rolling his R's, not in Uncle Jules' triumphant fashion but with a slight 'shushing' sound, and his sentences proceeded in a kind of sinuous and melodious singsong. He was kind and generous, but very susceptible: one day when Berlaudier called him 'figatelli'—the Marseillais nickname for Corsicans—he blenched and warned him that if he repeated that insult 'he would make him see stars in the darkness of the grave'. The other, who would not have liked to see them even in full daylight, was careful not to repeat the offence.

On the third form of the centre row sat our friend Nelps, whom we called the 'vicar of Saint-Barnabé' because he boasted of never having missed Sunday mass. He was good-tempered, patient, obliging, and the masters quoted him as an example. However, he took a very great interest in the misdeeds of the 'bad uns', and kept himself closely informed of the punishments that would rain down all around him, like those painstaking criminologists who write books on the psychology of murderers or compile data on penitentiaries. Although he never cared to join in a rag, he would give excellent technical advice and help to perfect the original plan: boys would come and consult him from afar, even from Middle School, to inquire what risk one ran in breaking a window, throwing a stink-bomb or making a torpedo explode. In this way, the pious and virtuous boy roamed on the borders of crime as a dilettante, and kept garnering good marks and honourable mentions when all the time he'd have deserved old Socrates' potion of hemlock twenty times over.

Finally, far in front of us, in the second row, there was Oliva, little Oliva who liked to enjoy a laugh, expertly juggled with fractions and was able to do three-figure multiplications with his eyes closed.

I also spent a lot of time with the handsome Carrère whom I used to see in the courtyard, and with three of the day-boys: Picot, Zacharias, and Bernier, the shipowner's son. Those were my friends and formed my little universe, in which events of major importance continually occurred. I realize today that our life at school had almost detached us from our families, whom we never mentioned among ourselves: only twenty or thirty years later did I learn something of the origins of some of my best friends.

At a dinner party one night I met a captain in our navy: that was Oliva, whom Naval College had turned into an athlete. He told me then that he had lost his parents at the age of six and had been brought up by his two brothers, one of whom was a bricklayer and the other a docker. I was sorry I had not known it at school; I would have loved him all the more dearly for it. Similarly, I never suspected that Zacharias's father owned a fleet of sixty ships nor that Galubert's mother was a famous actress. Our existence was confined to ourselves, and the appearance of a father at school would greatly embarrass his son.

On the other hand, our families were almost completely ignorant of our school lives: I told at home only amusing or glorious episodes, such as Blue Ginger's tumble down the stairs on his way to dining hall, or our victory at pelota over the Middle School team. Anyhow, the language I spoke was rendered obscure by surprising abbreviations or strange metaphors, which were the—temporary and changing— idiom of the boarders.

The only accurate news our families received came to them via the end of term reports, and mine, I must confess with regret, were a pretty grim disappointment for my dear Joseph.

CHAPTER THIRTY-THREE

Thanks to the years I had spent at the elementary school I obtained honourable results in sums and spelling; on the other hand, my passion for words had enabled me to achieve fast progress in English and, with the help of the learned Bigot, some small success in translations from the Latin. When it came to translating *into* Latin, I was completely at sea: though I learnt my grammar lessons by heart and crammed my head with rules and examples, I never grasped the use of them and believed in perfectly good faith that it was enough to be able to reel them off by rote. When I had to translate a sentence I would look up the Latin words in my dictionary and line them up, one after the other, in place of the French words; that is why Socrates alleged that I was an outstanding manufacturer of solecisms and barbarisms when I did not even know what they were.

As for history, it no longer interested me: I just could not tell apart, despite their numberings, all those kings endowed with Christian names only, who were all related and kept waging wars against one another, and it seemed to me absurd to learn by heart the clauses of two consecutive treaties the second of which had cancelled the first. Besides, all those people had been dead for ages, there was nothing they could give or take from me: all history ever talked about was the past. What interested me was the coming Thursday; Monsieur Michel's tales of bygone eras, which had used up their allotted years, were of no more interest to me than a walk through a graveyard.

Geography would amuse me now and then, because you would meet some rather likeable characters in it: Marco Polo, who had a faked cane full of silkworm eggs; Christopher Columbus's 'Land! Land!' and the egg, flattened at one end, standing upright in the middle of the plate (which, incidentally, strikes me today as a solution that is just as silly as Alexander's for the problem of the Gordian knot) and La Pérouse, roasted on a spit by cannibals in his admiral's outfit. But the isthmuses, peninsulas, capes, confluences and tributaries were really too numerous for me, and I was utterly stupefied when I saw on the map that the left bank of the Seine was on the same side as the right bank of the Rhône ...

That is why, though the frail Oliva in Sixth Form B was carrying high the banner of the Rue de Lodi School, I did not add much to the glory of the Chemin des Chartreux.

*

There were some excuses for this mediocrity.

Doubtless on account of my age and the mysterious changes that were transforming my organism, it was very hard for me to concentrate my attention on a given subject: I managed it only by dint of very great effort. I might, of course, have got the better of this physical sloth if I had been sustained by the hope of resounding victories; but unfortunately, there were Picot and Gillis in my form who vied for all the first places.

Picot was a rather tall and distinguished-looking boy, who often offered me liquorice drops but who never smiled because life for him, on account of Gillis's existence, was hell.

When Picot placed second, he would be unable to speak for several days, and two or three members of his family would—secretly—come, one after the other, to ask the *Censeur* how such a strange accident could have happened.

As for Gillis (a skinny boy with big ears), he had tamed fractions and handled the absolute ablative as a Red Indian handles his tomahawk. He knew the list of sub-prefectures as well as a post office sorter on the railways, and talked of the Pharaohs with the volubility of a resuscitated mummy.

Moreover, his keenness and his memory had a powerful support in his mother's active piety: on the eve of every test paper she would burn a candle to the patron saint of the fatal day. But this intervention—which to my mind was unfair—did not always succeed: when it came to the arithmetic paper the burnt offering of the bribing candle must have offended some strict, stiff-necked old saint, for Gillis was not merely beaten by Picot, but came fourth! Flushed with fury and shame, his father—a big, bearded fellow from the wealthy Rue Paradis, led him at a fast march to a doctor who gave him injections in his buttocks, and engaged a tutor to give him two hours' coaching every night, plus four more on Thursdays. The struggle between the two rivals soon became so ruthless that our masters chose to place them first, on equal points, in almost all the papers.

One could not even dream of beating those two fanatics, nor did their glory strike me as enviable: the rings under their eyes, their wan cheeks, their nervous strain proved the dangers inherent in a frenzy for work, and I was really scared when I saw Picot bite his india-rubber or when Gillis, without knowing it, would suddenly twitch his face into grimaces. Lagneau was of the opinion that if those two unhappy creatures were not lucky enough to die young they would certainly end up in a padded cell . . .

It was obvious, therefore, that all my diligence would never be able to lift me above third place.

Now, who would stake all his savings on the purchase of a lottery ticket if he had the dead certainty of not drawing the first prize? I decided that the game was not worth the candle, and I used my best efforts on football, bare-handed pelota, prisoner's base, leapfrog and the assiduous reading of the exploits of Buffalo Bill, Nick Carter and Nat Pinkerton. Lagneau would buy three numbers every week and I would read them entranced, never noticing that it was always the same old story.

*

My father, who had been hoping for a triumphal year, was thus painfully disappointed by the mediocrity of my general average, and he admonished me to work harder. I promptly told him of Gillis and Picot, menaced by lurking anaemia and meningitis, and I complained of a pain in my knee, which was genuine, and of headaches which were not.

When he said, in a lugubrious voice: 'Twenty-ninth in Latin composition, with four marks out of twenty!' my mother parried immediately:

'But he is first at gymnastics and he's growing half an inch every month! You can't do everything at once!'

'Quite so,' said my father. 'But we must warn him that if he goes on in this way he will never be a secondary-school teacher, and we shall be obliged to turn him into a tram conductor or a lamp lighter, or perhaps a road mender.'

Those prospects did not frighten me, for I would much rather have conducted the whizzing Aubagne tram than Socrates' class.

I was stirred by alarm, however, when one night through the partition I overheard a conversation between my parents.

It was rather late but I was not yet asleep because I had made a pig of myself with a pound of roasted chestnuts.

Joseph was reporting to my mother on a visit he had paid to the *lycée* without telling me. He had had a long talk with Socrates.

'According to Monsieur Lepelletier,' he was saying, 'the boy's mental development is somewhat lagging behind his physical one. He's not lacking in intelligence or memory, but for the time being he is a little retarded.'

'What?' cried my mother. 'Why not say right out that he's a mental defective?'

'Why, no,' said Joseph. 'Monsieur Lepelletier is of the opinion that he will certainly wake up soon and that he'll surprise us before he is thirteen! Besides, his marks are passable, after all, except in Latin. But on the whole . . .'

'On the whole who cares about Latin!' said my mother. 'Do you want to make a priest of him? Retarded indeed! I've seen that Lepelletier of yours. No one can say *he* is retarded! He's as fat as a leg of ham, and he has the backside of a cart-horse!'

'Since I was facing him,' my father remarked, 'I did not notice that peculiarity.'

'Well, I did! One Saturday when I went to fetch the boy at four, he showed me that gentleman in the street: all I can say is that he's a fine hypocrite, for he bowed to me with great politeness and not at all as if I were the mother of a mentally deficient child! The truth is that they are all against my boy because he comes from an elementary school and is a hundred times more intelligent than all the rest of them put together! Retarded indeed! I've heard some tall stories in my time, but never one like that! I'll talk to my sister about it to give her a laugh . . . My poor Rose never guessed she was the aunt of a retarded boy! When I think that he could read when he was three!'

'Don't talk so loud!' said Joseph. 'You'll wake the children.'

The conversation went on for another few minutes but I could only hear a dim buzz, and I fell asleep vaguely troubled by that mysterious word.

*

Next morning, no sooner had I arrived in the schoolyard than I sought out Carrère, our scholar. I found him in the gallery. He was walking slowly and alone, carrying in his hand a book closed over his forefinger, and he was moving his lips noiselessly like a curé reading his breviary. When he saw me approach, he stopped suddenly in his track, assumed a fierce expression and, pointing his finger at me, cried:

> *'Misfortune had abated not her pride*
> *She even wore that borrowed brightness still*
> *That she would spread upon her face erewhile*
> *To cover o'er the ravages of time . . .'*[1]

'What does "retarded" mean? What's a person like who is retarded?'

Instead of answering me with so many words he suddenly drew in his head between his shoulders, stuck his elbows into his sides and, raising his wrists to breast level, let his hands dangle, twitching spasmodically. Finally, a lolling, slobbering tongue protruded through his half-open lips and his eyes converged towards the tip of his nose, while he uttered inarticulate sounds.

He then resumed his normal face and walk, bellowing:

> *'Tremble, she said, O worthy daughter mine!*
> *The Jews' cruel God against thee doth prevail . . .'*

I followed him, persisting:
'And tell me, do you think *I'm* retarded?'
He replied with grave solemnity:

[1] The famous Dream Scene from 'Athalia' by Racine. Translation by Lacy Lockert, Princeton University Press.

202

'It sticks out a mile, like the nose in your face.'
'And how do you see it?'
He answered:

> '*I grieve for thee that thou must fall as well*
> *As I, my child, into his fearful hands.*
> *These words of horror ending, as one bends*
> *Above my bed her shadow seemed to stoop,*
> *And longingly my arms stretched out to her!*'

He had uttered the last line with a pathetic quaver and was holding out his hands and his book towards me, when the drum rolled peremptorily.

I realized he had been joking, but the memory of his pantomime did not make me laugh, and I began to ponder upon my case with real concern.

*

In the midday break I told Lagneau—in a joking way—the whole story. He could see that I was a bit bothered and wanted to comfort me.

'What?' he cried indignantly. 'You're taking notice of what Socrates says? The old doy doesn't understand anything except the absolute ablative . . . I'm telling you that you're the smartest one of the lot! You aren't first, you aren't last, you get a good laugh out of the other fellows' jokes but you never get caught . . . You've found the cushiest place because you go unnoticed. That's why I'm telling you that you've outsmarted them all!'

Now like most children I liked to strut and swagger: a fault of which I have corrected myself, probably only to add to the list of my virtues a most ostentatious modesty. Lagneau's compliment therefore cut me to the quick, for it revealed that even in my friend's eyes I enjoyed no moral standing whatsoever in our little world.

Lagneau was the reckless collector of detentions, Berlaudier the ringleader of rags, Schmidt the uncontested football champion, Zacharias the model dunce. Vigilanti never drew back even before big boys, Oliva was considered a certainty for the class prize. Nelps wrote poetry, Carrère was the scholar, the sage, the arbiter—they all had a personality.

As for me, on the one hand the road to school honours was barred by the Picot-Gillis tandem and Socrates treated me as 'retarded'; on the other hand, paralysed by the fear of being kept in, I could not gain the notice of my school-fellows and so was vegetating in the shadows and in mediocrity. This situation suddenly seemed to me intolerable, and I decided to put an end to it by some sensational exploit: if by evil chance I was sentenced to be kept in, I would explain to my father that I had been compelled to run a risk for the honour of our name.

CHAPTER THIRTY-FOUR

ONE afternoon during the four o'clock break, we found Oliva sitting all alone on the bench in the gallery, as was his custom: but I noticed that his nose was swollen and that he seemed stricken.

'What's the matter with you?' asked Lagneau.

'It's Pégomas,' he said, and he showed us his deformed and purplish nose.

Pégomas was a day-boy—tall, big, fat and extremely insolent: he liked to bully weaker boys and boasted in public of his family's wealth.

'What did you do to him?' I asked.

'Nothing . . . He's jealous of me because he's always at the bottom of the class. So he said to me, "They only give you good marks out of charity. The day-boarders are all little runts, and the scholarship boys are just penniless riff-raff." So I said to him, "And you're just a big belly full of soup," and suddenly he hit me in the face with his fist.'

I did not know what a runt was but it was obviously an insult. In any case, I turned red with anger because that fat money-bag had said that we were penniless riff-raff. The story of this vile infamy quickly made the rounds of the courtyard, and Oliva's nose became the centre of attraction of a circle of indignant spectators, who were already putting their heads together with a view to wreaking exemplary vengeance. But as they talked of ganging up, four or five of them, to chastise the offender, I declared that this would not be fair and coolly remarked:

'Just one will be enough.'

'You're right!' cried Berlaudier, who was always spoiling for a fight, 'I'll attend to him tomorrow morning!'

'No,' I said, 'you're not a scholarship boy. It's got to be one of us.'

'Who, then?' asked Lagneau.

I looked round the company, frowned and said: 'Me.'

There was a moment's silence, followed by some smiles which proved to me that my reputation was not up to the level of this heroic decision. Berlaudier declared:

'Even supposing you don't back out, he'll just give you the same bloody nose as he gave Oliva.'

I looked him straight in the eye and replied:

'We'll see about that tomorrow in the ten o'clock break, in the day-school yard.'

I saw the expression of astonishment on several faces, and I myself was startled by the decisive words I had just spoken. Lagneau, however, put his hand on my shoulder and announced with sovereign authority:

'Don't you worry: you don't know him. But I do!'

I said no more, but to corroborate my friend's statement I dug my hands into my pockets and gave a somewhat sardonic grin, like someone who had been hiding his game for a long while but was now going to put his trumps on the table.

This attitude seemed to make a certain impression on the attendance. It comforted me, anyway, and so it was with a peaceful yet dignified gait that I answered the drum-roll.

*

The two hours' prep was glorious; the news spread like wildfire from desk to desk. Everyone in turn looked at me and expressed by gestures or grimaces his approval, admiration, alarm or incredulity.

Monsieur Payre's attention was soon caught by this unusual atmosphere; and just as the pessimistic Nelps was making negative signs to me he accused him of 'having played the clown for five minutes' and threatened him with a bad mark for behaviour, which would have been the first of his school career. Then he asked Vigilanti if he were suffering from a crick in the neck that forced him to keep his head turned towards me. The pantomimes stopped, but notes were discreetly passed up to me, signed by distant winks: 'If you strike the first blow he'll pipe down' (Schmidt)— 'Stamp your heel on his toes' (Rémusat)—'Don't eat too much tonight' (Nelps)—'Tickle him, he's afraid of that'

(Oliva)—'If you back out, I'll step in your place' (Ber-laudier)—'A pinch of pepper in his eye, that'll do the trick' (Cabanel, known as 'The Truffle').

I answered with nods to show my thanks and grinned to prove my self-assurance. And because I was the centre of interest in the prep room I felt ever stronger, I was drunk with confidence and conceit.

Lagneau saw me all the way home. On the way, he changed his tune, for he said to me all of a sudden:

'I say, there's something you've forgotten.'

'What's that?'

'What if you're caught and kept in?'

'Well, I'll tell my father the truth and he'll congratulate me!'

'It's just a suggestion, you know . . . 'cos if you decide to pack up at the last moment, I could explain to the others that you're afraid of being kept in on account of your scholarship.'

'So you think in the back of your mind that I want to back down?'

He did not answer at once, then said gently:

'Pégomas is bigger than you, and what's more he's vicious.'

This solicitude should have touched me; instead, I was irritated by the lack of confidence it proved.

'So you're afraid for me now?'

'That's to say . . .'

'Well, tomorrow morning at five past ten you'll jolly well see what I can do!'

*

After dinner, as I was undressing, my mother came into my bedroom and said in a low voice:

'What's the matter with you? Have you had some bad marks?'

'No, Maman, I assure you.'

'You've hardly eaten a thing.'

'That's because I had too much at four. Lagneau treated me to two *croissants*.'

'You mustn't always accept,' she told me. 'Tomorrow I'll give you twenty *sous* so that you can buy him something. Try and sleep: you seem on edge. You haven't got a sore throat, have you?'

'Not for the moment.'
She kissed my forehead and went out.

*

Her anxiety, which confirmed Lagneau's, made me aware of my own, which I had so far refused to admit. I now realized that the verbal and glorious period of my adventure was over . . . Tomorrow morning I would have to fight in earnest.

Actually, Pégomas's reputation was disturbing, and the fact that he went for the weaker boys did not in any way prove that he was weak himself: it even meant, if you looked at it closely, that he often had fights and always won . . . I had only caught a passing glimpse of him in the day-school yard: as I considered that fleeting vision I realized that he was as tall as Schmidt and much heavier. 'A big belly full of soup', that is easy to say, but you never know what people are full of. He was perhaps 'full of muscles' and would knock me down with the first blow, and if I got up with Oliva's nose all my verbal swagger would founder in ridicule.

One technical point caused me the worst fear: that dreadful day-boy had given his victim only one taste of his fist, a simple warning blow, and yet the outcome had been disastrous. Of course, Oliva did not have my strength, but the nose of a weak boy is no softer than that of a sturdy fellow, and mine would not resist any better. I had seen it in profile in the three-sided mirror at the 'Belle Jardinière'. It was fairly small, perfectly straight, and I had thought it rather pretty: this brute would perhaps flatten it out for life; I would look like a Chinese who had been bleached with washing soda and my mother would worry herself sick over it . . . What madness had made me stick out my neck—and my nose—to court this ridiculous tragedy? I tried to reassure myself by calling to mind the fuss my classmates had made of me and the moral support they had so spontaneously offered: but I suddenly realized that their startled admiration was no proof at all of their confidence in my strength, that they had rather applauded the foolhardy courage of my weakness.

Naturally they did not hope for my defeat, but they would laugh about it mercilessly, while Oliva and Lagneau would apply damp handkerchiefs to my squashed nose between two black eyes . . .

At that point, I was frozen with pallid fear and I groped for some means of escaping the massacre without loss of face . . .

*

Cowardice is always ingenious, and I had soon thought up an artful scenario.

My mother had shown herself worried for my health. I only had to complain of the beginning of laryngitis and she would keep me at home for two or three days during which, on the pretext of finding it hard to swallow, I would eat next to nothing. This comedy would see me through till Friday morning. Then I would return to school with wan complexion and hollow cheeks and, on account of the pain in my knee, would be limping.

Many would welcome me with unpleasant sneers or offensive 'ahems'. I would pretend not to see them and would say to Lagneau, as if in confidence:

'The doctor did not want me to go out, but I have come to settle accounts with Pégomas.'

Then Lagneau, Berlaudier, Oliva, Vigilanti would all fling up their arms and cry:

'You're mad!'—'You're not going to fight in the state you're in!'—'It's unbelievable to have such guts!'

I would persist and, in the ten o'clock break would set out —still limping—in search of Pégamos: my friends would run after me and would bodily hold me back, while I would struggle furiously, uttering yells of rage, and finally Berlaudier would be the one to go and chastise Pégomas.

This seemed to me an admirable plan and I laughed silently at my ruse, which I thought diabolical . . . Reassured and satisfied, I was about to fall asleep, when I heard Joseph's voice: he was walking along the corridor to go to bed, and singing in an undertone:

> *La victoire en chantant*
> *Nous ouvre la barrière . . .*[1]

[1] 'Victory, as we sing, opens the barrier to us . . .' A verse of the revolutionary song, *Le Chant du Départ*.

Then I felt my cheeks burn and hid my head under the sheet.

*

A kick in the shin and two socks on the jaw—was it really worth while to dodge them by playing an ignoble comedy which would fool no one, and in any case not me? What would my father have said, what would Paul have said if they'd known of my cowardice? Since I had promised, I would go and challenge Pégamos—and if he knocked me to the ground I'd get up and charge again. Twice, three times, ten times, until he would take to flight, screaming with fear; and if I came out of the fight with a black eye and my nose askew my friends would carry me in triumph, because nothing is more beautiful than a wounded victor . . .

Calmly and with wide-open eyes in the dark, I went over my chances.

I had never yet had a serious fight. At elementary school the situation of being Joseph's son had always conferred complete immunity on me; at the *lycée* the fear of being kept in had made me shun big battles, though in the course of rather rowdy games, such as the Attack on the Stage-coach or Roland at Roncevaux, I had given proof of fairly great skill in the difficult art of tripping up; in the sham boxing-matches my quickness had often caught my opponent by surprise; one day I had even blackened Rémusat's eye without meaning to, and he had afterwards said the memorable words: 'I know you didn't do it on purpose; you just don't know your own strength!'

A precious declaration, the memory of which now gave me wonderful comfort. Moreover, I remembered that when playing with Lagneau or Nelps I had often managed to put into practice the arm-twists dear to Nick Carter or the crank-handle jerk which had brought Nat Pinkerton fame. Also I had recently found that by dint of looking at my biceps they had begun to take shape and that they were as hard as wood . . . All these points restored my confidence, and I resolved to go to sleep at once so as to be dead ready for the battle.

My night was, however, very agitated, for I fought against the awful Pégomas till morning.

He was really very strong, but I was much quicker than

he, and I pummelled him with a shower of straight hits, hooks and swings. I first blacked both his eyes with a straight right and left of such elegance that they produced a rousing cheer. Then I aimed at his nose, which was as soft as a pillow and which instantly grew to enormous size.

He was trembling with hate and fear, but instead of taking to flight he gave me vicious kicks which I cleverly dodged by frog-leaps of supernatural ease . . . When I woke up, I was holding his left wrist with both my hands, for I had just severed his arm from his shoulder with a twist à la Nick Carter, and I was about to smash him with this weapon while Lagneau was trying to hold me back, saying 'All right, all right, that'll do now!'

CHAPTER THIRTY-FIVE

I ARRIVED at the *lycée* long before classes began. While I was putting on my smock in the empty prep room, Lagneau, Oliva, Berlaudier and a few others appeared: there were even two boarders from the next-door prep, Ben Seboul, an African, and the small Japanese boy whom we called 'Little Lemon'.

They all looked at me with curiosity and Berlaudier asked me banteringly:

'So your mind's still made up?'

I answered gravely:

'I'm as good as my word.'

Lagneau, visibly worried, cried:

'You didn't give your word! You simply said—'

'I said I'd smash Pégamas' face in, and I'm going to do it at ten o'clock.'

'Do it if you like,' said Vigilanti, 'but nobody's forcing you.'

They all feared the worst for me because they didn't know about my victory during the night.

Just then Carrère appeared; he put his left hand on the desks, in passing, in order to lessen his limp.

I thought he had come to smooth things over and forbid me to fight. But he simply said, with a grave face that was as beautiful as a man's:

'I'm proud to be your friend and I think it's jolly decent to have a shot at a boy who's sure to be much stronger than you. I'm certain you'll give him a good hiding, because you're fighting for a question of honour. Now what may be bothering you is being kept in after hours or even detained for a half-day. But there I may be of help to you.

'Blue Ginger will be supervising the break. Generally he never says a word to anyone but a fight might interest him . . . So I'll make sure he's kept busy by asking him for a tip on some problem of algebra . . . X's make his mouth water, like fudge. You can fight in peace.'

Little Lemon was chirping in his soft voice:

'Come into the courtyard with me, I'll show you a trick.'

'What trick?'

He explained obligingly:

'You take his middle finger and turn it backward. There's a crack, his finger sticks up in the air, and he begins to blubber right away.'

'That's complicated,' said Ben Seboul. 'Much better butt into his bellee with your noddle. Then he bends down, you lift your knee to meet his nose half-way and it bursts like a ripe fig.'

'You're all very kind,' I said, 'but I know what I'm going to do.'

'Yeah,' sneered Berlaudier, 'what *you're* going to do you know, but what *he's* going to do you don't! At all events, if he smashes you to pieces, I've got a roll of sticky-paper!'

'Shut up, you!' I said brutally. 'Don't get me worked up or I'll start with you!'

I took a step forward with squared shoulders and clenched fists.

Berlaudier assumed a look of terror, flung up his arms and cried in a shrill, girlish voice:

'Help! Maman! He wants to hit me! Help!'

And he fled towards the yard amid a general roar of laughter. However, the roll of the drum and Monsieur Payre's entrance put an end to the comedy.

*

Before the gory recess I had to live through an hour of French grammar, then an hour of Latin. The distant voice of Socrates was once more speaking of his beloved absolute ablative. Lagneau, meanwhile, in thrilled expectancy of the drama, was suggesting plans of battle out of the corner of his mouth.

'If you like, I'll go and talk to him first. You come up from behind . . .'

I whispered: 'No, I want to attack him face to face.'

'Let me tell you . . .'

I gladly would have let him tell me, but not so Socrates.

'Monsieur Lagneau,' he said; 'I see a rather disturbing twitch on your face which might lead me to believe that your mouth is below your left ear. If you wish to avoid two hours' detention I advise you to replace it under your nose.'

Lagneau was thus reduced to silence, but Berlaudier now and then showed me from a distance his roll of sticky paper. I pretended I did not see it. I had folded my arms, as well-behaved pupils do; actually I did it to feel my biceps and I made the bumps quiver to prepare them for battle . . . But time was not moving on: my legs were full of pins and needles, the absolute ablative had invaded the blackboard, Lagneau made his knees jump up and down on his bobbing toes, causing a ripple on the surface of the ink-well. Through the plane trees the June sun filled the empty yard with a golden-green light, the yard which presently perhaps would be running with blood . . . No, I was not afraid any more, and I felt ready to avenge Oliva's nose, the glory of our prep room, and the honour of my name: but it was really agony to have to be ready for so long, and I was straining my ears with all my might for the chime of the great clock: at last the little bell struck once. It was 'five to', and the drum sounded the charge.

*

Through the crowd rushing to leave, I advanced resolutely towards the door of the Sixth B. Lagneau was on my right, Berlaudier on my left, and we were followed by a dozen day-boarders: Oliva, whose nose had turned blue, ran to meet us: Nelps was accompanying him.

'Don't go!' Oliva cried to me. 'I was wrong to tell you about it: don't go!'

I nobly shoved him out of the way and discovered Pégomas: leaning with his back against a pillar of the gallery, he was stuffing a *croissant* between his fat cheeks. He was a head taller than I, but he was not as big as my fears had painted him, and as a little crease of fat was bulging at his knees it pleased me to think that he was really full of soup.

Amid a deep silence I went and planted myself in front of him, and said:

'Are you Pégomas?'

Voluptuously munching his *croissant*, he answered with great simplicity:

'Yes, and bugger to you.'

I heard bursts of laughter but did not take up the paltry insult.

'It appears you said that the day-boarders are all little runts and that the scholarship boys are penniless riff-raff. Have you the guts to repeat that?'

I had counted on this preamble, uttered in an aggressive tone, to intimidate the adversary and was half hoping that he might make grovelling apologies. But he stared at me with surprise charged with contempt and proclaimed, stressing each word:

'The day-boarders are little runts and the scholarship boys are penniless riff-raff. And the proof of it is that the government lets you eat here because there's nothing to put in your bellies at home.'

And he stuffed the second half of his *croissant* into his jaws.

A buzz of indignation ran through the crowd and I was suddenly incensed with a blazing fury, a cat's fury. The big belly full of soup had just spoken of Joseph's poverty! I rushed at him with a single leap, and with the base of my open palm struck him an upward blow under the nostrils with all my strength, which anger rendered ten times more powerful. This was Nat Pinkerton's blow which 'bewilders the opponent'. Mine had a twofold success, for not only did I tilt his nose up to the ceiling but my open hand, in passing, had thrust the—pointed—half of the *croissant* right up against the sacrilegious glottis.

At the same instant I received a somewhat violent blow on my left eye, then I heard the awful noise of a racking retch followed by a nauseous gurgle. I took a step back, rushed forward again, and hit him twice in the pit of the stomach. Vomiting the remnants of the *croissant*, he bent double and turned his back to me, presenting his vast behind: I pressed my heel against it and with a violent push projected him into the yard, where he went sprawling flat on his belly, while the audience clapped and cheered.

I followed him and, addressing his horizontal back, shouted:

'Get up, you big coward. Get up because I haven't finished with you! I've only just begun!'

He turned over and vainly kicked sideways, while Vigilanti shouted his advice to me:

'Jump on his belly!'

I was certainly about to trample him when Oliva and Nelps each grabbed me by one arm and I heard Lagneau's voice saying the words of my dream:

'All right, all right, that'll do now!'

The fat boy suddenly got up and I jerked my friends away to rush forward to meet him.

But Blue Ginger, escaping from Carrère's mathematical enticements, had just popped up behind a pillar, and his face for the first time expressed a certain interest in topical events. The big coward flung himself upon him, screaming:

'Sir! Sir! Look what he's done to me!'

In falling flat on his face he had scraped his upper lip, which was bleeding and swelling before our eyes.

Blue Ginger looked at this phenomenon with genuine curiosity, then answered without the least emotion:

'I see. Besides, I've seen and heard it all. Dismissed.'

The amazed Pégomas insisted:

'A day-boarder did it! It's that one!' And he pointed at me.

'I know,' said Blue Ginger, 'I know.'

Then, thoughtfully, he fell silent. I was waiting motionless for the fatal words which were going to announce the punishment for my victory; perhaps he would take me to the *Surveillant général*?

The drum gave a long but vain roll. The crowd of bystanders around us remained mute and motionless, in expectation of the verdict.

Then Blue Ginger suddenly frowned and said sharply:

'Well? Haven't you heard the drum? Dismissed!'

He turned on his heels and walked away with even strides through the rush of schoolboys, while my friends, drunk with joy and pride, followed me in a triumphant procession up to the English classroom.

*

This victory was the talk of the day in the boarders' house. Lagneau related the battle in a Homeric vein and concluded by saying:

'If I hadn't been there, he'd have killed him!'

Berlaudier discussed the matter as a technician and greatly appreciated the open-hand cut under the nose, of which I gave several demonstrations amid a circle of connoisseurs.

The crowning glory was that the only blow I had received had resplendently blackened my eye, which first glowed red, then in the course of the afternoon, became surrounded with multicoloured rings of gorgeous effect. It was really a glorious day, hardly dimmed by the fear of the possible consequences of my victory, for Blue Ginger's attitude remained a mystery to us. Some thought that the few words he had spoken represented the complete cycle of his reactions and definitely wound up the Affair; others feared it might rebound on Pégomas' swollen jowl and that the rumour of my fame might reach the ever-receptive ears of *Monsieur le Censeur*. As this perturbing hypothesis concerned only the following day—that is to say the remote future—I resolved not to think of it before its time and to enjoy my promotion peacefully.

During prep Monsieur Payre looked at me with interest and came up and asked, 'who had fixed my face like that'. I answered modestly that I'd been hit in the eye by a ball while playing pelota: a perfectly plausible explanation, which Joseph too accepted that very night without argument.

*

Next morning, in the empty prep room, I was buttoning my smock and chatting with Schmidt and Lagneau. The swelling round my eye had diminished but the colours were enhanced, for by means of nocturnal friction I had managed to cancel out the healing effect of my mother's compresses: in her naïvety she would have effaced the glorious wound, not knowing its worth.

Lagneau was just admiring it, when the drummer-cum-doorkeeper stuck his head and shoulders through the half-open door, motioned towards me, and cried:

'To *Monsieur le Censeur!*'

Lagneau, aghast, said under his breath:

'That's torn it! Blue Ginger has reported you!'

This dreadful news hit me in the pit of my stomach and I must have paled for Schmidt, the good fellow, tried hard to reassure me:

'What's the worst you can get?' he said. 'Two hours, perhaps. Being kept in for that wouldn't scare me. It isn't as if it were for bad work or conduct. You wanted to defend a friend. You ought to get a medal!'

'Maybe,' I said. 'But if they withdraw my scholarship?'

Vigilanti had just come in with Oliva in his wake.

'What?' he cried. 'Now that would be criminal! I'm telling you he'll give you a warning, that's all.'

Oliva stepped forward, distressed.

'I want to go with you. I'll tell them that it's all my fault!'

'That isn't true,' Lagneau replied. 'It's all the fault of that big belly full of soup! Explain to the *Censeur* that Pégomas was the one who attacked you, and everybody will back you up!'

'That,' said Vigilanti gravely, 'wouldn't be honest, because it's not true!'

'What?' cried Lagneau indignantly. 'We've got a right to swear that it was Pégamos who started with a sock on the nose! No need to say that it was Oliva's nose!'

'He's right!' Schmidt declared. 'Let's go, all of us.'

The slanting torso of the doorkeeper reappeared and cried:

'Now then, are you coming?'

We walked out into the corridor, all together, and found the doorkeeper waiting for me there.

'What do all those want?'

'We are witnesses!' said Lagneau. 'We're going to tell the *Censeur* that he's in the right and that the other one started it!'

'If the other one started it he made a big mistake!' said the doorkeeper . . . 'He's got a nose like a tomato and a mouth that looks as if he were whistling. And his father is kicking up a hell of a row. He's asked the *Censeur* if this is a *lycée* or a slaughter-house.'

Now I was really scared and Lagneau himself seemed alarmed.

'Has his father been here?'

'He's been and still is. There's his father, there's him, there's the *Censeur* and Monsieur Berniolle, who is about to explain things.'

Monsieur Berniolle was Blue Ginger. I realized that I was lost. I leaned on Lagneau's shoulder.

'You did the right thing, all the same,' said Vigilanti. 'Your conscience is clear and honour bright!'

My conscience! What good could my conscience do me? If Pégamos was disfigured, I would certainly be hauled before the Disciplinary Council, I would lose my scholarship, and there would be nothing left for me but to flee with Lili into the hills . . .

Oliva was marching ahead of me. From time to time he turned round and looked at me humbly.

I began to detest him. He was really my bad angel. At the scholarship exams he had stolen the First Place from me, and now on account of him and for the glory of his nose I would be driven out of the *lycée*, to my father's disgrace. I cursed him from the bottom of my heart and bitterly regretted the disastrous victory which was sending me to the scaffold and ravaging my family . . . Moreover, I suddenly thought of that enraged father who would perhaps box my ears in front of everybody . . . Now that would be the limit . . . At this thought my ribs tightened round my chest and I was compelled to stop and take a deep breath, before the worried eyes of my friends. The doorkeeper, who was walking ahead of us, turned round and said once more:

'Now then! Are you coming?'

We arrived at last in front of the double door, out of which every day for years so many condemned men had passed: never yet had I walked through it, and I stopped again.

The doorkeeper, without any sign of emotion, shoved my escort aside, took me by the shoulder, knocked discreetly, strained his ear, opened the door, pushed me in and closed it after me.

*

The first thing I saw was Blue Ginger's back: he was standing, and his left hand was clasping his right wrist behind his back. On the other side of the writing-table *Monsieur le Censeur* was sitting motionless, before an open register.

To the left of Blue Ginger's back there was the back of Pégomas; he turned his face as I came in: I saw with amazement his bloated lips and swollen nose, yellow as the saffron in a *bouillabaisse*. It looked like a carnival mask, whose involuntary grimace—perhaps fixed for ever—proclaimed my ferocity. I had hoped for a moment that my black eye, supported by the exhibition of Oliva's nose, might be deducted from the damage which the day-boy had suffered: but a comparison between my black eye and this glowing disaster could only have aggravated my case, and I gave up in advance.

Next to Pégomas, there was a very tall man, richly clad in a navy-blue suit and holding a grey felt hat in his hand . . . The little finger of this hand was adorned with a very thick gold ring, which must have cost a fortune. Raising my eyes, I saw that he was red-haired, like Clémentine. She had often told me, with pride: 'Redheads are either all good or all bad.' Which sort was he? One could not say at first sight, but according to the doorkeeper's words I was afraid he was not good . . . I became aware that Blue Ginger was speaking. In a tone of perfect indifference and like someone reciting a lesson, he was murmuring:

'At that moment I heard the pupil Pégomas saying emphatically: 'Day-boarders are little runts and scholarship boys are penniless riff-raff. And the proof of it is that one lets them eat at the *lycée* because there's nothing to put in their bellies at home." And then . . .'

'Excuse me!' said the man with the ring. 'Forgive me for interrupting you.'

He turned to his son and asked:

'Do you admit having said those words?'

Pégomas, with scowling eyes, painfully articulated through his meaty mouth:

'I said it because it's the truth.'

There was a short silence, during which the red-haired man, to my great surprise, pulled his ring from his finger, while *Monsieur le Censeur*, with a frown on his face, gazed at Pégomos disapprovingly; he was going to speak but was given no time.

The red-haired man's right hand shot out in a flash and

sparked off a little blaze on the cheek of the offender, who gasped and tottered.

Monsieur le Censeur smiled, while the administrator of justice, putting his ring back on his finger, turned to me.

'My young friend,' he said, 'I congratulate you on having chastised this idiot in the proper fashion, and I hope *Monsieur le Censeur* will not follow up this regrettable incident.'

Then he took his son by the shoulder and pushed him towards me.

'Apologize to this boy,' he said.

Pégomas looked at me wild-eyed. To his father's exhortation he replied:

'I don't know what to say.'

'Repeat: I am sorry to have said such odious words and beg you to forget them.'

He hesitated, looked in all directions, then closed his eyes and repeated the sentence, groping for the words.

'Very well,' said Monsieur Pégomas. 'And now, *Monsieur le Censeur*, I myself must apologize for having made you lose your valuable time: this affair, which my son explained in his own way, needed clearing up.'

Monsieur le Censeur accompanied him to the door, talking politely. But when he opened it, Lagneau, bent double, fell ear forward onto Monsieur Pégomas's chest, as if he wanted to listen to his heart . . . His surprised patient pushed him back rather vehemently, which enabled Lagneau to take to his heels before he was recognized.

When the Pégomas family had gone, the *Censeur* came over to me, raised my chin with the tip of his forefinger, examined my eye, and said: 'That'll be all right.'

And as the drum-roll was sounding, he added:

'Thanks to Monsieur Pégomas' magnanimity you will not be punished this time. Dismissed!'

*

I walked out, dizzy with joy. In the corridor I found not only my sincere false witnesses but also a dozen other 'supporters' whom the faithful Lagneau had recruited—in the course of his flight. They were grinning with pleasure, admiring me, clinging to my shoulder. Little Oliva was laughing nervously and along his bluish nose there gleamed the trace of a tear of joy, but he did not dare approach me: so I pushed the others aside and clasped my glory to my heart.

*

The very next morning I wrenched three buttons off my smock, which left three frayed little gaps behind; then I tore the thread of one seam, made two rips in the everlasting sateen which my mother had chosen, and pushed my socks down onto my shoes.

From that day onward, whenever Pégomas saw me arrive in the courtyard he would glower at me and move away hugging the walls, or slip behind a pillar of the gallery in a semi-circular flight, and my reputation glowed afresh.

I revelled in it peacefully, but without going in search of fresh fights: I was thinking of the second half of the *croissant*. I knew quite well that that little horn of pastry, so imprudently crammed in just before the battle, had been the principal weapon of my victory: it would have been unreasonable to hope that destiny would always offer me opponents equipped with a *croissant* pointing at their uvula . . . That is why I confined myself to showing my strength by the sole authority of my glance, the calm violence of my words and Pégomas's repeated flights.

This is how, at the end of my year in the Sixth Form, I had asserted my personality without effort and settled down for good to a rather handsome situation as a redoubtable fighter and a redresser of wrongs.

PART TWO

The Time of Love

ONE

The Secret Society

Although I did not realize it until much later, the most surprising change wrought by my new life as a daily boarder at the Lycée was that my family, my beloved family, ceased to be the centre around which my life revolved. The only time I saw them was when we assembled for our evening meal, and, when I talked about the Lycée, in reply to my father's or Paul's questions, I did not tell them everything, but gave them an edited version of events, like a traveller describing Brazil or Canada to people who have never been there, and whose understanding must therefore, of necessity, be limited.

Paul, at least, was keenly aware that I had become a stranger to him. He was no less fond of me, and his admiration for me had grown, but we no longer played together. On Thursdays, his little friends would come to the house, while I would join up with Lagneau and Schmidt for a game of football, or a bicycle ride in the Parc Borély. I had my secrets, and I lived in another world, a world in which I was a different person, one whom they would certainly have failed to recognize.

When I look back upon the long list of roles that I have played in the course of my life, I sometimes wonder who I really am. With my mother, I was an affectionate little boy, sometimes daring, sometimes timid, but always obedient. With Clémentine, I was a dazzled spectator, in spite of my vastly greater physical strength, as compared with hers, that is to say. With Isabelle I had been an abject slave, until I had at last broken free in disgust. And now, at the Lycée, I was an organizer, a bold and calculating leader, and I had only one wish, to exclude my family from my new-found kingdom, knowing full well that they would seem out of place in it.

We had only one real friend among the day boys, and his name was Mérinos. He was fairly tall and very dark, with a nose which was already prominent, although he himself preferred to call it 'aquiline'. He prided himself on his sartorial elegance, with some justification, I must admit, though his fine feathers were usually somewhat bedraggled by the end of the morning recess.

His strong language alone, not to mention his imaginative capacity for mischief, would have won him a place in our counsels, but what we admired most of all was the extent of his medical knowledge.

His father was, in fact, a distinguished physician in Marseilles, as much respected for his dedication and goodness of heart as for his diagnostic skill.

As was to be expected, he possessed a very large library, and since he was forever toiling up and down the staircases of tenements to minister to the poor, his son had ample opportunities for making use of it. At night in bed, with the avidity of youth, he would read everything he could find concerning the reproductive functions, and would arrive at the Lycée next day laden with the fruits of his labour. Lili, a local shepherd, blushing a little, had furnished me with a vague notion of the manner of my birth, whereas Mérinos, in the space of ten minutes, explained the whole process in detail with no trace of a blush, but many a wink and snigger. Then, as his reading progressed, he initiated us into the most horrifying diseases, and even went so far as to bring us an astonishing photograph, torn out of the medical Larousse, which portrayed an unfortunate Abyssinian, suffering from some form of tropical elephantiasis, as a result of which he was constrained forever to push a heavily-laden wheel-barrow before him. All this information, passed on in the day boys' playground, proved extremely profitable, and it is no exaggeration to say that I owe more to Mérinos even than to my philology teachers, who made it possible for me to read Ulfilas's Bible in the original mediaeval Saxon.

That year in the Sixth Grade was not distinguished by any outstanding event, unless it were the foundation of a Secret Society, whose only aim, however, was to remain secret, and which, far from having any revolutionary or doctrinal basis, came into being entirely by accident.

Berlaudier's father was an importer of Mocha coffee, and he

sold this precious commodity in little paper bags, each one secured by a tin fastener in the shape of a four-leaf clover, with dazzlingly bright red, enamelled leaves.

Berlaudier had pinched some twenty of these trinkets, and brought them to school, with no very clear notion of what to do with them.

I can claim for myself the merit of having taken one look at them and realized that we should have to found the Red Clover-Leaf Secret Society, which we proceeded to do (in secret) during the lunch-hour recess.

At first there were only four initiates, Berlaudier, Nelps, Lagneau and I.

We began by pricking the tips of our forefingers (using a new pen-nib), and mingling the four drops of our blood on a portrait of Vercingetorix, torn out of Lagneau's history textbook. This hallowed page was then folded in four, and we took it to a distant corner of the playground, and set fire to it. I wonder now what the connection was between this native of Auvergne and our little enterprise. Presumably, we wanted to establish a link with our country's remotest past while, at the same time, paying tribute to a brave and ill-fated man. And besides, it must be admitted that Lagneau just happened to have the picture in his pocket at the time, and that it was intended to be used for a very different purpose.

Next, we fastened the red emblems to the front of our shirts, so that they were concealed beneath our black overalls. It was later decided that whenever any two initiates met, they should hastily unbutton their overalls and whisper: 'Vercingetorix'.

Berlaudier, who was essentially a prosaic character, protested that, since we were all so well known to one another, such signals of recognition were pointless. Nelps retorted that anyone who could say such a thing was obviously an idiot, and I said (in an undertone):

'There are only four of us now. But what about when we have a thousand members?'

This optimistic forecast resulted in my being elected Supreme Chief, with the privilege of wearing two clover-leaves instead of just one.

That same night I invented a secret cipher, consisting of circles, triangles, crosses, numbers, letters turned on their sides, question marks, and a variety of squiggles, copies of which I distributed among the initiates. We then proceeded to despatch messages by means of the password: 'Hand it on.' That is to say, I would entrust the message, folded in four, to Rémusat with the whispered instruction: 'Hand it on to Berlaudier.' He, in turn, would pass it to Schmidt, who sat in front of him. Schmidt would hand it on to Beltrami, who would finally give it to the addressee. Needless to say, not one of these helpful intermediaries omitted to unfold the message, and con the hieroglyphics with the liveliest interest, mingled at times with incredulity. When the message finally reached Berlaudier, the intermediaries would watch him closely, eager to see what he would do with it.

First, Berlaudier would make sure that Monsieur Payre's attention was engaged elsewhere (that is to say, that he was reading his newspaper). Next, he would unfold the despatch and, to all appearances, decipher it at a glance. Then, he would turn to me and, with a solemn nod, acknowledge receipt of the Supreme Chief's orders.

These machinations—conducted repeatedly in lessons and study periods—soon had all our school-mates agog with curiosity. We were delighted, for what was the point of having a Secret Society if no one knew of its secret existence? The one secret that must be kept at all costs was the object of our activities, and this was not too difficult, since there was none.

Mérinos was the first to apply for admission. His application was discussed at great length, and, although he was a day boy, it was decided to admit him. Nelps proposed Valabrègue for membership. He, too, was a day boy, but in Form B2 in the Sixth Grade. He also was admitted. It seemed to me sound political sense to have a tame spy in that remote classroom, which was situated right at the far end of the corridor.

Every Saturday, I received a report—in cipher—on the events of the week from each individual member. I would then make a summary of these, and read it aloud to the Grand Council during the afternoon recess.

It was not long before the society numbered some twenty members, scattered among the five forms of the Sixth Grade. Many of the day boys were all too eager to bribe their way in with toffees, humbugs, rare stamps and agate marbles. All such attempts at corruption, however, were scornfully rejected.

All the same, I made a big mistake in refusing admission to Carcassonne, on the grounds that he had once tripped up Lagneau, while he was belting downstairs to his drawing class.

We were the losers, for, while Berlaudier's father used the red clover-leaves, it was Carcassonne's father who manufactured them, by the million, a fact which the scoundrel omitted to mention, since he planned thereby to have his revenge.

One day, he arrived with a fistful of these mysterious emblems, and secretly distributed them to all sorts of undesirable individuals in the Fifth and Sixth Grades: to such good effect that the Grand Council, assembling in the day boys' playground for the evening recess, suffered a severe public humiliation. For there were thirty great idiots, each wearing a red clover-leaf in his buttonhole, performing a grotesque parody of our recognition signals.

And then Carcassonne, watched by a semi-circle of sniggering spectators, solemnly handed me a square of cardboard covered in hieroglyphics, and announced to all and sundry that he brought me greetings from Vercingetorix, which provoked a thunderous round of hoots and shouts.

I responded with a smart kick on the shin, while Lagneau spat in his face. At this, the initiates closed ranks behind me. We were just moving in to do battle on the grand scale, when the Waterloo drum sounded a general retreat.

And thus it was that the Red Clover-Leaf Secret Society, after six weeks of glory, foundered in a blaze of public ignominy, and was soon forgotten.

TWO

The Hangings

Far from experiencing the slightest twinge of anxiety, I was truly filled with joy, when I left home one morning in October for the Lycée, to start the academic year as a member of Form A2 in the Fifth Grade. No one came with me. With my satchel on my back and my hands in my pockets, I did not even have to look up to read the names of the streets. I was not on my way to an unknown prison, teeming with strangers. On the contrary, I was looking forward to a thousand reunions with boys of my own age in familiar corridors and playgrounds, the ticking of a friendly clock, the shade of plane trees, and the exchange of secrets. I bundled the new overall that my mother had made me into my locker, and wore last year's tattered garment, which I had secreted in my satchel. It was limp with age, and snagged and frayed, and it no longer rustled when I moved, but it proclaimed my status. I made a triumphal entry into the playground. No longer was I the 'new boy', the lonely outsider, standing rooted to the spot, peering anxiously about in the hope of eliciting a smile or friendly gesture. No sooner did I appear in my ragged overall than Lagneau, Nelps and Vigilanti were rushing up to me with welcoming cries. In response I burst out laughing, Lagneau broke into a joyful dance, and then we all ran off together to welcome Berlaudier. He had spent the summer in the mountains, returning with cheeks so puffed up that his eyes were little more than slits, and the sleeves of his overall now barely reached below his elbows. To mark the opening of the academic year, he took a fire-cracker from his pocket, and aimed it adroitly between the legs of a new boy, who happened to have his back to us. The boy leapt into the air, as if lifted by the blast, and fled to the far end of the playground, without venturing so much as a single backward glance. Whereupon we went and sat on the bench under the colonnade, and began exchanging gossip.

We were looking forward to this coming year in the Fifth Grade, with high hopes of our new form master, Monsieur Bidart, in whose classroom bedlam reigned. Whenever we went past his door, we could hear shouting and bellowing, interspersed with snatches of song and gales of laughter so infectious that even the best-behaved among us yearned to join in. One day, the temptation became too great even for Berlaudier. Squinting, limping and stammering, he had introduced himself as a new boy, and the unsuspecting Bidart had enrolled him in the register as Patureau, Victor, from the College of the Sacred Heart in Palavas-les-Flots. For more than an hour, the 'new boy' had performed such extravagant antics that the entire class could be heard bellowing through the party wall; so much so that, in the end, Bidart sent him out of the room with the sanction of Sunday detention. No doubt the official chit is still being passed around in the hope that it will eventually catch up with Patureau, Victor.

Thus it was that we were looking forward ecstatically to spending a whole year in this pests' paradise. And, what was more, Lagneau and Berlaudier had made their preparations in advance, and I knew that they were determined to set the tone right from the start. Berlaudier had in his pockets four 'Martinique stones', which were little round pebbles dipped in phosphorus. When rolled on the floor, these fiendish stones emitted a shower of crackling sparks. He also had some glacial fluid, with which he intended to anoint Bidart's chair, and a pair of little leather bellows, intended for snaring thrushes, which chirruped at the slightest pressure. Lagneau, for his part, produced a very large matchbox, and held it up to my ear, whereupon I could hear a good deal of scratching, and a few very sharp taps. These sounds were made by a couple of crickets that he had brought back from the country, and which he proposed to release in the classroom, having first coated them with an appropriate quantity of ink. We were about to inaugurate a veritable festival of fun in Bidart's circus, and I felt positively ashamed of having nothing to contribute but goodwill.

When the drum-roll sounded for the first time that year, far from answering its call at a run like new boys (or, indeed, mere day boys), we remained seated, serenely unhurried, like the veterans we were. It was not until the last beat that we strolled off in leisurely fashion to the classroom.

We still had another year ahead under the tutelage of Monsieur Payre, and we were delighted to see him again.

He gave us a beaming smile, before bellowing out his usual greeting:

'It's been a long time, gentlemen, a long time!'

To our great indignation, we found that two new boys—in all innocence—were occupying our seats! With magisterial authority and in complete silence, we took them by the scruff of the neck and dislodged them.

Then, while Monsieur Payre was delivering his little speech of welcome (it seemed to me that I had heard it at least ten times before), we settled down to an exchange of news.

Schmidt showed us a two-note wooden whistle, which he had brought back from Switzerland for use in Bidart's classroom, and which (he told us) imitated the call of the cuckoo to the life, while Vigilanti produced a box of tintacks as big as carpet tacks, 'for the day boys,' he said, explaining that he intended to scatter them, point upwards, all over their benches.

Finally, we marched upstairs to the day boys' floor, in such a state of excitement that even Bluebeard noticed it, and halted the column, to restore order in the ranks.

At last we reached the door of Form A2 in the Fifth Grade, adjacent to our former classroom. The day boys were already there, and not a sound was to be heard. Lagneau turned the brass doorknob, and abruptly stepped backwards.

'This isn't it,' he said. 'This is the Sixth Grade.'

But the voice of Socrates suddenly rang out:

'Come in, gentlemen!'

And coming to the door himself, he greeted Bluebeard with a nod, and repeated, with a touch of impatience:

'Come in!'

We did so, filled with consternation, while he returned to his seat on the rostrum.

Then, when we were all seated, he said, smiling broadly and stroking his handsome beard:

'Gentlemen, I too have been passed fit for promotion. That is to say that my colleague and friend Monsieur Bidart having reached retirement age, the Headmaster has been good enough to entrust his form to me, and it gives me great pleasure to see you all again. I trust that this pleasure is shared, if not by all of you, at least by those who intend to devote this year to work.'

The day boys in the front row, smiling from ear to ear, responded with murmurs of satisfaction. Meanwhile Zacharias's head drooped, and he covered his face with his hands, and Lagneau repeatedly muttered the *mot de Cambronne* under his breath at a prodigious speed.

Whereupon Socrates, opening a cardboard-covered exercise book, announced:

'Before we tackle the *De Viris Illustribus Urbis Romae*, we shall begin this academic year by concentrating on the ablative absolute.'

All this while, Berlaudier scarcely dared to move for fear of activating the dreaded Martinique stones, and I could hear the crickets in Lagneau's pocket, gnawing their way out of the matchbox.

The stubbornness of Socrates was not all we had to endure. We also still had Pitzu for English, Pétunia for Mathematics, and Monsieur Michel for Ancient History. It was small consolation to us that, instead of plugging the Pharaohs and the Obelisks, he now endeavoured to interest us in that ludicrous fellow Romulus, who, not content with being suckled by a she-wolf with grubby teats, went on to murder his brother and found the Roman Empire, much to the detriment of the curriculum of secondary education.

Fortunately, however, we still had Tignasse, upon whom we were able to unleash all the artillery of the Bidart festival in the afternoons. But for him, that year in the Fifth Grade, so similar to the year before, would have left me with no memories worth recording, for it was indeed in his form that the Lagneau affair began, arising directly as it did from the Hangings.

I feel I owe it to the reader at this point to explain the techniques involved. Lagneau, who was no mean draughtsman, would draw a full-length, highly-coloured portrait of one of the masters, using an entire page of his exercise book. He would then cut round it very skilfully with a penknife.

All this time, Berlaudier would be busy chewing blotting paper to the consistency of a glutinous paste. Thanks to the

233

strength of his greedy jaws, and the viscosity and abundance of his frothy saliva, he could provide us, in a matter of minutes, with a ball of paste, as smooth and sticky as could possibly be desired. I would then embed half a matchstick in this paste and fasten to it a length of thread, at the other end of which I had tied a slip-knot. This I would attach to the neck of the cut-out figure, so that it took on the appearance of a hanged man. Next, I would wait until Tignasse had his back turned, and with a sudden jerk I would throw the adhesive pellet up to the ceiling, where it would remain stuck, so that the hanged man would swing gracefully from side to side every time anyone opened the door.

Tignasse was the first of our victims, but he did not deign to notice the effigy, and it was still there two days later, swooping and fluttering with every puff of wind. Next, we executed the caretaker, then Pétunia, Monsieur Michel, Bluebeard, the Senior Tutor, and even the Deputy Head in charge of the boarders. Fear alone deterred us from hanging the Headmaster, but, in vetoing the execution of Pitzu and Monsieur Payre, I was moved solely by affection.

It was good fun, but, owing to the caddish indifference of Tignasse, it created very little stir. And besides, at the end of two or three weeks, by which time Berlaudier's paste had dried out, the hanged men had fallen down one by one, and been swept away. In the end our hopes of having a complete rogues' gallery hanging from the ceiling were frustrated, and we abandoned the game.

It was some three months after this that Socrates began making my life a misery. Just because I had been imprudent enough to turn in one or two good pieces of work, he saw fit to shatter my tranquil existence. Every morning, he would insist on testing me in grammar or recitation, and would pester me in class with questions so esoteric that Lagneau became indignant on my behalf, and even Zacharias was moved to pity at my plight. I endeavoured to discourage my tormentor by nonsensical answers. On one occasion, when he asked me to cite an example of the ablative absolute, I replied "*Subito presto*", which earned me a few sniggers from the day boys, and an imposition requiring me to translate three extra paragraphs of the *De Viris Illustribus*.

*

But, far from losing heart, this scourge of a man continued to persecute me, so much so that I began dreaming about it at night, and I resolved to have my revenge.

One morning, I informed Lagneau and Berlaudier that I had decided to hang Socrates in his own classroom, and I requested Lagneau to devote the next study period to drawing as life-like a portrait as he could manage.

He seemed somewhat daunted at the recklessness of my plan, but Berlaudier exclaimed:

'He's right! Socrates has been hounding him. You can't expect him just to knuckle under and do nothing!'

'What if he cops a detention?'

'If he follows the usual procedure, Socrates won't notice a thing.'

'But what if someone gives him away?'

'Well, for one thing, those swots in the front row won't see, and, for another, all the ones at the back are decent types. And what's more, if he does cop a detention, it can only do him credit. All the time he's been at the Lycée, he's never once been in serious trouble. That's a pretty feeble record for a daily boarder. You do that drawing of Socrates, and be sure and give him a long, protruding tongue, all blue and swollen, and he's got it made!'

The artist pleaded for a respite of twenty-four hours, on the pretext that he had not brought his crayons with him. The truth was that he wanted to give me time to think it over. But Berlaudier immediately countered by offering to lend him his own paint box, and Lagneau was obliged to set to work without further delay.

He made the drawing during the maths lesson, and spent the lunch-hour break lovingly colouring it in. But he refused to depict Socrates with his tongue hanging out, on the grounds that this would conceal his handsome golden beard, thus rendering him unrecognizable. Berlaudier, acknowledging the claims of artistic integrity, did not insist, and during the next one-and-a-half-hour study period, dedicated himself to the chewing of a sheet of high-grade blotting paper.

It was a quarter to three, just as the twelve strokes of the school bell were sounding, when Socrates rose from his chair and, with a piece of chalk in his hand, turned his back on us, to write a sentence in Latin on the blackboard.

235

This was the moment I had been waiting for.

Not forgetting to keep a sharp eye on him, with a single swift and possibly even graceful flick of the wrist, I launched the sticky pellet towards the ceiling, the pellet at which Berlaudier had worked so hard in the name of friendship. Not daring to look up, I heard the tiny 'clunk' of impact: but at the same time, I also heard behind me a faint cry. That idiot Zacharias, whom I had foolishly omitted to take into my confidence, had been unable to master his terror at such an occurrence taking place in his immediate vicinity. Socrates had a very keen ear. He heard both the 'clunk' and the cry, and turned sharply to face us. My head was already bent over my exercise book, and, as a good boy should, I was writing with a little frown of concentration. I was prepared for anything, but for a full thirty seconds no sound broke the lowering silence.

Lagneau had the gift of double vision, by which I mean that he was able to watch Socrates while seeming to keep his eyes fixed on his exercise book. He whispered:

'Watch out! He's seen it!'

Then I heard the low murmur of voices, and I could sense that the boys in the front row had turned round to look at us. I went on writing with an air of great absorption. But then I felt something soft land on the top of my head, and the whole form burst out laughing. Lagneau murmured: 'Oh! calamity!' Perhaps the blotting paper had been too well chewed, perhaps the pellet was too big, perhaps the ceiling was too far gone in decay; be that as it may, the apparatus had just fallen on my head, and the paper Socrates was fluttering under my nose.

I picked it up instantly, and looked at it in surprise, as if I had never seen it before. Then, with every appearance of indignation, I was crumpling it between my fingers, when Socrates, the real Socrates, he of the ablative absolute, stopped me with an imperious gesture.

'Stop that, sir. Bring that thing in your hand to me, and be quick about it.'

Moving like an automaton, I went up to the rostrum, pretending to myself that all was not yet lost.

Socrates took the crumpled wad of paper and deftly opened it out, while Berlaudier's paste dropped like a meteor at his feet. Whereupon he said:

'Plainly this is a portrait of myself. The beard is a fair like-ness, and the blue of the eyes is flattering.'

This was greeted with gales of laughter, and I did my best to join in the general merriment, to show that I was in no way responsible for the incident.

But Socrates went on:

'However, this is a personal insult to me, and the culprit will have to be punished. I did not see him do it.' (He turned to me.) 'However, unfortunately for you, this caricature fell on your head, and it seems to me self-evident that, in falling, it retraced its upward path. All the evidence, therefore, points to you as the culprit.'

Once again, the whole form burst out laughing. With my hands clasped behind my back, I bent my head and remained silent.

'And what's more,' continued Socrates, 'you seemed to me very anxious to destroy this work of art. And finally, you have not the impudence to protest your innocence. Admittedly, the evidence is all circumstantial, but the case against you is so strong that I have no hesitation in pronouncing you guilty, and I am in duty bound to punish you accordingly.'

He picked up the hanged man by the cord, and held it in front of his eyes for a second or two.

'You sentenced me to be hanged. I shall be less severe with you. I will merely inflict two hours of detention on you, the sentence to be carried out next Thursday. In addition, since it seems to me that you are in need of a little time to meditate upon the respect due to your teachers, you will spend the rest of the morning in the punishment hall, where you will find the atmosphere wholly conducive to reflection. Allow me to furnish you with your passport.'

He returned to his chair, wrote a few lines on a sheet of paper, and handed it to me. I returned to my seat to collect my text-books and exercise books. Lagneau was as white as a sheet, but Berlaudier winked joyfully at me.

An awesome silence fell upon the room as I went out.

The playground was deserted except for a few pecking spar-rows, and the long colonnade was empty as far as the eye could see. I stopped under an archway, and unfolded the dreaded piece of paper. On it was written my name, followed by the words:

'Attempted to suspend a caricature of his form master from the ceiling.'

It was no more than the truth, and I had no cause for complaint. I resumed my solitary journey. As I went past the row of classrooms, boys made faces and cocked snooks at me through the windows.

It occurred to me, all of a sudden, that I might well be about to encounter the day boys' Housemaster, the dreaded Vulture. Then I shrugged, and said aloud: 'What worse can he do to me than this?' I felt that I had touched rock-bottom in terms of scholastic misfortune, and that the magnitude of the catastrophe was such that not only Fate but the Vulture himself could do me no more harm, in other words, I was as invulnerable as the dead.

I walked on towards the punishment hall. It was a sort of concentration camp for those under sentence of punishment or expulsion, for outcasts. I had never yet been inside, but had often gone past the door on the way to my drawing class. It was a tall, narrow, double door. One day I had seen a crowd of boys of all ages coming out through that door. They had not tumbled out with open mouths and shouts of joy, but had processed slowly, like penitents, some sullen-looking, others ferocious, and still others sniggering gloomily.

I paused for an instant on the threshold of that fateful door. I drew several deep breaths, fastened the buttons of my overall, and, with a hand that shook a little, opened it.

I found myself in a long, narrow room. At the far end glittered a tall window, beneath which, silhouetted against the light, sat a man, bent over a broad, funereally black table. On my right, a bare wall. On my left, two long rows of desks already occupied by delinquents.

I approached the seated man, and saw that he was engaged in copying individual detention notices from a huge punishment register, which lay open at his left hand. In front of him, spread like a fan, were the detention notices which he had already completed, and which would be sent out on the following Wednesday. He was manufacturing these detonators without any visible emotion, apparently indifferent to the explosions of parental wrath that they would surely touch off. His smooth,

238

hairless face wore an unwavering expression of cold majesty, reminiscent of the Recording Angel.

He surveyed me without surprise, and said, without pausing for breath:

'Surname, christian name, form, form master?'

I replied in a voice that I did not recognize as my own, and handed him the note from Socrates.

He read it, shook his head, and then proceeded to make an entry in the huge punishment register open in front of him: in the first column, my name, stiff and stark on the page, in the second, very neatly, A2, in the third, the name Lepelletier, and finally, in the fourth column (the widest), my offence.

His handwriting was beautiful.

Without raising his head, he said, 'Go and sit down,' and went on with his work.

I went and sat in the back row, next to one of the 'big boys', who was probably in the Second Grade. I opened my *Epitome*, and looked about me.

My companions in misfortune were of every size, some tall, some of medium height, and others small, but they were all equal in adversity. Daunted by the bleakness of their surroundings, they concentrated in silence on the homework that they had failed to do, the lesson that they had omitted to learn, or meditated humbly upon the terrible consequences of bad behaviour, to such an extent that this gathering of dunces, rebels and jokers, brought together by laziness, insolence and mendacity, wore the appearance of an assemblage of academic excellence. From time to time, the door would open, and we would look up discreetly to witness the arrival of the latest outlaw.

He would shut the door as if entering a sickroom, and advance on tiptoe for the brief interrogation, then, duly enrolled, he would come and sit in our midst, in deathly silence.

One solitary incident disturbed us at our peaceful toil, the irruption of the young victim of a judicial error. What an uproar the innocent can create, protesting, squealing, weeping and snuffling, and they never seem to carry a handkerchief! Ours (a small red-head in the Sixth Grade) literally danced with rage, so much so that, in the end, he fully deserved the two hours' detention awarded him by the black master of silence himself.

At this, the innocent—now at last truly guilty, and no longer labouring under a sense of injustice—shut up, swallowed his tears, and came to take his seat among his sneering fellow-sinners.

Socrates had been quite right to tell me that this place was conducive to meditation. But my meditations were not concerned with the respect due to my teachers. I spent the time bitterly reproaching myself for the failure of my plan, considering all the possible alternatives that might have succeeded. The best of these would have been to have obtained permission from Monsieur Payre to go upstairs to the day boys' wing during the evening study period, on the pretext of fetching a text-book or exercise book deliberately left behind. Then, alone in the deserted classroom, I could have placed my hanged man directly above the master's seat, or, even better, directly above that of the senior scholar, Picot, making sure this time, however, that the adhesive was well and truly fixed. Thus Socrates could not possibly have suspected me, and, as he would have been unable to dislodge the effigy without the help of a longish pole, he would have had to send for the caretaker, or even perhaps the Deputy Headmaster, which would have given us all a good laugh. Alternatively, he might have pretended not to notice it, in which case it would have remained there, slowly rotating above his head for two whole hours, a circumstance so disconcerting that even the great Socrates might have confused an ablative absolute with a future participle. But, alas, it was too late. My hair was still stuck together with Berlaudier's paste, and I was in the punishment hall . . . Presumably criminals serving their term in prison meditate in this fashion, taking advantage of their hours of enforced idleness to perfect their nefarious skills.

Thus I did not reproach myself for my crime, but for my failure to commit it undetected, and I blamed my sorry plight on my own foolishness.

I was not in the least daunted at the prospect of being kept in at the Lycée from eight to ten on the following Thursday morning. Lagneau, who had attended many of these dunces' gatherings, had made them sound rather fun. On the rostrum sat a junior master reading the newspapers, while the malefactors openly sat reading whatever they pleased, or chatting among themselves in undertones. This ordeal held no terrors for me, and besides, I agreed with Berlaudier: a day-boarder who had never been punished was rather like an officer who had never been to war. My only anxiety was on Joseph's account. I could already see him turning pale when I showed him the chit, requiring that he sign it with the name I had dishonoured. He would reproach me with ingratitude towards the bountiful state which had awarded me a scholarship, and, even as he was speaking, he would fly into a rage, and it would all end up with a box on the ears. Paul would burst into tears, my mother would bring my dinner up to my bedroom on a tray, and Joseph would be thoroughly upset. Admittedly this catastrophe lay some way ahead. Today was Friday, so there were nearly six days to go before the fateful Wednesday evening, on which all would finally have to be revealed at home. But what agony I should have to endure between now and then! I endeavoured to work out a plan of campaign.

I could, for instance, take my mother into my confidence, so that she might forewarn Joseph. Or I myself could introduce the subject at the dinner table, remarking on the number of detentions that were meted out daily all around me, and adding that it was a wonder that I had so far managed to escape. I could go on to explain that it was often the innocent who were punished, but that it was a law of the Lycée that it was in the highest degree dishonourable to denounce the true culprit. Needless to say, I would shift the blame for my exploit on to Berlaudier, making a jest of the whole business, which would make little Paul laugh, and then my mother, and then—who could tell?— even perhaps Joseph. Although I was much impressed by the astuteness of this plan of campaign, I immediately set about devising another, for fear had greatly stimulated my imagination.

Might it not be possible, in the course of five days, to obtain Socrates' forgiveness, and persuade him to rescind the detention order? But how? By learning the rules governing the ablative absolute. I would work at it day and night. I would seek help from Uncle Jules, and would perform so brilliantly in the classroom that Socrates, touched on his weakest spot, would, of his own volition, tear up the fateful chit. For a while, I was greatly cheered by these musings, until I suddenly noticed that the sombre scribe on the rostrum had reached the last entry in the register, and, from the look he gave me, I knew that he was writing out my sentence.

When he had finished, he beckoned me to approach, and addressed me in ringing tones:

'For an offence such as yours, you are being let off lightly with a mere two-hours' detention. A whole day would be more appropriate, and it would not surprise me if the Deputy Headmaster were to vary your sentence accordingly. I think it only fair to warn you. You may return to your seat.'

All my hopes and plans were shattered. I knew that I was utterly lost, and my chin began to quiver.

It was then that the door opened, and Lagneau appeared. He was carrying his books under his left arm, and he had a piece of paper in his right hand.

Neither faltering nor cringing, he pushed the door shut with his elbow, marched up to the desk, brandished the paper under the scribe's nose, turned to look about the room for me, and gave me a cheerful wink. I thought that he must have deliberately done something foolish, just for the sake of keeping me company, but he had acted more nobly than that.

The supervisor, after having read Lepelletier's latest note, which appeared to be somewhat longer than the first, raised his eyes to Lagneau.

'So it was you who threw your form master at the ceiling?'

'Yes, sir,' said Lagneau, 'it was I.'

I was choked with emotion. My fellow-captives looked up as one man, to gaze half-incredulous, half-amused, at this twelve-year-old kid, who had had the gall to admit to having thrown his form master at the ceiling.

'And you were prepared to let your friend take the rap for it?'

Lagneau shrugged his shoulders, and said:

'I was too scared at first to confess. When I'd had time to think it over, I remembered that he was a scholar, and that, because of this business, he might lose his grant. So I told Socrates—Monsieur Lepelletier, I mean—that I was the one who had done it, and he revoked his detention order, and sent me to take his place in the punishment hall. Where am I to sit?'

'You're an odd fish, I must say,' remarked the supervisor.

Lagneau shrugged again, as if to say that there was nothing he could do about that.

The supervisor looked at me:

'And what about you? Why didn't you speak up for yourself?'

I was in no state to reply. My eyes were brimming with tears.

'Take your things, and go back to your classroom.'

I stood up, shaking from head to foot. Lagneau laughed delightedly.

'So you think it's a laughing matter, do you?' said the supervisor reprovingly.

'I'm not laughing,' said Lagneau. 'I'm smiling, not because I mean to, but because I can't help myself.'

Meanwhile, the supervisor was tearing up one of the detention forms, and as I went past the rostrum, he handed me the pieces.

'This is yours,' he said. 'Keep the pieces as a reminder. And you would do well to learn to stand up for yourself in future, otherwise you will spend the rest of your life paying for the misdeeds of others. You may go.'

I was reluctant to leave. I did not want to abandon my heroic friend, and I was on the point of asking permission to remain at his side, which would have plunged the Recording Angel into an abyss of perplexity, when the drum-roll sounded.

Two or three delinquents stood up, only to be quelled by a thunderous glance from the supervisor. They hastily resumed their seats. Then, with calm deliberation, he recorded Lagneau's misdemeanour and sentence in the register, and, using a ruler, erased mine with two lines in red ink. Outside in the corridor could be heard the thunder of feet galloping to freedom. Impassively, he closed his books, gathered up the detention chits, and locked them away in a drawer.

He coughed, rose to his feet, picked up his felt hat, brushed it with his sleeve, put it on his head, went to the door and opened it. But he did not go out. He remained there on guard.

'Get into line.'

The prisoners formed up in two rows, which the gaoler proceeded to straighten. At long last, he said:

'You may go.'

We went out to freedom.

243

Out in the playground, I put my arms round Lagneau and hugged him.

'You're a real brick—but I shouldn't have let you do it.'

'For you,' he said, 'detention is a catastrophe, but it doesn't make a scrap of difference to me. This year alone I've been in detention a dozen times, and, on top of that, I've had three suspensions, one whole day and two half days, and I'm still laughing.'

'But what about your father? What has he to say?'

Lagneau burst out laughing.

'He doesn't say anything.'

Seeing that I was on the point of questioning him further, Lagneau, looking serious for once, went on:

'He doesn't say anything, because I've got a dodge.'

'What dodge?'

'I've never told you, because my mother made me promise I'd never tell anyone. But it must be at least two years since I promised not to tell! So!'

He shrugged, as if to say that promises, like people, lose their potency with age. All the same, he was careful to extract a brand-new, and consequently binding, promise from me.

'If you swear you won't repeat it to anyone, I'll tell you about my dodge in the playground, in the lunch-hour recess.'

And thus it was that, having duly extracted a solemn promise from me, Lagneau led me to a remote corner of the colonnade in the junior playground, and, for the first time, told me about his private life. But I share Lagneau's views on promises, and since mine was given half a century ago, I now propose to betray it without remorse.

THREE

The Tragedy of Lagneau

Lagneau was the only son of a haulage-contractor in the port of Marseilles. This powerful employer of labour owned some hundred horses, housed in extensive stables, for in those days 'petroleum spirit' was used only for cleaning gloves or turning the stains on garments into haloes, and also in little lamps for heating the breakfast coffee, which, although guaranteed to be perfectly safe, occasionally exploded. Monsieur Lagneau's horse-power, therefore, was not yet harnessed to an engine under the bonnet of a car, but trotted about freely by day. They were enormous beasts, with each shod foot the size of four cobble-stones. Their owner was built on much the same massive scale. To give me some idea of this, Lagneau said:

'You know the bookcase in the reading room? Well, then, every time I see it, I think of him! He's very nearly as broad, though not quite so tall, and a lot thicker. He has a huge black moustache, and so much hair on his hands that he sometimes combs it with a special little comb. And, what's more, he has a fearsome voice, which puts a terrible strain on his vocal cords.'

This outsize father prided himself on having made his fortune with his own strong arm, and this was no metaphor, because it needed an arm of iron to drive a team of three Percherons. At the end of twenty-five years of labour, with precious few hours of sleep, he owned fifty wagons, with his name painted in white letters on the back and sides, and under the name was a number which in some magical way corresponded (as if it were a name itself) with a hand-operated telephonic instrument, that was kept in a box screwed to the wall. By means of this instrument, it was possible to talk, without having to shout, to someone at the opposite end of the Vieux-Port. I had heard tell of such things, but had had no idea that people could have them in their homes, like a sewing machine or a coffee percolator. The haulier, himself a man of little education, had great faith in the value of learning, and, in this regard, was very strict indeed with his son. And this was why, during his first year in the Sixth Grade, Lagneau had been subjected to 'correction' several times, that is to say, he had been severely caned, so much so, that on one occasion, according to him, he had almost landed up in hospital. He told me in confidence that his person was striped like a zebra with deep scars, but that these, unfortunately, were so awkwardly placed that it was impossible for him to display them at the Lycée, even in the seclusion of the colonnades.

I was horrified by the very thought of such savage brutality, and I gazed at him pityingly, but he retorted with a wink:

'But that's all in the past. It's over and done with, because my mother and my aunt, having given the matter much thought, came up with this terrific dodge, and now I can indulge in the luxury of a couple of detentions a week, and laugh them off, without fear of reprisal. And now I'll tell you about this dodge of theirs.'

I had seen his mother a few times after school in the evenings, because she sometimes came to meet him, and would wait for him outside in the little square, but I had never seen her close to. Lagneau, with very natural concern for his self-respect, had forbidden her to show herself when he was in the company of his friends.

It was therefore her habit to keep a lookout from the corner of the narrow Rue Mazagran, where ladies painted like dolls were to be seen taking the evening air, pacing back and forth indefatigably. When we came out of school, Lagneau would pretend not to see her, and she would follow behind us at some distance. She was rather a fat lady, who wore splendid hats, trimmed with flowers and birds, and a little veil over her face, but, seeing that her hair appeared to be white, I had taken her to be his grandmother, as indeed she might have been, since, according to him, she was nearly fifty.

This soft-hearted mother had a sister, who was not only Lagneau's aunt, but also his godmother. I had seen her only once (in the distance), but she made such a deep impression on me that I never forgot her. She was very tall, with sloping shoulders, like a bottle of mineral water, and, as she walked about the streets, she gesticulated so wildly that it was a wonder she never hit anyone. Lagneau assured me that she had 'a heart of gold', which I found hard to believe at first, until I realized hearts of gold were often concealed in ungainly bodies, as in the case of Don Quixote.

These two women adored Lagneau, an only son and only nephew respectively. They were sickened and shattered by the haulier's brutality, and each time Lagneau got a severe caning, his mother chewed her handkerchief to bits, and his aunt was unable to sit down for two days.

That first year in the Sixth Grade, ravaged by the detentions which were meted out almost every week, was a year of prolonged martyrdom for them. The whole of every week was nothing but a prelude to the dreaded Wednesday, when the inevitable beating would fall due.

On that day, however hard they tried, they could scarcely eat a morsel at lunch, as they sat at table watching the haulier wolf down game paté, rumpsteak and *pommes dauphinoises* as callously as an ogre, and trembling to see him thus build up his strength for the evening beating. The afternoon would be spent in the exchange of reassuring conversation, the optimistic tone of which was belied by the mother's sighs, and the aunt's nervous tics, the latter sometimes even going so far, in an attempt to comfort herself, as to give strident voice, with quivering chin, to some old sentimental song.

At last, round about seven, Lagneau would arrive home. Sometimes he would call out from the stairs:

'I shall be having pudding for dinner tonight!'

These were such joyful occasions that the aunt, leaning over the banisters, would burst into tears, and the mother would rush off and take her 'drops', to calm the thunderous beating of her heart.

But when he crept silently up the stairs, and took the punishment chit out of his satchel, then, after the first few tremulous questions, they were struck dumb and motionless with shock, though shaken with tremors when the mournful tones of the striking clock announced the imminent homecoming of the executioner.

And this was why, during the respite afforded by the summer holidays, they had, after long and careful planning, set the wheels in motion which would put an end to their tripartite martyrdom.

While the family were spending their holiday in a villa near Allauch, the aunt, to the utter amazement of the haulier, announced that she had always nursed a passion for hill-climbing, and thereafter, every other day, she would set out at seven in the morning, armed with a knapsack and a stout, steel-tipped walking-stick.

Her brother-in-law, far from disapproving of this craze for exercise, declared that it was only natural that an old maid should feel the need to do something to steady her nerves, and that it was better to resort to mountain climbing than to gigolos. Presently it occurred to him that 'the kid' would be better employed breathing in the mountain air than romping with the village hooligans. Lagneau at first pretended to jib at this suggestion, but, in the end, yielded to his father's wishes. Not that he had any enthusiasm for hill climbing, but he was in his aunt's confidence, and he knew that these healthful excursions would take them no further afield than the market square, where, after a copious meal in a well-stocked local bistro, he could spend the whole day larking about with lads of his own age.

This regimen was so beneficial to his health that the haulier was overjoyed. And thus, as soon as they got back home, the two tender-hearted schemers suggested to the father that, during term-time, Thursday afternoons should be devoted to similar healthful excursions.

At this he frowned, and then sniggered:

'Thursdays! In this family, Thursday is detention day!'

'There will be no more detentions!' declared the aunt. 'You will never again be required to sign a detention chit! Never!'

'Please God!' said the haulier, incredulously.

'Well, we shall see . . .'

Which was why, every Thursday morning, the aunt-godmother, disguised as a mountain-climber, would rouse her nephew-godson, and the pair of them, shouldering their Tyrolean knapsacks, filled with the appropriate provisions, sliced sausage, tomato pancakes, raw chops and bread, in addition to woolly waistcoats and mackintoshes, would set out in all their glory, their hobnailed boots ringing on the pavement, so that the sentence of two, four or even sometimes six hours of detention could be carried out. As the aunt had promised, the haulier was never again called upon to sign a detention chit. After long training in secret, it was upon his wife that this task now devolved. On reaching the corner of the street where the Lycée stood, the aunt would relieve the nephew of his knapsack, and Lagneau would scamper off cheerfully to the detention room, his hobnail boots striking showers of sparks on the marble floors of the corridors. When lunch-time came, and he was set free, he would go to his aunt's house, to eat not the frugal fare of the hardy mountaineer, but a dish of pilaf of mussels, fragrantly spiced with saffron, followed by spit-roasted spring chicken, garnished with potato puffs, or mushrooms grilled over charred vine twigs. Afterwards, he would crunch a piece of hard nougat from Arles, or chew some creamy *calisson* from Aix, finishing up with a little glass of the liqueur known as *crème de cacao*.

Sometimes, he had to return to the Lycée, to be incarcerated anew until four o'clock, or even occasionally until six. But, more often than not, he would spend the afternoon in the Parc Borély, cycling or boating. Finally, before going home, he would pore over a ramblers' map of the Marseilles region, and work out the route of his imaginary excursion, so as to be ready to give an account of himself in the evening, in reply to the haulier's questions.

This stratagem worked to perfection, and Papa Lagneau himself was overjoyed to see his son so miraculously transformed by the beneficial effects of climbing and wholesome mountain air. In short, the family was aglow with happiness.

Thus it was that my friend, not without proper pride, revealed his 'dodge' to me. I was the more impressed, seeing that he had made use of it to save me, and I pledged my eternal gratitude. It was not until three months later that I at last had an opportunity of proving it.

It was the month of March that saw the beginning of the stink bomb affair.

These bombs were really no more than big glass tears, filled with a yellowish liquid, which I later learned was hydrogen sulphide. They broke at the slightest tap, and instantly poisoned the atmosphere with a revolting stench.

The first to throw a stink bomb, or rather, I should say, the first that year to create something of a sensation by doing so, was a boy in Form 4B called Barbot, who unintentionally achieved a master-stroke. This fragile projectile of his, aimed at nothing in particular, happened to land on the top of Tignasse's head. The resulting pollution of his long hair was such that he had to resign himself to having it shaved off, and we were at last able to see his chubby face for what it really was, that of an amiable clown.

The perpetrator was never unmasked, but those in the know basked in Barbot's reflected glory. And that was why Soliman, a Turkish boy in 5B, resolved to outshine him, by the ingenious deployment of a novel technique. He began his experiments in Monsieur Verdot's class. This master, grave-faced and melancholy, taught mathematics. Nothing was yet known about him, for he had only recently come to us from another Lycée. It was said of him that he had never been seen to smile, and we called him the Undertaker.

Soliman, who seemed to have vast sums of money at his disposal, bought (from the oriental bazaar in the Rue Sibié) five stink bombs of an exceptionally large size. But, instead of scattering them at random (a practice both dangerous and inconsiderate, since it might involve an innocent bystander), he slunk into the classroom early, and laid them out in a clump under the master's desk, just about where the Undertaker might be expected to put his big feet.

'This way,' announced Soliman, 'he'll be the first to get the benefit!' This forecast was to prove correct.

As soon as all the boys were seated, the Undertaker went to his desk. He began the lesson, without preamble, by reciting the jingle stating Pythagoras' Theorem.* But he only got as far as the famous '*si je ne m'abuse*', that golden nail which fixes the square of the hypotenuse in our memories, when we heard a small cracking sound amplified by the echoing floor-boards of the rostrum.

Abruptly, the Undertaker stopped abusing himself. He lowered his head, snuffed the air, and, for the first time since we had known him, smiled the smile of one witnessing a Mystery, like the Pythian Oracle, for like her (or, for that matter, like a smoked ham) he was enveloped in a cloud of pungent vapour.

* *Le carré de l'hypotenuse/Est égal, si je ne m'abuse,/A la somme des carrés/Construits sur les autres côtés.*

Without haste, and still smiling his ineffable smile, he pushed back his chair, peered down at the floor-boards under his desk, then bent down four times, and laid out the four unbroken capsules in a row in front of him. Presently, turning a terrifyingly amiable smile on every boy in the class, he broke the ghastly silence.

'There is someone in this class who, knowing that I adore the pungent scent of hydrogen sulphide, H_2S, has made me a present of these five little phials of it. I don't want to know his name, but I thank him most cordially. But please, on no account open any of the windows, or we shall lose the full benefit!'

He stood up, and watched by the whole class, frozen with horror, he flung the four bombs, one after another, against the wall at the back of the room. They left stains on the wall in the shape of four grey asterisks.

He sat down, snuffed the air greedily, and declaimed, in bantering tones:

'Est égal, si je ne m'abuse,
'A la somme des carrés
'Construits sur les autres côtés.'

Asking no questions, making no further reference to the incident, he proceeded to treat us to a scintillating lecture, which lasted a full hour.

Soliman had to wait until the end of the class before his ingenuity was duly rewarded. But as soon as they were outside, the day boys, with red noses and streaming eyes, and seemingly inebriated by their long exposure to the stench, fell upon him and kicked him heavily all the way to the boarders' staircase. One would have thought that the failure of his plan, followed by his ignominiously assisted flight, would have exposed him to ridicule. But quite the reverse. The tale of the Undertaker's lunacy spread through the whole school, and Soliman, as the prime mover, suddenly found himself a celebrity. It was from this episode that I learned that it is always profitable to be involved, in any way whatsoever, in great events, and that notoriety and glory are one and the same. Lagneau was consumed with envy, and one Monday morning, at round about a quarter to nine, while a history lesson was in progress, he threw two stink bombs.

*

The first was a huge success, because Monsieur Michel had his back to us, and was writing on the blackboard, names and dates bracketed together. He saw nothing, he heard nothing, he knew nothing about the exploit of the nameless joker, until he was assailed by the appalling stench. Since the windows were open, he supposed that it must be coming from outside. He ordered that they should be shut, and then, chalk in hand, turned his back on us again.

Lagneau, glorying in his initial success, suddenly half-rose in his seat, and threw the second glass capsule. It broke against the flue-pipe of the stove with a metallic ring. Monsieur Michel spun round, with his hands on his hips, frowning angrily. He was looking our way. But Lagneau, who had promptly resumed his seat, was carefully putting brackets round his notes, with his head a little on one side. I, too, was writing busily, as were my neighbours, fearful that they might be unjustly accused. Only Mérinos, sitting in front of me, was caught short. He was struggling to suppress a fit of the giggles, and his neck was swollen with the effort. I felt sure that he was lost. But just then the door was flung wide, and the Headmaster, in morning coat and top hat, strode purposefully into the room. He was followed by the Deputy Head, who was carrying a sheaf of foolscap paper. These dignitaries had come, with their customary solemn formality, to read out the history class reports. As was the custom, the whole class rose to its feet as one man. Even Mérinos, son of Ulysses (or was it Achilles?), had stopped laughing. The situation was desperate, and Lagneau went as white as a turnip.

And, indeed, the Deputy Headmaster's nostrils were already flaring. His glance rested on the floor at the foot of the stove, where a few tiny slivers of glass were clearly visible.

In less than a second, he collated the evidence afforded by his nose with that which glittered before his eyes.

Then, with a sweeping gesture of his baleful forefinger, he pointed at Lagneau, and said, in a voice which brooked no contradiction:

'Stand up!'

Lagneau, pale and trembling, did not stand up. Instead, he looked hastily over his shoulder at the desks behind him, as if, knowing that the order could not possibly concern him, he was curious to discover whom the Deputy Head was addressing. But this artless demonstration of innocence had not the slightest effect, and the voice, sarcastic now, thundered:

'You! Yes. You! It's no good playing the innocent. I saw you through the window! Yes, I saw you throw something, and now we know what it was! Your name?'

'But, sir,' said Lagneau, 'maybe you did see my hand move, but it wasn't me! I was just trying to catch a fly, and then . . .'

The pathetic stupidity of this excuse sent a ripple of muted laughter round the class.

'Be quiet!' thundered the Deputy Head. 'Your name?'

'Lagneau.'

The Deputy Head took a notebook from his pocket, unscrewed the cap of his fountain pen, and recorded the name, the form and the offence. All this time, the unbearable stench, seemingly intensified by the deathly silence, spread and seeped into every corner of the classroom, so that Lagneau's offence seemed more iniquitous, more poisonous, with every passing second.

The day boys, hardened hypocrites that they were, held their noses in indignation. The Headmaster, whose status forbade him to do likewise, in quiet and solemn tones gave the order:

'Open the windows!'

The day boys hastened to obey. Finally, the Deputy Head tore the page out of his notebook, and held it out to Lagneau, saying:

'Get your things together, and take this to the punishment hall!'

Lagneau, crushed, collected his textbooks and exercise books, came down the three steps from the rostrum, walked slowly to the door, opened it a little way, and disappeared.

Presently the Deputy Head, resuming his normal tone of voice, began reading, and announced, as usual:

'First, Robin, 19½. Conduct 10, homework 9, class work 10.'

I went in search of Lagneau, and found him in the boarders' playground. To my great surprise, he seemed very worried.

'What's the matter?' I said. 'What about your dodge?'

'My dodge is all very fine for a four-hour detention, or even a whole day. But this time, the Headmaster and the Deputy Head are mixed up in it . . . And, what's more, that murderer in the punishment hall says that I shall probably be hauled up in

253

front of the disciplinary committee, and suspended for a whole week.'

'He only said that to frighten you.'

'Maybe, but one can't be sure . . . And, to make matters worse, one of the seniors told me that, when you're suspended, the Headmaster sends for your father! Just think what that would mean!'

Seeking to reassure him, I invited Nelps and Carrère, a slight, good-looking boy with a limp, in Form 3A2, to join our counsels.

Nelps cited five cases of stink-bomb throwing, and informed us that the severest penalty, inflicted upon Barbot, was a full day's Sunday detention. He concluded with reassuring authority:

'You're good for a full day's detention next Thursday, but nothing worse.'

Carrère, of a more reflective turn of mind, attempted to evaluate the additional severity of the punishment generally inflicted when the offence was committed in the presence of the Deputy Head. As in this case, unfortunately, the gravity of the situation was even greater, owing to the involvement of the Headmaster, he was pessimistic.

All the same, in view of the fact that the missile had been thrown before the entry of the two dignitaries, and in ignorance of their imminent arrival, he finally concluded that, in his opinion, a full day's detention would be amply sufficient. He did not believe that the powers of the disciplinary committee would be invoked, and, in this, Nelps, sounding very confident, supported him, adding:

'And besides, if anything worse than detention was in store for you, the Deputy Head would have sent for you before this!'

'He's right!' exclaimed Lagneau. 'And if it's nothing more than detention, I don't give a damn! I've got two *Buffalo Bills* and three *Nat Pinkertons*. They should be enough to keep me occupied for the day!'

And he broke into a dance, accompanied by hoots of laughter.

And it was then that the voice of doom rang out. It came from beneath the moustache of the caretaker, the words being loudly and slowly intoned, so that the whole playground re-echoed with them:

'Lagneau, Form 5A2, to report to the Deputy Headmaster!'

Then this herald, indifferent to the terrible import of his words, retreated without so much as looking back.

Lagneau blenched, cleared his throat and, with a pitiable little giggle, said:

'What a swine!'

Then, with shoulders drooping but fists clenched, he walked away.

We waited under the plane trees for his return, and discussed his case. I was a little uneasy on my friend's account, because it seemed to me that our two advisers were less optimistic, now that the culprit had left us, and Nelps even went so far as to draw attention to a new factor in the situation, namely, that the throwing of stink bombs had become altogether too wide-spread of late, declaring that he feared that the Deputy Head might be intending to make an example of Lagneau, in order to put an end to the practice. To make matters worse, time was passing, and Lagneau had still not returned, and this seemed to me a very bad sign. But Carrère allayed my anxiety by telling me that 'the longer the jawing, the lighter the punishment,' and that Lagneau might well be let off with four hours' detention and a severe reprimand. At this point, fortunately, an entertaining diversion occurred, which greatly alleviated the agony of our suspense. Marion, of Form 5B, having dipped a stick into the entrails of an earth-closet, went up to Schmidt, and abruptly accosted him with these words:

'Let's see which of us is stronger, you or me!'

And he held out the revoltingly slimy end of the stick to him.

Schmidt, suspecting nothing, seized it in his fist and tugged. The stick slid away from him, leaving his palm smeared with a thick, greasy mess, and Marion ran away, sniggering. Schmidt, though quick to grasp the nature of the jest, did not relish it in the least. In three bounding strides, he caught up with his persecutor, pinned him to the wall, and lingeringly wiped his hand on his face, whereupon the nasty little squirt began to vomit noisily on the spot.

I did not witness the end of this interesting interlude, because at this juncture Lagneau came out through the door. He wore an expression of dismay. He came towards us hesitantly, with bowed head.

'Well?' said Nelps. 'What is it to be? Detention?'

Lagneau nodded.

'On Thursday?'

'Yes,' he whispered.

He wanted to say more, but instead he burst into tears. He ran up to the wall, rested his forearm against it, cradled his forehead in his hand, and wept to his heart's content.

I was very much puzzled by these signs of despair, and I went to him, and whispered:

'Why should you worry about detention? You've got your remedy, haven't you?'

Without saying a word, he turned and looked at me with reddened eyes, shrugged, and scraped the ground with his toecap.

The others had come to join us, but no one ventured to ask any questions, and we stood around in respectful silence, until the drum-roll sounded.

In class, he resumed his customary demeanour. With his Latin Grammar open in front of him, he sat, with arms folded, staring at a sentence printed in heavy type: 'Noctua cicadam interfecit, quanquam clamitabat' or 'quamvis clamitaret'.

But that his mind was far, far away from such linguistic subtleties could be deduced from the tremendous sighs he heaved from time to time. At last, when a quarter of an hour had gone by in this fashion, he whispered the truth to me.

The Deputy Head had imposed an eight-hour detention on him, from eight in the morning to midday, and from two in the afternoon until six.

A negligible punishment in itself, and capable of being neatly cancelled out by the time-honoured stratagem. But the Deputy Head had gone on to say:

'The thought has crossed my mind of late that the signatory of your detention chits might be Madame your mother. Hitherto, however, I have been content to give you the benefit of the doubt. But this time you have gone too far. To clarify the situation, once and for all, I feel I have no choice but to send a copy of your detention chit to Monsieur your father's office address, with a covering note expressing my apologies for troubling him.'

This revelation was imparted to me in broken snatches, because, every now and then, Monsieur Payre would direct a look of stern inquiry at us, thus reducing us to silence for the time being.

When I was at last in possession of the full facts—I had been studiously leafing through my Latin dictionary as I listened—I thought it over for a moment, then, pretending to write, with my head bent over my exercise book, I said, out of the corner of my mouth:

'It's a nuisance, of course, but it's not a tragedy. As far as your father is concerned, this will be the first detention you have had this year ... No one has ever been slaughtered for a first offence.'

He did not reply immediately, because at this point Monsieur Payre's powerful voice rang out, informing Berlaudier that the classroom was not a dormitory.

At the end of this interruption, Lagneau whispered:

'He's bound to come and see the Deputy Head, and ask for an explanation, and then he'll find out about all the other times.'

Privately, I agreed that his fears were justified, and I could think of nothing to say. However, after thinking it over for a few minutes, I came to the conclusion that, if his father were to learn at one fell swoop that his son had been in detention twenty times, he could scarcely punish him more than once, so that on balance Lagneau would still have the advantage. I was about to offer him consolation in these terms, when he suddenly said:

'And worse than that, much worse, he'll find out about that business of the end-of-term reports.'

This was news to me.

'What business?'

He did not reply immediately, because Monsieur Payre had just stepped down from his rostrum, and was making his usual tour of inspection. With his right wrist clasped in his left hand behind his back, he walked slowly between the rows of desks, pausing here and there, to bend down over someone's exercise book. His advice and comments were often far from flattering. This was the best time for talking, because, with the sound of his own voice buzzing in his ears, he could no longer hear us whispering.

So now Lagneau told me the whole dreadful story. It was long and involved (desperation not being conducive to coherence), indistinctly articulated, and punctuated by convulsive silences.

All the same, I did in the end hear the whole saga of the end-of-term reports, and here it is, for the benefit of my readers.

The fraudulent activities of the mother and the aunt did not end with forging signatures on detention chits. One crime invariably leads to another, for the malefactor is in the toils of Satan. All of a sudden, it occurred to them that the end-of-term report, when it arrived, would brutally reveal three months of idleness and misbehaviour, and might even list the punishments incurred.

Horror-stricken, they resolved to intercept and falsify the report.

The aunt had only to refer to one of the detention slips to learn the name of the printer employed by the Lycée. She then proceeded to suborn a drunken employee of the firm, who gave her twelve blank report forms in exchange for twelve bottles of *absinthe*, and twelve envelopes printed with the letter-head of the Lycée for six bottles of *Amer Picon*.

As the end of the first term approached, the mother and the aunt endured a week of crazed anguish. Armed with a skeleton key to the letterbox, they watched in fear and trembling for the arrival of the postman.

As good luck would have it, the genuine report arrived at nine, after the haulier had left for work, for it was his invariable custom to be at the depot by six every morning. The two guilty women seized the fateful letter, and hastened to lock themselves in the dressing-room. There, with the aid of a steaming kettle and a knitting needle, they succeeded in unsticking the glue. Presently, they took refuge in the bedroom, to pore at great length over the all-too-accurate report.

There were several noughts, which caused them to tremble, and a number of threes and fours, over which they sighed. An eight quite melted their hearts, and a fourteen (for drawing) had them smiling. But the comments of some of the masters were what really crushed them.

'Has learnt absolutely nothing' (Mathematics).

'Impudent, lazy and inattentive' (English).

'Incapable of concentrating. Keeping the boy at this school is a waste of time.' (Latin.)

These assessments—according to the aunt—clearly proved that some of the masters had 'taken a scunner on him.' Some of the comments, on the other hand, were a little less harsh.

'Progress patently inadequate' (French).

'Inadequate,' said the aunt. 'But still there has been progress!'

And both of them were delighted with 'Could do better.'

'Naturally,' said the mother. 'One can always do better. That's no criticism!'

'Quite the reverse! Now, if they had said: "Could do well", it would mean that he was not doing well. But "Could do better" means: "He's doing well, indeed very well, but he could do even better!"'

Then—just like a full-scale meeting of the disciplinary committee—they discussed the proper allocation of marks as between the various subjects. Their scale of measurement was not the dear boy's scholastic achievements, but the expectations of his father, although care was taken to see that these were not wholly satisfied.

'Let's not overdo it!' said the aunt, altering a three to a ten. 'It would never do if Edouard were led to expect him to get the form prize!'

Thus it was that the noughts were altered to sixes or nines by a simple stroke of the pen. The five for Latin was altered to a ten ('Let's not overdo it!'), the three in history shot up to nine, and the seven in French, in a burst of patriotic fervour, broke the mediocrity barrier to become thirteen, which was, besides, a lucky number.

As for the unjust comments, these were replaced by others, but the aunt was scrupulous about retaining at least some of the original words. For instance, 'Progress inadequate' became, more simply, 'Making progress', 'Does not do anything and has no wish to', was translated into 'Could do better if he wished'.

Finally, again prompted by the niceness of her scruples, and to counterbalance these improvements to some extent, the hardhearted aunt lopped two off the good mark awarded for Physical Training.

This report was found by the haulier in the letter box the following evening. He read it aloud at the dinner table, commenting on it as he went along. He had reservations about the thirteen for French, which he considered not quite good enough; but he conceded that, on the whole, it was an improvement on last year's report, and that it at least showed that the boy had made a good start. The mother and the aunt, however, even while trembling at the very thought of what he would have said if he had known the truth, began to regret the niggardliness of their comments, and resolved to do better next time. And they were as good as their word, because the following end-of-term report needed even more drastic rewriting than the first. In the same way as a forger of hundred-franc notes, having taken the first guilty step, eventually realizes that he might just as well progress to thousand-franc notes, so they did not hesitate to turn a six into a sixteen—after all, the figure sixteen also contained a six—and to apply this principle in general, their task being much simplified by the fact that most of the marks were below ten. The haulier was won over. The future of his stables and the perpetuation of his telephone number now seemed assured, and he secretly rejoiced.

Meanwhile, the two women lived their life of deceit in torment. At any moment, a chance encounter between the haulier and the Deputy Headmaster could bring their happy family life crashing down in ruins. Their nights were made hideous by the dreams brought on by remorse, and even the use of sleeping draughts could not alleviate their plight. In her dreams, the aunt saw a great swarm of buzzing noughts, and the father, in a burst of insane fury, lashing out at them with his whip. The mother's recurring nightmare was different. She saw her husband lying on the carpet in his splendid office, his body stiff, his face purple, his mouth twisted, holding a genuine end-of-term report in his clenched fist.

This was the story told to me by Lagneau. I listened in consternation, all too conscious of the magnitude of the catastrophe that might ensue, and my friend's demeanour all through that day broke my heart. We went down to the refectory. He ate nothing. White-faced and speechless, he wept into the sausage and beans. Then he offered his portion to Berlaudier, who, although laughingly complaining that it was somewhat over-salted with tears, nevertheless devoured the lot.

During the recess, he retreated under the colonnade and, with arms crossed and cheek pressed against the wall, he sat motionless for a whole hour, as if paralysed by shock. I spoke to him, but he was no longer in any condition to listen to me.

His desolation was soon apparent to his other friends, and they asked what was the matter. I put them slightly off the scent by saying, without going into any details, that he was to be kept in all day on Thursday, and that this was likely to cause serious trouble at home. A few of our more case-hardened friends were much amused at this, especially Péridier (of 5B), whose widowed mother had always believed that the 'optional extra classes on Thursdays' were a privilege reserved for the brightest pupils. That afternoon in class, Socrates—oblivious of his distraught appearance—ordered him to recite the set passage of Latin verse. He stood up, crossed his arms, gazed at him with haggard eyes, and stumbled through the first stanza (considerably garbled) of the legend of Phaedra. Then, having earned a nought, he sat down again, murmuring:

'What difference can it possibly make to me now?'

He made these words sound like a death-bed valediction.

During the four o'clock recess, we strolled gloomily through the throng of boys at play, striving to find a solution to an insoluble problem.

He toyed briefly with the idea of escaping to a foreign land— that very night—hidden in a goods wagon. I pointed out that, as we still had twenty-four hours ahead of us, he would do better to ask his mother for enough money to enable him to travel comfortably by passenger train.

Presently, I had another idea. Why should he not go into hiding in the hills around my home? I knew the terrain intimately, having studied it over a long period, with a view to possibly escaping there myself. I put this plan to him, but he rejected it, saying:

'No, no. What happens to me is nothing. He can kill me, for all I care. It's my mother and my aunt I'm worried about. I bet you anything you like, he'll divorce the pair of them . . . that is, if he gets the chance before my mother takes poison, and my aunt throws herself under a tram. I'm not joking. She told me so herself: "There'll be nothing for it, but for me to throw myself under a tram!" And it's all on account of me! I'm to blame for everything!'

In his mind's eye, he could see the severed, bleeding limbs of his aunt rolling over on the rails, and at that same instant his head jerked convulsively, as a leather ball, thrown from the far end of the playground, hit him in the left eye. His hands flew up to his face, and he sat there, swaying like a dancing bear, and moaning rhythmically. I hastened to pull his hands away from his face. His eye was watering and turning red, but otherwise he appeared unharmed. I ran across to the tap, steeped my handkerchief in water, and proceeded to bathe the swelling with lingering care. As I did so, he exclaimed emphatically:

'And a good thing too! All the better! If I lose my eye, it will be no more than I deserve!'

It was as if this premature punishment had, in some way, diminished his guilt.

That evening, during the study period, I handed him the rough draft of my Latin translation, so that he need do nothing but make a fair copy of it, but he pushed it wearily aside, and, turning to look at me through the slit of his black eye, he said:

'It's for Friday . . . and by Friday, who can tell where I'll be?'

Nelps sat three rows in front of us. Lagneau's distraught appearance had touched his soft heart. This was why, every now and then, he would turn round to look at us, with a smile, a shrug, a wink and a dismissive wave of the hand, all by way of consolation. But he got so carried away by these good intentions that, all at once, there was Monsieur Payre's powerful voice resoundingly accusing him of having spent the last quarter of an hour dancing about like a puppet on a string, and threatening him with a nought for conduct, which would have been the first such black mark of his scholastic career, and might have become the first of a long series, since there is nothing like lost innocence for leading to other and worse excesses.

Terror-stricken, he spent the rest of the period with his back studiously turned to us, while Lagneau stared gloomily at a book lying open at random in front of him. And when the seven o'clock drum-roll sounded the hour of our deliverance, he said, as he got to his feet:

'It would have been better for me if I had crunched those two stink bombs between my teeth and swallowed them.'

As we went out, he took my arm, and walked with tottering steps. Looking back, I suspect that he was piling on the agony a little, even though his distress was unquestionably genuine. Nelps caught up with us, with friendly expressions of sympathy, whereas Berlaudier, the mean beast, asked, shouting from a long way off and at the top of his voice, whether he had any idea how far his father would be able to propel him, with his first kick in the pants. We accompanied him all the way to his own front door, then Nelps jumped on the running-board of the tram to Saint-Barnabé, and I made my way towards La Plaine, uneasily convinced that merely to share such a secret was to be tainted with guilt, and filled with shame at conveying it into Joseph's house.

Wednesday dawned at last, the fateful day appointed by Destiny and the Authorities. As surely as night follows day, the caretaker would appear, sometime between eight and nine, while the English class was in progress, carrying under his left arm the big black register, in which Pitzu would enter the names of any absentees, and, in his right hand, ten or so buff envelopes, each containing all the detention chits for one particular form. He would deliver ours to Pitzu, who would then distribute these infringements of personal liberty to those concerned. The little ceremony was ineluctable. Nothing could delay it or prevent its taking place, except perhaps the death of the caretaker as he was getting out of bed, or an earthquake, or the end of the world, none of which was a very likely contingency. All the same, I felt there was still a ray of hope. It was a very faint hope, and no doubt illusory like almost all other hopes, but it was just conceivable that the Deputy Head had omitted to make a note of the offence, as he had in the case of Barbey, when he had been caught smoking in the lavatory. There was also the case of Rémusat, who had planted a bottom-pincher on Tignasse's chair. The Deputy Head had given him a sound wigging, and sentenced him to four hours of detention, but nothing was ever heard of it again. It was therefore not absolutely inconceivable that he should have forgotten about Lagneau's offence. We had an outside chance, even if the odds were impossibly long, and that entitled us to just a very little hope. At a quarter to eight I sought out Lagneau in the playground. With drooping head and hands in pockets, he was leaning against a plane tree, being eloquently reassured by Nelps. Nelps's reasoning, however, was inevitably faulty, since he knew nothing of the plotting that had gone before. The fact was that Nelps believed that Lagneau's father must have long ago become resigned to having to endorse detention chits, and this last one was, after all, no worse than all the others. On the contrary, it seemed to him that there was a comic side to this stink bomb business, which would probably not escape Monsieur Lagneau. But our friend's only response was a sad smile, and a shrug, as of one resigned to his fate.

We spent the first half-hour of the English class waiting for the arrival of the caretaker, sinister emissary from the punishment hall. The door opened suddenly. I felt my face twitch. Lagneau hastily lowered his head, as if to duck the arrow of Fate. But it was only a day boy, arriving late, though safely armed with a note of explanation. At the end of the hour, the half-time bell sounded. Lagneau was growing more and more agitated. Feverishly, he scribbled illegible notes in his exercise book, while Pitzu, for the umpteenth time, expounded the use of the present instead of the future tense after *when*—which was to him what the ablative absolute was to Socrates—and I understood that in thus applying himself to the lesson, Lagneau was driven by some obscure notion of bribing the gods to cancel his detention. Another hour or two passed, and the clock chimed a quarter to.

He gave me a feeble smile, a mere twitch of the lips, for his eyes were not smiling. The caretaker was late. Perhaps he wouldn't come at all? Perhaps he had died in the night? Perhaps ... But there he was, opening the door, a figure of dread as he approached the rostrum, with the buff envelopes gleaming in his right hand.

He put down the register, open to its full extent, in front of Pitzu, for him to enter the names of absentees. Then, callously, he searched through the envelopes for the one addressed to Form 5A2. Having been through all of them, he looked puzzled. Apparently ours was not there! Under the table, Lagneau nudged my knee with his, and the look of despair was wiped off his face. But the caretaker was going through the bundle again, and, all of a sudden, he plucked out the fateful envelope. With a hideous grin, he put it down on the master's desk, picked up the register, tucked it under his arm, and went out, smugly self-satisfied at the harm he had done.

264

Lagneau, crushed by the workings of destiny, planted his left elbow on his desk, leaned his icy forehead on his hand, and waited to hear Pitzu call the malefactors one by one up to the rostrum, in order to place their detention orders in their own hands.

In spite of everything, there was still one glimmer of hope. True, there was the envelope containing the detention chits for all to see, but was Lagneau's necessarily among them? He too was still hopeful, for he was shaking so much that I could see ripples on the surface of the inkwell. We waited. Suddenly the voice of Monsieur Pitzu rang out, proclaiming in English: '*When I am in England, I shall eat plum pudding.*'

Lagneau raised his head. The buff envelope gleamed on the corner of the desk, apparently forgotten.

'That is to say,' pursued Monsieur Pitzu, 'that, as the English see it, the speaker will already be in England when he eats the plum pudding, and consequently the occurrence, for him, will be in the present. Monsieur Robin, please translate the following sentence: "*Quand mon père sera vieux, il aura des cheveux blancs.*"'

Unhesitatingly, Robin replied:

'*When my father is old, his hair will be white.*'

'Perfect', said Monsieur Pitzu, with genuine pleasure.

He turned to us, and spoke in English:

'*Master Lagneau, will you translate into French this sentence: "When I am at home, I shall have a pleasant dinner with my family."*'

Lagneau stood up and, while pretending to pause for thought, strained his ears to catch the whisperings which were coming to him from all directions. Schmidt and Berlaudier having exerted themselves to the uttermost, Lagneau was enabled to stammer out haltingly:

'*Quand je serai . . . à la maison . . . je dînerai agréablement . . . avec ma famille . . .*'

'Thank you,' said Monsieur Pitzu. 'I will award ten marks to Monsieur Schmidt for having translated that sentence, and a nought for conduct for having whispered it to you. As for you, I am giving you a nought for having repeated what Monsieur Schmidt whispered to you without understanding a word of it. Sit down!'

*

Then he turned his attention to the rules governing the use of *shall* and *will, should* and *would,* of which we understood not a single word. We were wholly absorbed in watching his movements. Would he pick up the envelope? He was not even looking at it. Next, he proceeded to go into ecstasies over a poem which sounded pretty foolish to me. First, it exhorted a star to twinkle, and then asked it what it was. Lagneau, in a perfect frenzy of nervous agitation, was kicking the bar under his desk so hard that it shook.

All of a sudden, the drum-roll sounded. Pitzu stowed his books away in his brief case, and Galliano, as was his wont, had reached the door in a single flying leap, when Pitzu cried out: 'Stop! Silence!' and, at long last, picked up the fateful envelope from the edge of his desk.

He opened it, drew out five or six detention chits, and announced:

'Galliano! It just so happens that I have here a communication which concerns you!'

He held out the first of the detention orders, whereupon the would-be fugitive stopped dead in his tracks, and then went forward, while at the same time putting on a remarkable display of mime, expressive of stupefaction and indignation.

Next to be called up was Péridier, who received his invitation to attend 'an optional extra class on Thursday' with perfect equanimity. He was followed by Vernet, who shrugged discreetly, and by Gontard, who looked at his chit, and was so far unable to contain his delight that he gave vent to a loud guffaw.

'What's the meaning of this?' asked Monsieur Pitzu sternly. 'Are you so hardened to punishment that you can take it as a joke?'

'Sir,' said Gontard, 'I was expecting a whole day's detention, and the Deputy Headmaster has put me down for only four hours!'

'I trust,' said Monsieur Pitzu, 'that Monsieur your father will find it less amusing than you do, and I really can't think what there is to prevent me from extending your period of detention, since you find it so short!'

Even as he was speaking, Monsieur Pitzu was gesturing with the last of the detention chits in his hand. I felt Lagneau's nails digging into my biceps.

'That's mine,' he whispered. 'I'm sure it must be mine.'

And so, indeed, it was. Monsieur Pitzu glanced at the chit and said:

'And talking of a "whole day's detention", here we have one ... It is in consideration of the activities of Monsieur Lagneau, who, it seems, threw a stink bomb during a history lesson! He is therefore required to attend tomorrow between the hours of eight in the morning and six in the evening, and, considering the gravity of the offence, he is being let off lightly.'

He held out the fateful chit. Lagneau went up to the rostrum to receive it, but he had not the courage to look at it there, where so many eyes were upon him. He slipped it into his exercise book, and was about to leave the room, when Monsieur Pitzu added:

'A long detention such as this can be extremely beneficial, and I would like to help you make the most of it. Accordingly, to ensure that your time is well spent, I wish you to use it in translating the first twelve exercises in your *English Companion*. This will, I am sure, give a tremendous boost to your command of the language!'

Lagneau was quite simply stunned by the imposition of this additional punishment. Berlaudier, however, burst out laughing, and there were murmurs among the crowd, protests from the dunces and sycophantic giggles from the swots. I could see that my friend was on the verge of saying something that he would later regret, so, elbowing the spectators aside, I led him away towards the day boys' block.

In a remote corner of the playground, we studied the chit. There was nothing at all remarkable about it, it simply stated that the boy Lagneau, of Form 5A2, would be detained at the Lycée tomorrow, Thursday, from eight o'clock in the morning until six o'clock in the evening, for having 'thrown a stink bomb during a history lesson.' One stink bomb. I immediately seized upon this diminution of his offence. A solitary stink bomb was one thing, two smacked of recidivism. Nelps, when consulted, was emphatic. One was nothing to worry about. Lagneau could tell his father that he had been handed the thing in class, and had thrown it away in disgust, without even knowing what it was, and that he was the first to be taken by surprise, and even terrified, by the revolting and sickening stench. I thought this a brilliant strategy, and, in a burst of friendly feeling, declared:

'All you have to say is that I was the one who passed it to you!'

'While I'm about it,' said Lagneau, 'why shouldn't I say you were the one who threw it?'

'Do, by all means. Your father doesn't know my father, so he won't be able to tell him!'

'Yes,' said Nelps. 'But what if he were to come to the Lycée, to complain to the Deputy Head, and tell him that you were the real culprit?'

'The Deputy Head wouldn't believe it,' said Lagneau, 'seeing that he saw me through the window with his own eyes. And besides, if my father should ever come to the Lycée, they'd have more important things than that to talk about, and that would be the last you'd ever see of me in this place!'

There is no point in relating any more of what we said to one another that day, since it consisted of repeating the same thing over and over again.

During the evening study period, a storm broke. Heavy rain beat a rapid tattoo on the windows, and, from time to time, these were shaken by claps of thunder.

It was very quiet in the classroom. Monsieur Payre was at his desk reading a newspaper. Nelps turned round every now and then to cheer us with a friendly smile, but without any accompanying gestures. We listened to the hiss of the gas jets, and watched the smoke-absorbers fluttering above the glass funnels of the lamps.

Just to be on the safe side, I had warned my mother that I should be at least twenty minutes late getting home that evening, saying that I had to look in on a friend to borrow some books.

Lagneau was ready five minutes before the drum-roll sounded.

'I've told them what to expect,' he said, 'and they're both waiting for me outside. Come with me. Come on, and you can tell my mother that you're quite willing for me to say that you were the culprit.'

I closed my text books and exercise books. The drum-roll was still sounding as we went out of the classroom. The storm had died down, and a fine drizzle glittered in the yellow light of the gas lamps. They were waiting, motionless, on the corner of the little street, sheltering under one umbrella.

The aunt, very tall and very thin, was wearing a hat that looked like a Salvation Army bonnet, and she had enormous blue eyes, as blue as the sea.

We went up to them.

'Here we are,' said Lagneau. 'This is Marcel.'

Without even looking at me, the mother asked in a choking voice:

'Have you got it?'

Lagneau handed her the chit.

When she saw it, the aunt gave a strangled cry. 'My God!' she exclaimed, and rested her cheek against the palm of her hand to hold up her drooping head.

The mother unfolded the chit, and hastened across to the nearest street lamp. The aunt followed, holding the open umbrella over her.

The poor woman endeavoured to read the cramped black writing, which might well be about to shatter the peace of her household. Through a film of rain, glittering under the street lamp, I saw her hand tremble. It was a plump, white hand, with a ring on every finger. Seeing that she was unable to decipher the note, the aunt took it from her. In a broken voice, she read out:

'He threw a . . . stick? . . . stake . . . ?'

'A stink bomb,' said Lagneau.

She repeated the words several times, varying the pitch each time, as if, by so doing, she hoped to alter the meaning. Then she said, with angry emphasis:

'Well, for one thing, it ought to be forbidden to sell stink bombs to children. They'll be selling them revolvers next, I shouldn't wonder! That's Government policy all over! It's the manager of the Oriental Bazaar who ought to be in detention. If anyone threw a stink bomb during the history lesson, he did, when he put it in the hands of this poor, innocent child!'

'Calm down, Anna,' said the mother. 'And don't shout so.'

She turned to her son.

'Are you sure your father has been told?'

'He told me he'd be sending a copy to him at his office.'

'At his office!' repeated the aunt indignantly. 'At his office! What a nasty, suspicious mind the man must have!'

269

It seemed to me that his nasty suspicions were, on the whole, justified, but, of course, I realized that women, and especially aunts, saw things in a somewhat different light from ourselves.

The mother was bracing herself, but I could see that there were tears in her eyes. She murmured: 'If it was sent off this morning, it will have arrived by the six o'clock post, so we'll find it waiting for us at home.'

'Listen,' said Lagneau. 'We'll have to tell papa that I've done nothing to deserve such punishment, because I wasn't the one who threw the stink bomb. We'll say it was Marcel who did it.'

'He won't believe it!' said the aunt.

'And if he does believe it,' said the mother, 'he's bound to go to the Lycée tomorrow morning to protest . . . And then . . .'

They stood there, all three of them, in the miserable, drizzling rain, mute and motionless. Then, all of a sudden, Lagneau dropped his books, flung himself at his mother and, throwing his arms round her waist, burst into loud sobs. The aunt melted into tears under the quivering umbrella. I was deeply distressed by this pitiful scene. I bent down to pick up the unhappy boy's scattered books, feeling very close to tears myself.

Then, I recalled the sacrifice that Lagneau had made in taking upon himself my detention over the hanging, and I made a heroic decision.

'Listen, madame. I've just had an idea!'

The aunt, hiccuping, opened her great eyes very wide.

'What idea? Irène, he's had an idea. What idea?'

'If you like, I will go and see Monsieur Lagneau myself, and tell him that I was the one who threw the stink bomb. And then I'll explain to him that I'm a scholar, and that if he were to go and see the Deputy Head, they'd take my scholarship away, and my father, who is a schoolmaster himself, would very likely die of shame!'

'You really would do that?' said the heartbroken mother.

My heroic resolve stiffened.

'Yes, I'll do it at once.'

The aunt gazed at me out of her great, mad eyes. She gave a little moaning cry, and said:

'This child was sent to us by God!'

With rapid strides we walked down La Canebière towards

Lagneau's house in the Rue Paradis, where most of the rich merchants of the town lived. And, as we walked, the two women coached me in my part, giving a final polish to the script of the tragi-comedy about to be enacted.

Lagneau clung to my arm, murmuring between sniffles:

'It's going to work! It's going to work!'

I was beginning to feel uneasy. Heroism, like a cheese soufflé, does not improve with keeping. Suddenly ī said:

'He won't belt me, will he?'

'Certainly not!' said the mother. 'He's very strict, but he's not mad.'

'And besides,' said the aunt, 'we shall both be there!'

'He might decide to write to my father, though!'

'I don't think so,' said the mother. 'But in any case, if he does, I shall go and see your father myself, and tell him the whole truth! And you can take it from me, he'll be very proud of you!'

The aunt put her hand on my shoulder, as if to make sure that I should not escape, while Lagneau was still clinging to my arm. The two of them, in fact, were urging me on, like a lamb to the slaughter.

It was a truly splendid house. The staircase was lit by electricity and carpeted in red, and, instead of a finial at the foot of the banisters, there stood the marble figure of a woman wearing bronze draperies. It was magnificent.

Slowly, and without making a sound, we went up to the first floor. At every third step, the two women paused to listen. Had he come home yet? Were we going to find him waiting for us on the landing, a towering figure with his cane in his hand?

No, he had not yet arrived. Lagneau's mother led me into a drawing-room so beautifully furnished that it was like a small museum, and she sat me down in a magnificent black armchair made of ebony, carved all over in twists and spirals. Then she said to me:

'Wait here. It wouldn't do for him to see you right away. When he gets home, we'll prepare the ground, and, when the time is ripe, I'll come and fetch you. Don't be frightened. Everything is going to be all right.'

Just as she was about to leave the room, she changed her mind and went to a drawer, from which she took a large cardboard box filled with chocolate acorns, and a little round basket with a bow of ribbon on the handle containing crystallized fruits of every colour.

'Help yourself to these', she said, 'and don't worry.'

It was easy enough to say, but I could not help thinking that, tender-hearted though Lagneau's mother might be, her solicitude for my buttocks was probably less acute than for her son's, and that I might well be about to pay for his misdemeanours.

Well! What of it? I owed Lagneau a debt of gratitude. And besides, once the die is cast, one must accept one's fate. I stuffed two chocolates into my mouth at once, suspecting that I might not be left alone for long to enjoy them.

There was not a sound to be heard in the house. With my mouth full of chocolate, I looked around admiringly at the splendid furnishings, and got up to take a closer look at all those marvellous treasures. On the chimneypiece, between two great, branched, cut-glass candelabra, stood a gilded clock, surmounted by a little statue of a naked girl. She was running so fast that she had only one foot on the ground, or rather not even one foot, but just the tips of her toes. Her other foot was stretched out far behind her. Even as she ran, she was drawing the bow she held in her hand, and all around her dogs leapt and pranced. I went up to her, and put out my finger to touch her bosom, which was superb. But then I noticed that there was one vital element missing from this magnificent tableau: there was no string in the bow! I thought this a great shame, and resolved to suggest to Lagneau that he string the bow with a strong elastic band, sprinkled with gold powder.

As I could still hear no sound, I hastily stuffed a soft-centred chocolate into my mouth.

On a sort of table, also gilded, I saw a great many things to admire: small china elephants, little brightly-coloured soldiers, Japanese dolls with real hair, and a little donkey, also with real hair, whose head nodded when touched. It was enthralling to find so many decorative objects all together. It was like looking in the window of a gift shop.

Presently, having helped myself to a crystallized orange, I gazed admiringly at the chandelier hanging from the ceiling. It had at least six electric bulbs, each nestling inside an iridescent tulip! And right in the middle, underneath the lights, a white glass angel, with green wings spread, was playing a golden trumpet. What a magical sight it must be, I thought, when all the lamps were lit for a party. Overwhelmed as I was by the sight of so much wealth, I was filled with admiration for my friend's character. I had only to look around at all this luxury to realize how unassuming he was, for he had never spoken to me of his riches. He was as kind and friendly as if he had been poor. Accordingly, I did not scruple to help myself to a crystallized apricot, glazed all over with sugar, and I had just begun to savour it when I heard a door slam, and then an angry voice, thick and muffled, then a woman's voice talking rapidly, then both voices at once. Presently, another door slammed, and then all I could hear was an indistinct murmur of voices, and my mouth was full of the taste of apricot.

I thought: 'They are preparing the ground.'

I hoped these preliminaries would last long enough for me to swallow the remains of the apricot, half of which was still stuck to the roof of my mouth. Suddenly the door swung open, and there was the aunt. She was smiling, but I could see well enough that this was merely to reassure me. With a jerk of her head she beckoned me. I followed her out of the room.

Lagneau had not exaggerated. His father really was as tall and broad as a cupboard. His grizzled hair, cut very short, bristled all over his head, and his small, piercing black eyes, with crow's feet at the corners, were overhung by massive eyebrows.

Standing beside his desk, he was holding the detention chit in his hand.

No sooner had I come into the room than he addressed me in the harsh, hoarse tones of a military commander.

'So you, sir, are the young man who goes about throwing stink bombs in the classrooms of the Lycée?'

I bowed my head submissively, and said nothing.

'And what's more, what's more, you are willing to allow your friend to be punished for your offence?'

While maintaining the posture of one thoroughly cowed, I examined the carpet, which was embroidered with abstract designs on a red ground.

Then, in a voice even more thunderous than before, he demanded:

'Do you realize what you have done?'

He stood, with arms folded, waiting for an answer, but the apricot had rendered me speechless, so he repeated:

'Do you realize?'

The aunt spoke up for me.

'Of course he does, Edouard!'

'Oh! no!' he said explosively. 'He does not truly *realize* what he has done. I shall have to dot the i's and cross the t's for him.' He pointed to his son who, though apparently not in the least discomfited, assumed a wan and martyred expression and smiled pathetically.

'Here is a boy,' he said, 'who, since the beginning of this school year—since October—has made a considerable effort to mend his ways. According to his end of term reports, his marks for conduct are above the average, and he has not incurred a single punishment in the last eight months, and now, thanks to you, he is saddled with a full day's detention! All his efforts cancelled out! He'll have to start all over again from scratch! Yes, from scratch!'

Lagneau said coldly:

'You can safely leave that to me!'

'Do you hear that, Edouard?' said the aunt. 'You can safely leave that to him!'

'That's easy to say, but he doesn't appreciate the gravity of the situation either. As I see it, his teachers are bound to think that he has lapsed into his old ways, and from now on they will be keeping a very sharp eye on him. And when the notion gets around that a boy is capable of throwing stink bombs, he is the one liable to be blamed for everything. From now on he'll have to watch his every step, or, the next time anyone does anything foolish, whatever it may be, he'll be the one to be punished for it. That is what you have done to him!'

'Edouard', said the mother, 'I really think that's going a bit too far!'

'Especially when you consider,' said the aunt, 'that his other teachers don't even know he's been punished. Isn't that so, Jacques?'

Jacques looked up, and said softly:

'Monsieur Michel is the only one who knows . . . besides the Deputy Headmaster. But he dishes out so many detentions that he can't possibly remember them for more than a week. . . !'

The huge man reflected for a few seconds, and then said sharply to me:

'I suppose it is only to be expected that you should act foolishly at your age, but you should, at least, be prepared to take the consequences. If I were in your place, young man, I should own up.'

'He can't do that,' said the mother. 'As I have already told you, he is a scholar, and his father is an elementary schoolmaster . . . Schoolmasters are not well paid. If the child were to lose his scholarship, he would not be able to stay on at school!'

'He should have thought of that before! And besides, a scholar ought to know how to behave. Let's not forget that it's out of the taxes I pay that the state finances these scholarships —and this fellow here has the nerve to spread noxious fumes all over the place, and then stand by and see my son punished for it! What an extraordinary way to behave! If this is a typical example of modern youth, what will the next generation of soldiers be like? It's not by throwing stink bombs that we shall recapture Alsace-Lorraine!'

This absurd notion struck me as comical, and I could not help smiling.

'He's laughing!' exclaimed the haulier. 'Our lost provinces are a laughing matter to him! That really is the limit!'

Timidly, the mother interposed:

'Listen, Edouard, you mustn't forget that he had the courage to come and tell you the truth.'

'And wasn't it you who made him come?'

'Not at all!' said the aunt. 'It was entirely his own idea!'

The father took a few turns about the room, then went back to his desk, and addressed his son:

'And what about you? Why didn't you speak up at the time?'

'I said it wasn't me, but they didn't believe me.'

'When was this?'

'Monday morning.'

'And in all that time, it never occurred to you to name the real culprit?'

Lagneau's face was a study in indignation and amazement.

'What, me? Inform on a friend? Oh! no, that sort of thing just isn't done!'

'Even though you knew you would be punished for it?'

'Yes, I knew. But I intended to tell you the truth, and you would have believed me, at least I hope so.'

'That's where you're wrong! If he hadn't come, I should not have believed you!'

'There you are, Edouard,' exclaimed the mother. 'You see how unjust you can be at times!'

'How true!' chimed in the aunt, pathetically. 'You're always ready to think the worst of the poor child!'

The father thought for a moment or two, and then declared:

'Well, taking one thing with another, I suppose you could say that there are redeeming features in this case.'

He turned to me:

'As for you, you certainly don't show up in a very good light! True, you came here of your own free will. But you would have done better to give a thought to Monsieur your father before throwing that stink bomb. Monsieur your father is a gentleman. What would he have to say to your conduct?'

The thought of my beloved Joseph being mixed up in this tissue of lies and deception was fearfully distressing to me. He persisted:

'What would he have to say? What would Monsieur your father have to say?'

I was sorely tempted to retort: 'He'd say you must be off your head!'

But, it must be admitted, I lacked the courage, so I shook my head sadly three or four times, while at the same time endeavouring to dislodge the apricot, still stuck to the roof of my mouth, with the tip of my tongue.

There followed a longish silence. The huge haulier paced back and forth slowly between the door and the window, seemingly plunged in deep thought. The women, mute but already confident of the outcome, waited. Lagneau was sitting with arms folded, in an armchair, gazing at the carpet, but whenever his father's back was turned, he put out his tongue at him, and gave me a wink. At long last, the thinker ceased his pacing, and said:

'So be it! Seeing that he came here of his own free will, and confessed, I won't say anything about it, either to his father or to the authorities at the Lycée.'

'Bless you!' said the aunt. 'Bless you, Edouard. You're a generous and magnanimous man!'

'But let there be no repetition of this!' he added, pointing a menacing forefinger at me.

'There will be no repetition!' cried the mother, shedding tears of joy. 'Isn't that so, Jacques?'

Infamously, Jacques was all wide-eyed innocence.

'Why ask me?' he exclaimed. 'It's got nothing to do with me!'

'He's right,' said the father. 'All he did was to take the blame himself, rather than inform on a friend. I take due note of that. I take due note, and it is by no means to his discredit.'

Even as he spoke, he went up to his son, and laid his great hand on the curly head of the little rascal, who assumed an air at once deprecating and embarrassed.

'He took the blame for someone else's offence, because he didn't want it said that young Lagneau, the haulier's son, informed on a friend. It does him credit. I must remember that.'

And, it seemed to me, he was not likely to forget it, for he seemed suddenly to have increased in stature before my very eyes. As I watched him, I saw that fleshy face irradiated by a brilliant smile, and those big eyes shining like two rain-washed lamps.

The changes wrought by this adventure were spectacular.

For a start, Lagneau woke up two days later to find, propped up against the foot of his bed, a gleaming bicycle with a three-speed gear, a padded saddle, and rubber-coated pedals. The fearsome haulier had got up in the middle of the night to play Father Christmas (albeit at Whitsun). This undeserved reward, placing, as it did, a heavy moral responsibility on his shoulders, terrified Lagneau. As a result, he buckled down to work with astonishing energy. That is to say, he bribed Bigot with a regular supply of toffees to do his Latin proses. He borrowed my exercise books, and carefully copied out my answers to problems in mathematics. He spent every Thursday composing French essays in collaboration with his aunt.

Furthermore, he would copy out the Latin verses for the day in large letters on a page torn out of an exercise book, and wedge the top of the sheet under the jacket collar of Remusat, the boy who sat in front of us. Thus, in the guise of a sandwich-board man, though visible only to those in the row behind him, Remusat displayed between his frail shoulder blades the legend of Phaedra or the rules governing the superlative. All these stratagems were to have a very great influence on Lagneau's future, for they earned him excellent, if at first undeserved, marks, and filled him with pride and self-confidence. Moreover, by dint of the efforts he put into cheating, he gradually came to take a genuine interest in his work, and to realize that it took less trouble to learn his lessons than to expend his energies in elaborate deception. Finally, no sooner did his teachers begin to look upon him as a promising pupil than he actually became one, for, to get the best out of people, it is first necessary to show that one has confidence in them.

No, he was not awarded the form prize, but he was placed third in Latin and fourth in French. As a result, at the end of the school year, when the aunt, delirious with joy but still a prisoner of her past, was once again obliged to forge her nephew's report (because a change of handwriting might have put the haulier on enquiry), she did not have to falsify a single mark or comment. Thus the gleaming bicycle, though obtained by fraud, was, in the event, no more than a premature reward for genuine merit.

As for me, my loyalty to my friend was amply rewarded. For one thing, the mother and the aunt declared themselves eternally grateful. Now that Lagneau no longer had to spend his Thursdays in detention, the weekly excursions had become a reality, and I always made one of the party. On these excursions, we visited La Treille and La Bouilladisse, and climbed the hills of Allauch. But, at midday, instead of bread and sausage, the aunt, who was a rich woman, treated us to a proper lunch in local restaurants, many of which even went so far as to serve *hors-d'oeuvre*. (When I told Paul that for starters in such restaurants one would be served with ten or a dozen little dishes of 'everything you could wish for', and that one could have as much as one wanted, his naturally hearty appetite was greatly stimulated, and later he asked my father whether such prodigality was really possible.)

*

Round about four o'clock, we would go back to Lagneau's house, where his mother would have tea waiting for us. Tea, on these occasions, included rum babas, meringues, *choux à la crème*, and marzipan figs with thick green skins. One sank one's teeth into the soft flesh of the fruit, and one's mouth was filled with the delicious flavour of almond paste. Sometimes, round about six, Monsieur Lagneau would appear, and remain to look on at our games. The first time this happened, I was startled and somewhat uneasy when I heard his footsteps on the landing. He opened the door of the drawing-room, to find us lying full-length on the carpet playing draughts.

'Oh! so you're here, are you, you young ruffian!' he said to me.

And he shook me by the hand, as if I were a man.

Then he turned to his wife:

'You've given them some tea, I trust?'

Then, without waiting for an answer—for he could see the plates scattered about on the floor—he pretended to sniff the air, and said:

'Well! well, no stink bombs today, I see, unless perhaps they were filled with confectioners' cream!'

And he laughed so heartily that the glass angel swayed gracefully to the tinkling of the drops on the chandelier.

At the Lycée, although we had sworn one another to secrecy, Lagneau simply could not resist telling the whole story to Berlaudier, with embellishments, needless to say. In his version of the story, his father, in an exaggerated frenzy of rage, had already raised the cane to strike his son on his bare buttocks, when I flung myself on my knees, and sobbed out the heroic confession which stayed the hand of the tormentor.

Berlaudier began by berating him for his cowardice, and then proceeded to extol my heroism, declaring, as he squeezed both my hands in his, that I was 'a proper man' and a true friend. This public eulogy intrigued Zacharias, who would not rest until he had got the whole story out of Berlaudier. And having done so, this son of Homer waited until the four o'clock recess, and then declaimed the epic saga to a circle of attentive listeners, who afterwards carried me in triumph on their shoulders from one end of the playground to the other.

My heroism was lauded, my loyalty admired, but it was the

ingenuity of my stratagem which won me the esteem and gratitude of the whole of the Fifth Grade, and even of the Middle School.

As long as Lycées had existed, detentions had always led to slaps, kicks in the pants, irate threats of instant incarceration in a factory, and prolonged parental fury and lamentation.

I had succeeded in transforming these miseries into bicycles, orgies of cream cakes, and repeated felicitations in the midst of a fond and happy family, and the stratagem I had devised was there at the disposal of anyone who cared to make use of it.

And make use of it they did. And thus it was that Berlaudier called at the home of Duvernet one evening, to confess that it was he and he alone who was responsible for having planted a bottom-pincher on Pétunia's chair. Three weeks later, he was amply rewarded, when Duvernet, all aglow with gratitude, flung himself at the feet of Papa Berlaudier, and meekly claimed responsibility for the 'loud and prolonged hooting in the corridors' for which his son had been unjustly punished.

Thus the spurious culprit would escape with no more than a volley of reproaches, harsh perhaps, but painless, from a father other than his own, while the spurious victim of injustice would submit to his 'undeserved' punishment, to the plaudits of his entire family, filled with pride and emotion at the dignified resignation with which he accepted the sacrifice of a whole Thursday in the interests of self-respect, schoolboy honour, and friendship.

The only dissenting voice was that of our criminologist friend, Nelps, and he, I suspected, was moved by a touch of envy.

'It's a marvellous dodge,' he said, 'but unfortunately it can only be used once!'

'Only once in any one family!' cried Berlaudier. 'But it can still be used in thousands of families! It's an absolutely terrific idea for anyone to have thought up, all the same, and I think he ought to write novels when he grows up!'

FOUR

Joseph and the Boule Match

That summer vacation, which brought to a close my year in the Fifth Grade, I found that Lili had undergone a transformation. He was now almost a young man, with a patch of soft brown fluff sprouting under his childish nose.

He had joined forces with Mond des Parpaillouns, the most notorious poacher in the district. As Uncle Jules had bought himself a dog, a small golden retriever, I persuaded Joseph that he no longer needed me to flush out or retrieve game for him, and threw in my lot with Lili and Mond.

He lived in a 'croft', which was really nothing but the ground floor of a long barn for storing grain, with a pigsty built on to one end, in which he kept an alarmingly thin but abnormally long sow, which wallowed up to its chest in its own excrement, and squealed with hunger all day long.

The outer walls of the croft were scaly and crumbling, but two large mulberry trees, formerly used for the cultivation of silk worms, shaded it delightfully.

Through the shutters, always kept half-closed, at the far end of the big, dim kitchen, wasps danced and glittered in a narrow beam of sun-gilded dust. They flew in to feed on the meagre remnants of food on the table, greasy plates streaked with dried broth, brittle thrushes' feet, cheese rinds, rotting grapes, and pear and apple cores.

Hanging on the walls were strings of garlic, shallots and dried tomatoes. The uneven tiled floor was littered with rubbish of all sorts, chairs with no seats, earthenware saucepans with no handles, jugs with no lips, buckets with holes, bits of frayed rope, misshapen bird-cages, and a great assortment of obsolete farm implements.

A long paliasse, laid on the floor in a corner, and covered with a torn counterpane, constituted the sleeping quarters. In appearance, the owner closely resembled his home.

He always wore an ancient pair of light-brown velveteen trousers, wonderfully threadbare, with grey velveteen patches over the knees and buttocks. His shirt was also grey, although it had not been so originally. It always hung open to the waist, to reveal a mat of grey and white fur, like a badger's.

He dry-cleaned himself by scratching, and on Sundays trimmed his beard with a pair of secateurs. Long ago, he had broken his forearm when his staircase collapsed under his weight. Since he had stubbornly resolved to treat the injury himself, the bones had never knitted, with the result that he had an extra joint between his elbow and wrist. He could do the most amazing things with his hand, even making it turn a complete circle, until his arm was as twisted as the screw of a wooden press. He claimed that this was of great use to him, but for my own part I never looked too closely at him when he was demonstrating his skill, because it made me feel queasy.

He took a great fancy to me, and taught me how to set rabbit traps, which I was by now strong enough to handle.

The first requisite was to choose a site, sheltered from the wind between two rosemary or juniper bushes, and clear a small circular area, making sure that it was 'nice and clean'. On the edge of this round patch, a bunch of wheat or barley ears was wedged under a big stone. The rodents were quick to take advantage of this windfall, and, the next day, we nearly always found their traces on the site, and we could be certain that henceforth one of the gluttons would come back every night. Mond would say:

'He's hooked!'

Well and truly hooked! All that remained to be done was to bury the trap next to the bunch of grain.

We would catch two or three every day, and sometimes Mond would make me a present of one of the best, and I would take it home in triumph to my mother.

Then, one day, in the vale of Passetemps, we came upon a bunch of wheat that was not ours. Mond flew into a rage, and heaped fearful curses upon the unknown thief who had invaded our territory with his traps, but when I bent down to pick up the bait, he put out his hand to stop me.

'Don't touch it. If we remove his bait, he'll simply put down more, here or elsewhere. We can do much better than that. The

282

thing to do is to piss on it! He won't know a thing about it, and the rabbits won't come near. If we do it on all his bait, he's bound to lose heart in the end. Come on now, boys, piss!'

Obediently we did so. But the ruffian was not so easily discouraged, and the number of enemy traps increased, which was why Mond insisted, before we set out, on making us drink three or four large glasses of water, by way of ammunition. He made each of us in turn contribute our mite, which was very painful, since we had to stop on command, and start again on the next bunch of grain. But it was only fair that we should pay for our apprenticeship, and we soon became accustomed to this interrupted micturition.

All this while, Jules and Joseph were having grand sport with their dog, of which they spoke in glowing terms. The little retriever was adept at gliding through the undergrowth, and flushing out the unsuspecting game, and he never failed to retrieve the wounded partridge or rabbit. But one day, catching sight of a hare streaking through a thicket, they took aim simultaneously, and could not be said to have missed, since the poor retriever was killed outright.

Thoroughly ashamed of themselves, the two bungling novices explained the disappearance of the dog by saying that he had run off after a bitch on heat. It was not until several years later that they admitted the truth. Uncle Jules carried the deception so far as to ask more than once, on returning home from shooting, whether anything had been seen of the retriever, knowing all the while that it lay buried somewhere near Font Bréguette, under a mound of stones erected by his own hands. No doubt he sought forgiveness at confession for this shockingly brazen lie.

Be that as it may, the sportsmen were now once again in need of my services, but I was unwilling to spare them more than one day in two, the rest of my time being reserved for Mond.

Our happiness as a family would have been pretty well complete, and I should have been more than content, had it not been for the abominable incubus of 'holiday homework'.

Joseph harried me on the topic of cycle racing, so that it haunted me even in my dreams. Even now these miseries are still so vivid to me that I never read the newspapers during July, to avoid seeing any references to the *Tour de France*. Then, at six o'clock Uncle Jules would turn up, accompanied by Mucius Scaevola, Regulus, Scipio Nasica, the Gerundive and the Supine. It was the height of cruelty when he opened the proceedings with his favourite gambit: '*Eo lusum*', 'I am going to play'. To him, it was an agreeable game. But, however hard I tried, I could not help looking as miserable as I felt. So much so that my uncle remarked: 'You don't want to get your teeth into Latin, that's obvious.' I said not a word, but he was the one I wanted to get my teeth into, I thought. I considered myself very witty.

All the same, I must admit that Mond des Parpaillouns amply made up to me for Plutarch and Quintus Curcius, who were never anything more than mediocre journalists, whom we have turned into scourges for our children.

One fine September evening, my Latin lesson was miraculously interrupted by a visit from Monsieur Vincent, registrar of the Préfecture, a man of considerable influence in the village. Mond des Parpaillouns and Lili came with him. Not that his mission concerned them in the least, they had just tagged on behind for the pleasure of seeing me.

My father sat them down under the fig tree, and came to fetch Uncle Jules. I lost no time in following him. Mond gave me a wide, toothless grin through his beard. Monsieur Vincent talked earnestly, even a little anxiously, while Uncle opened a bottle of white wine and Paul, sucking a fruit-gum, climbed on to Joseph's knee.

'This is how things stand', said Monsieur Vincent. 'The Club *Boule* Competition this year will be a much bigger affair than usual. The Club is putting up two hundred francs in prize money, and the *Mairie* is subsidizing us to the tune of two hundred and fifty francs, which makes a total of four hundred and fifty francs. Then there are the entry fees. Thirty teams have already entered, and by Sunday I fancy the number will have risen to forty. At ten francs a team, that adds up to another four hundred francs, making nine hundred and fifty francs in all. We have reduced the value of the second prize, so as to raise the first prize to seven hundred and fifty francs'.

'Bless my soul!' said Uncle Jules. 'That's not peanuts!'

He was no miser, but, true to his peasant origins, he had a respect for money.

'Mind you,' said Monsieur Vincent, 'It's all to the benefit of the Club. It's the substantial first prize that has been the inducement, attracting forty teams of a hundred and twenty players in all, and it will no doubt bring in as many spectators again, which means that we should sell at least three hundred aperitifs, a hundred lunches and a hundred bottles of beer. That will give us an ample return on our outlay. But what is worrying us is that Pessuguet has put his name down for the match, and he's bound to sweep the board!'

This Pessuguet, who was the postman in Allauch, would strike five bowls out of six. Together with Ficelle, with his accurate placing, and the redoubtable Pignatel as second player, his team was the terror of the neighbourhood, and they were generally spoken of as 'real professionals'. Indeed, they themselves proudly shared this opinion, and because they all came from different villages, Ficelle from Accates and Pignatel from La Valentine, they called themselves 'The International Trio of the Bouches-du-Rhône'.

'If Pessuguet is competing,' said Mond, 'the result is a foregone conclusion.'

'Believe me,' said Joseph, 'I saw them play last year. They beat the Honoré team in the final, but that team was unlucky. Those foreign chaps are skilful enough, but above all, it seems to me, they're up to every trick. If you want my opinion, I don't think they're unbeatable.'

And he gave a little smile which warmed my heart.

'Bravo!' exclaimed Monsieur Vincent. 'That's what I like to hear! And what's more, this is not just empty flattery. If you really want to know, I think your aim is every bit as good as Pessuguet's!'

'You haven't seen me play very often,' said Joseph. 'I daresay you just happened to hit on one of my good days.'

'I've seen you play at least three times,' said Monsieur Vincent, 'and I've also watched your brother-in-law placing his bowls. His action may be a bit unconventional, but he manages to place them well more often than not.'

Uncle Jules, looking wily, smiled, wagged his forefinger, and said:

'The proof of the pudding is in the eating!'

'Absolutely!' said Monsieur Vincent. 'And then we have Mond, who is an excellent second, which means that we can field a first-class team, Les Bellons, to stand up to or even beat Pessuguet.'

'Unfortunately,' said my father, 'we are sadly out of practice.'

'You have six days in which to train, and familiarise yourselves with the Club court, where the semi-finals and finals will be played.'

'We can but do our best,' said Mond. 'What have we got to lose?'

'It's what we've got to win that counts,' said my uncle. 'Think of those seven hundred and fifty francs! Even the second prize of two hundred francs wouldn't come amiss!'

The village had succeeded in scraping together six teams, three of which had not the remotest chance of winning a single round of the contest, but it was all part of the stratagem devised by Monsieur Vincent.

Taking us into his confidence as regards his plans, he told us that, according to his information, Pessuguet tended to perspire freely, and could therefore easily be persuaded to partake of chilled beer. As a result, it sometimes happened that, towards evening, his deadly aim would falter. Thus it was essential to keep the match going for as long as possible, and this was why Monsieur Vincent had put so much effort into enlisting at least forty teams, thus ensuring that the final would be preceded by four elimination rounds of fifteen points each, and that it could not take place before six o'clock in the evening, when the sun and Pessuguet would both be in decline.

Accordingly, the Les Bellons team went down to the village to practise, on the very court where the final would take place, with the Honoré team providing the opposition. I sat on the parapet, with Paul and Lili on either side of me, and we encouraged our team with cries of admiration and applause. Uncle Jules and Joseph measured the slopes, made chalk marks on the trunks of the plane trees (to enable them to judge distances at a glance), and studied every pebble embedded in the ground with minute attention. Uncle Jules was elegant, Mond efficient, Joseph dazzling, and Monsieur Vincent radiant. By the fifth day, he was so satisfied with the progress of our team that he advised them to cease training, and to take forty-eight hours' rest, as if they were professional sportsmen. Thus, the bowls were laid aside, and I took the opportunity, with assistance from my mother and Lili, of giving them a thorough polish.

We rose early and, collecting first Lili and then Mond des Parpaillouns, made our way to the village. I was carrying two little bags containing my father's bowls and those of Uncle Jules. Lili was accorded the honour of carrying Mond's.

As we reached Le Baou, the bells of the church rang out. Uncle Jules stepped out at a brisk pace, anxious not to be late for the special Mass being held for the contestants.

I should have loved to attend, purely out of curiosity, but Joseph, a staunch freethinker, led me away to the Esplanade, where a number of players were already practising their shots and examining the court with expert eyes. Standing with his back against a wall, a man of medium height, with black hair and pale, hollow cheeks, was watching these manoeuvres with a frigid expression, but, hanging from a crooked forefinger, I saw a kind of leather muzzle containing two silver bowls.

'That's him, that's Pessuguet,' said Mond.

'I thought he was taller,' said my father.

'He looks it when he's playing.'

Monsieur Vincent came out of the church before the Mass was over.

'I have to see to the draw!' he said, hurrying off to the Club.

It was an impressive scene.

Under the plane trees opposite the Club, there was a crowd of at least two hundred people. The players could be recognized by the labels inscribed with the number of their team, which dangled from a piece of string slotted through their buttonholes. Les Bellons were number 33, and Pessuguet's team number 13, which we took to be a propitious sign for us.

At the far end of the pitch, in front of the Club, a platform had been erected, on which stood a long table. Behind the table was Monsieur Vincent, flanked by two dignitaries, the president of the Boule Joyeuse Club of Château-Gombert, thin and solemn-looking in a black suit, and the president of the Quadretty Club of La Cabucelle, a young man from the town, who was attracting respectful glances from the crowd, as he was reported to be a sporting journalist who would be writing about the contest in the *Petit Provençal*. Lastly, in front of the table, stood a very pretty little girl of six or seven, looking extremely apprehensive under a huge pink bow, which perched on her head like a gigantic butterfly.

Monsieur Vincent rang a little bell and said:

'Ladies and gentlemen, our thirty-first annual *boule* competition is about to begin. It will be played according to the rules of the Fédération Bouliste des Bouches-du-Rhône, copies of which have been distributed to all the teams taking part. In view of the large number of entries, for which I thank you, the first round will consist of nineteen matches, for which nineteen courts had to be found. Some of these courts are not of the best, but this will not be sufficient to discourage contestants of your calibre, and to avoid disputes, each court is numbered, and thus the teams whose numbers are drawn first out of the bag will play on court number one, and so on. As it is already half-past eight, I will not waste any more of your time with words, and I will ask this little Innocent here to draw the numbers.'

He had with him a bag of the kind commonly used in the game of Lotto. He opened it, and held it out to the little girl.

Shyly, she drew out two wooden discs, and Monsieur Vincent announced:

'Teams numbers 13 and 22 will play on court number 1, that is to say, at the far end of the Esplanade.'

Sighs of relief could be heard on all sides, and several of the competitors rubbed their hands gleefully; they were spared a confrontation with Pessuguet in the first round, at least. Team number 22 consisted of three farm workers from Ruissatel. They accepted their fate with smiling resignation, while Pessuguet, impatient to get it over, hustled them off to the Esplanade, like cattle to the slaughter. Fate decreed that the Les Bellons team should play against Eoures, competent but not formidable players, and, what was more, the court allotted for this match was the Club ground, which they had studied so minutely for so long. They were obliged, however, to wait until the end of the draw before the court could be used.

Needless to say, I stayed with Lili, François and some others, including Monsieur Vincent, to watch the Les Bellons playing the Eoures. Uncle Jules was brilliant, and, however erratic its course, his bowl nearly always came to rest on the jack. My father was unhappy, because he was failing on every second shot, and seemed to be suffering from nerves, but Mond, in spite of, or perhaps because of, his corkscrew arm, played like a champion. At the end of half-an-hour, they were leading 8–2. As they now seemed certain to win, I suggested to Lili that we should repair to the Esplanade, to see how the Pessuguet massacre was progressing. As we turned into the narrow little street, we heard the metallic clink of a *carreau** and Pessuguet's voice announcing:

'Fifteen to nil! It's a *Fanny*!'

The crowd roared with laughter, and cheered Pessuguet, while the men from Ruissatel gathered up their bowls and put them back in their little bags, without once raising their eyes. One or two people in the crowd shouted good-natured insults at them, and suddenly a group of youths started running towards the Club, yelling '*Fanny! Fanny!*' as if they were calling to some girl. Then Pessuguet took his bowls from an admirer who had picked them up for him, and murmured:

'I fancy it won't be the last!'

He looked so resolute that I was filled with alarm.

Outside the Club, a couple of dozen players who had already finished their matches were standing about. Among them, I was delighted to see our Les Bellons team, who had beaten Eoures by 15 to 8. It was easy to see who had won. The victors were knocking their bowls together or rubbing them with their handkerchiefs, and they were still in their shirtsleeves, whereas the vanquished had already resumed their jackets and put away their bowls in their bags or muzzles. Some were arguing among themselves, eager to shift the blame for their defeat.

At the official table, the newspaper reporter was conscientiously recording the results of each match in a small ledger, and getting the captains of the teams to initial each entry. Meanwhile, Monsieur Vincent was sorting the discs for the second round draw, removing those bearing the numbers of the defeated teams.

When these formalities were completed, Monsieur Vincent solemnly read out the results, which were greeted with applause

* Translator's Note: A *carreau* is scored when the bowl which is thrown at an opponent's bowl knocks it away and takes its exact position.

and a few murmurs of dissent. Then there was a hushed silence as he held out the bag to the little girl. Suddenly the voice of Pessuguet rang out:

'What about the ceremony?'

Whereupon a group of boys began shouting in chorus:

'The *Fanny*! The *Fanny*!'

'It's a long-established tradition,' said the reporter. 'I think we ought to respect it.'

At these words, two young men went into the club-room at a run and returned, amid general merriment, carrying between them a picture about three feet square.

The three members of the losing team, looking confused but attempting to laugh, went forward to loud applause from the crowd. I had wriggled through to the front row, and I saw with amazement that the picture represented a bare behind! Nothing else. No legs, no back, no arms. Nothing but a fat anonymous behind, a real behind for sitting on, which the painter had chosen to embellish with a rose, which looked artificial to me.

Voices in the crowd shouted:

'On your knees!'

Obediently, the three losers knelt down.

Two of them kept up the pretence of laughing their heads off, but the third, looking very pale, bowed his head and made no sound.

Then the two young men carried the picture across to the captain of the team, and held it against his face. The captain, embarrassed, planted a timid kiss on those bulging buttocks.

Then he gave a great shout of laughter, but I could tell that his heart was not in it. The youngest member of the team, kneeling beside him, bent his head, and the muscle at the corner of his jaw was knotted into a great lump. As for me, I could have died of shame on their behalf. All the same, one or two people clapped, as if in tribute to their participation in the traditional ceremony, and Monsieur Vincent invited them to take a drink with him, but the captain shook his head, and they withdrew in absolute silence.

The second and third rounds were completed without memorable incident. Pessuguet triumphed first over the Honoré team, and then over that of Les Camoins. But, in both cases, honour was satisfied by a score of 4 points and 2 respectively. Decidedly, the Triplette Internationale des Bouches-du-Rhône knew all there was to know about *boule*, and I was beginning to have my doubts about the victory of the Les Bellons team, in spite of their splendid victories over the Accates and Quatre Saisons teams.

By lunch-time only five teams were still in the contest: Pessuguet's, Les Bellons, Les Camoins, La Valentine and Roquevaire.

Glowing with pride at the success of our team so far, we returned to La Bastide-Neuve for lunch, accompanied by Lili and Mond as guests of honour, in spite of Mond's protests that he would not know how to behave at a proper, sit-down meal. Still, in the end he did agree to come, but not before he had slipped into his house to give a little extra trim to his beard with the secateurs, and even to take the unprecedented step of washing his hands.

And, what was more, his table manners proved to be excellent. During lunch, I asked my father:

'As there are only five teams left in the contest, how will they manage the draw?'

'It's quite simple,' said Joseph. 'The first team drawn will play the second, and the third will play the fourth. As for the fifth, it will go through to the last round, as if it had won in the previous round.'

'That's not fair!' said my mother.

'If we should happen to be the lucky ones,' said Mond, 'we wouldn't complain of unfairness!'

'And besides, how else could it be done?' said Joseph. 'As, in each round, the number of teams has to be divided by two, odd numbers are unavoidable, unless the total number of teams were divisible by two in geometrical progression, in the sequence 2, 4, 8, 16, 32, 64, etc.'

'But...' protested Uncle Jules, and launched into mathematical theory. I shut my ears to this extra-curricular arithmetic lesson, and could think only of the three men kneeling in front of that enormous behind, the significance of which I failed to understand, though I dared not speak of it, least of all at the table.

It was six o'clock in the evening, as Monsieur Vincent had so shrewdly predicted, before the final match could begin. Although the sun was declining rapidly, it was still very warm. The contestants in the finals were the invincible Triplette des Bouches-du-Rhône, who had demolished the opposition with the utmost ease, and our own beloved team of Les Bellons.

Lili and I were torn between pride at seeing our champions win through to the finals, and dread at the thought of the humiliating defeat that they might be about to suffer at the hands of the dreaded Pessuguet.

Striding onto the court, and catching sight of Joseph, captain of the Les Bellons team, Pessuguet smiled in a manner that I did not like. To make things worse, he won the toss, so gaining the advantage of being the first to throw the jack. This seemed to me an inauspicious beginning. Then the game began, between two solid ranks of spectators, lined up three deep. Every ball was launched in profound silence and, as it ran its course, the crowd encouraged it with little, anguished cries. When it stopped, a volley of cheering and cursing broke out, followed by expert comments on the play.

Unfortunately, luck was not on our side, and it was soon obvious that Mond had lost control of his extra joint. Pessuguet, who was a postman, could not contain his little burst of scornful laughter whenever Mond's bowl, spinning eccentrically through the erratic behaviour of his crippled hand, ran backwards after it had touched the ground. Joseph was pale, and Uncle Jules red as a tomato. Pessuguet's team, after only three shots, were 8 points ahead. Lili, heartbroken, sadly shook his head, and several of our supporters, out of consideration for the feelings of the players, left the field.

I was trembling with rage at the overweening good fortune of the opposition, and the incredible bad luck of our team. Uncle Jules, having carefully studied the terrain, threw his bowl so high that it hit the branch of a plane tree, and just missed falling on his head, which provoked unworthy guffaws from the opposition, and caused him, in uttering the *mot de Cambronne*, to roll the only 'r' in the word at great length.

When Pessuguet's team had scored twelve points in a row, Monsieur Vincent, the registrar of the Préfecture, anxious to divert the attention of the spectators from what looked like becoming a rout, gave the order for the open-air dancing to begin. All the spectators seized eagerly upon this pretext to escape to the village square. Lili and I followed them, and the baker voiced the general feeling by saying:

'It's a massacre!'

Monsieur Vincent, looking very uneasy, added:

'Let us hope, at least, that it won't be a *Fanny*!'

The very thought distressed me deeply. I could picture Joseph and Uncle Jules kneeling before that great behind, at the behest of the hateful Pessuguet. Our whole family would have to endure the shame of it for ever and ever! The prospect brought me out in goose-pimples, and Lili kept repeating:

'It's all Mond's fault; With that arm of his, as limp as a rag, he ought not to be playing *boule*. It's all his fault!'

I agreed with him, but that didn't improve matters in the least, and when the orchestra struck up a polka, I went and hid behind the trunk of the big mulberry tree, and Lili followed me without a word.

The band was making a fearful racket, especially the cornet, which I felt sure could be heard as far away as Taoumé. Everybody seemed to be dancing, which was a considerable relief to me, since it meant that there would be no one to look on at the ceremony of the *Fanny*, if the worst were to happen, and it were to take place.

At all events, I would not be there, and neither, I felt sure, would Monsieur Vincent, nor Monsieur Féraud, the baker, nor the butcher, nor any of our real friends. But what of the children? Would they scruple to go and giggle at my father in his humiliation?

In a trembling voice, I put this question to Lili.

'Come with me!' he said. 'Come on!'

He led me away into a little side street, where Monsieur Féraud's stable stood. He took the key from a hole in the wall, went in, and came out armed with a carter's whip and a long bamboo cane, which he held out to me.

'If they do go,' he said, 'they won't stay long when they see us with these!'

They were still dancing in the square. I stood there, my heart pounding, not daring to go back to the Club, where the good name of my family hung in the balance.

And yet, as at least ten minutes had elapsed since we had left the fateful court, I felt a sudden, faint stirring of hope.

'Surely, Lili, if it was all over, we should have heard by now. And if it's still going on, they must have scored at least one point. Because the others only needed three to win, and it wouldn't have taken them all this time to get them.'

'That's true', he said. 'Yes, they must surely have scored one point, or even two or three. I'm not suggesting that they're going to win, but at least it won't be a *Fanny*. Do you want me to go and see?'

He was gone before I had time to reply.

The cornet was blaring out a waltz, and all the young people were rotating in the square, which was now in shadow, the sun being out of sight behind the bell tower. I repeated to myself:

'One point at least! They must have scored one!'

Lili came into sight at the corner of the street. But instead of coming towards me, he stopped, cupped his hands to his mouth, and shouted, in clear, sharp tones:

'Les Bellons are leading by 13 to 12!'

The music ceased abruptly. The dancing couples looked about them uncertainly.

He shouted again:

'A 13 to 12 lead for Les Bellons! Come quickly!'

He ran off towards the Club, and I ran after him. The cornet player ran beside me, with the whole crowd following behind.

When we reached the *boule* court, the Club secretary hurried forward to meet us with arms outstretched and palms facing outwards.

'Take care, please!' he cried. 'Stay where you are! We don't want the contestants disturbed. Be quiet, for God's sake! THEY'RE MEASURING!'

The crowd formed up in ranks alongside the court, the men walking on tiptoe.

Under the plane trees, the six contestants were bunched together around the ten or so bowls which encircled the jack. Four of the men, including my father, were standing upright with hands on hips, watching Uncle Jules and Pessuguet, who were squatting over the bowls. Uncle Jules was measuring the position with a piece of string, and Pessuguet was watching him with a baleful expression. Suddenly he cried:

'You haven't scored that second point! I told you so!'

'That is correct,' said Uncle Jules, standing up. 'We have only scored one. But there is still one bowl to play.'

And he pointed to Joseph, who moved forward with a bowl in his hand. He was calm and smiling. He glanced at the bowls in play, and said:

'I can't win by playing for position, and I might even bring their bowl in.'

'If you take aim at my bowl,' said Pessuguet, 'You might put your own bowl out. And then, even if mine is put out, it won't make any difference because Pignatel's bowl is also in a winning position . . .'

'Yes', said Joseph. 'But if I bring off a *carreau*, it will give us fifteen points . . .'

With resolute step, he returned to the 'circle'. In the hope of putting Joseph off his stroke, Pessuguet ran up to him suddenly, and peered suspiciously at his left foot, squatting down to check that it was not over-stepping the line. Meanwhile, Pignatel, who was hovering nearby, moved three paces to the side, so that his shadow fell across the bowl at which Joseph would be aiming.

Monsieur Vincent, standing in the crowd, called out:

'Hi there, old fellow! Move your shadow out of the way. Let the bowl "see the sun"!'

But that scoundrel Pignatel pretended not to realize that he was the person being addressed. So then Mond des Parpaillouns went up to him and said, pleasantly:

'Come on now, Pignatel, move over a bit!'

And without waiting for him to 'move over' of his own accord, he laid his good hand on his shoulder, and sent him spinning a couple of yards out of the way, saying, with a malign look:

'Sorry! I do beg your pardon.'

'Those are the rules!' cried the Club secretary. 'The bowl must "see the sun".'

Pignatel gave no more trouble. Joseph, his left heel in the middle of the circle, and his toes raised, took aim with great deliberation, amid a reverent silence. But, just as he was about to launch the bowl, Ficelle was seized with a violent fit of coughing. Joseph stopped, showing no signs of irritation, but indignant murmurs rose from the crowd, and fat Elzéar, the Chick Peas King, cried:

'It seems that in Les Accates even the centenarians catch whooping-cough!'

Mond went up to Ficelle, and said loudly:

'The best cure for that is a slap on the back!'

But, just as he was raising his hefty paw, Ficelle stepped hastily backwards, saying: 'No thanks! That won't be necessary!'

Silence fell once more. Then Joseph, having completed the three regulation skips, threw his bowl, which flew through the air, glittering like a little sun. I found I could no longer breathe. I could feel Lili's hand suddenly tighten on my arm, and it seemed as if the last bowl of the match would never reach the ground. Then suddenly, a resounding thud could be heard, and Pessuguet's black bowl started to gleam like silver. Joseph had pulled off the *carreau*. Motionless, and barely smiling, he said matter-of-factly:

'And that makes fifteen!'

At this, there was much clapping, mingled with shouts of 'Bravo!', and the crowd streamed towards him, while at the same time the *curé*, the last words of the evening service scarcely out of his mouth, came galloping down the little street, holding up his cassock with both hands.

Then followed the drinking of champagne. Yes, Joseph himself was compelled to drink a whole glassful, after my mother, hastily fetched to the scene, had been persuaded to moisten her lips with it first. Then Uncle Jules raised his glass, and made a speech containing a great many flattering but well-deserved references to Joseph's admirable courage, his skill, his dexterity, his refusal to give up hope, and his admirable courage. (I have already mentioned his courage, but Uncle Jules repeated it more than once.) Then it was Joseph's turn to speak. Modestly, he declared that Uncle Jules had exaggerated (whereas, in fact, he had not exaggerated at all), and that it was he, Jules, who had really won the match by his strategy, quick-wittedness, subtlety and amazing knowledge of the peculiarities of the ground. But in my opinion, he would have done better to take his eyes off the ground from time to time, and watch out for the branches of the plane trees. Next, my father congratulated

296

Mond des Parpaillouns, and explained that, at the start of the match, his third joint had become jammed, and so let him down, but that after he had freed it by pulling at it, he had scored points which were every bit as admirable as those which had been applauded by everyone in the finals of the *Petit Provençal* Competition. Monsieur Vincent congratulated everybody, and declared that it was wrong of Pessuguet and his team to go off like that, for they would anyway have been offered a glass of champagne, because they had played extremely well, and it was not their fault that they had been beaten by a better team. Finally, after loud applause, which brought a blush to the cheeks of the Les Bellons team, he invited my mother to open the ball officially with him.

And thus it was that I watched her revolving in his arms to the sparkling music of a waltz. She was smiling with lips parted and head thrown back, and she spun round so fast that her skirt flew out and everyone could see her ankles. She looked like a young girl. But it did not escape my notice that she never took her eyes off her Joseph, who, one hand on his hip, was dancing with the baker's wife from Eoures, a dark-haired young woman, and very good-looking. As they waltzed, he talked to her, and I strongly suspected that he was paying her compliments. As for Uncle Jules, he was dancing very formally with an elderly spinster wearing a lot of lace, who danced with her eyes closed, while Aunt Rose rotated in the arms of a distinguished-looking but unidentified summer visitor.

FIVE

Zizi

It was in Form IV A2 that we came under the tutelage of Monsieur Galeazzi, better known by the nickname of Zizi.

He was tall, thin, slightly round-shouldered, with a pointed beard, already turning white. His aquiline nose was by no means small, and his grey-blue eyes were always fixed straight ahead of him, like glass eyes. When he looked to right or left, it was his head that swivelled, like a lighthouse. His voice was faint but clear, and he articulated every syllable with rigorous precision.

I can't say that we were exactly afraid of him, but he made us feel uneasy, like a lizard or a jellyfish, and I was convinced that his skin must be cold to the touch from head to foot.

His authority was great, as he demonstrated on the first day of term, when he banished the twins to the detention hall.

These two clowns were scions of a prominent Greek family living in Marseilles. Golden-skinned and handsome as a pair of statues, they wore identical clothes, and were indistinguishable from one another. One of them answered modestly to the name of Pericles, the other to Aristotle.

They had already been expelled from several boarding schools, where they had exploited their identical appearance to bedevil the lives of their unhappy teachers, and they had promised to entertain us in similar fashion. But they never got the chance.

Pericles had installed himself in the front row, near the door, while Aristotle had banished himself to the back row, near the window overlooking the boarders' playground.

Zizi was at first completely taken aback by the sight of one boy in two different places, and his head swivelled back and forth three times, before he was persuaded that he was not dreaming. Having once assured himself that he was not, he asked them their christian names, and when they told him, the whole form burst out laughing.

At this, totally disregarding the respect due to their august namesakes, Zizi declared that their total resemblance to one another disturbed him, and that he felt unequal to the strain of having a single boy in duplicate in his form.

He warned them, accordingly, that they would not be admitted to the classroom in the afternoon unless they were wearing ties of different colours. In the meantime, he would be obliged if the philosopher and the general would take themselves off to the detention hall, and spend the rest of the morning, together or separately, translating the first chapter of Caesar's *Gallic Wars*.

In the afternoon they returned, Aristotle wearing a scarlet tie and Pericles a grey one shot with crimson. Zizi installed them both in the very front row, side by side, facing the rostrum. Even though now distinguishable by colour and proximity, the twins did not lose heart. From time to time—often as much as twice in a day—they exchanged christian names and ties, and seemed to derive great personal satisfaction from these small deceptions.

Zizi, who must certainly have guessed what they were up to, did not condescend to take any notice. Trained in the harsh school of Stoicism, he confined himself to punishing or rewarding each of the two neckties, according to desert, addressing them by their appropriate christian name, without stopping to enquire into the identity of the wearer. The twins, depersonalized by this indifference, and reduced to the status of mere neckwear, felt so profoundly humiliated that Aristotle responded by having all his hair shaved off. But even at this Zizi manifested no surprise whatsoever. In the end, they resigned themselves, learned their declensions, and, before long, were equipped to tackle Caesar's *Gallic Wars*.

This fellow Caesar was Zizi's god. Just as the natives of the Pacific Islands derive everything they need from the same palm tree, fencing, roof, wine, bread, arrows and clothing, so our Zizi relied on Caesar to provide our exercises in grammar, translation and literary criticism, our recitations and our impositions. He had even turned the name of Caesar into a common noun:

'Monsieur Schmidt, you will kindly spend two hours in detention producing "a Caesar" for me,' by which he meant, 'You will translate a chapter of Caesar'.

At first I put a great deal of effort into participating in the conquest of Gaul, but it really was agony to follow the marches and counter-marches of those murderous legions through forests of barbed wire, with their advance posts consisting of squads of future participles, and their flanks protected by supines and gerundives, impregnable except by wading through swamps infested by croaking hordes of ablative absolutes.

Nevertheless, I took a sentimental interest in this war, on account of Vercingetorix, our local hero in Auvergne, and I secretly raged over Caesar's victories, won by treachery, tactical skill and superior armaments.

He had ballistas, catapults, battering-rams, sling-stones and the wrought-iron swords of the legionaries, whereas my ancestors, the Gauls, had only their long, bronze swords, which buckled at the first blow, and could only be straightened by laying them across the knee and pulling on both ends; and while they were so engaged, the legionaries would plunge their rigid swords into the guts of the Arvernian or the Segobrigan, impaling them beyond repair.

Even Lagneau was moved to indignation. As for me, I had a ferocious longing to play a personal part in these bloody skirmishes. I saw myself at the head of a detachment of day boarders, armed with Flobert rifles, such as are to be found in fair-ground shooting galleries. With these, and a liberal supply of cartridges, we could have reversed the outcome of these Gallic Wars, and driven the legions scurrying back as far as the Rubicon, led by the little bald man, who would not have hesitated to be the first to cross. But all this was only a day dream, and the nearer Caesar got to Gergovia, the more my bitterness increased.

Then, one day, a young pupil-teacher, who happened to be on playground duty during the afternoon recess, and who was in the habit of chatting to us boys like one of ourselves, told us that our ancestors, the Gauls, had been Germans, Swiss, and Flemings, and that the Roman legionaries had been Russians, Bulgarians, Serbs and Hungarians. On learning this, my sentimental interest in these wars between a lot of foreigners died instantly, and henceforth Caesar's *Gallic Wars* were nothing to me but an interminable collection of Latin proses.

It was at about this time that an event occurred which wrought a transformation in my scholastic career.

Lagneau, whose mother kept him supplied with vast sums of money—five francs a week, to be precise—had come upon three volumes of *Buffalo Bill*, in a bookseller's bargain tray, priced at a franc for the lot. Having stuffed himself with toffees the previous day, he had just one franc left. He was just about to treat himself to the three volumes, when he discovered at the bottom of the tray a little book, yellow with age, which he opened in a spirit of idle curiosity, and he saw that it was a French translation of Caesar's *Gallic Wars*, with the Latin text printed below. He hesitated for only a second before sacrificing Buffalo Bill to Julius Caesar, for he was nothing if not a realist, and the following morning, at a quarter to eight, at the beginning of the first study period, he put down on my desk the little bundle of yellowing pages, which was to prove as helpful to us as a banister on a staircase.

It must be admitted, without false modesty, that I made the best possible use of it.

Each week, having found the chapter from which our Latin prose had been taken, I would copy out the translation but, in order not to arouse Zizi's suspicions, for he was pathologically mistrustful, I added a touch of verisimilitude to our homework by including a few errors.

For Lagneau, two mistranslations, two distortions of meaning and two solecisms. For me, one distortion, one misreading of a dative as an ablative, and three solecisms.

Little by little, I reduced the number of errors, and made those that remained less serious. Zizi suspected nothing, and one day even went so far as to congratulate us on our progress in front of the whole class, which caused me to blush to the very roots of my hair. For I was ashamed of having cheated, and was feeling extremely uneasy about the forthcoming test, which would take place in the classroom under the supervision of Zizi himself. When the day came, he dictated a passage of Livy to us, and I was at first appalled. Then, on rereading the passage, I found that I understood it quite well, and was pleasantly surprised when it was announced that I had been placed third, whereas Lagneau had been placed eleventh. I realized then that I had greatly benefited from my use of the crib, which had not only sharpened my innate ingenuity, but developed in me a taste for work.

SIX

I Become a Poet

The time had now come for us to leave the Junior playground, where we were the Big Boys, and move to the Middle School playground, where we would be the Little Ones. A somewhat humiliating position, but not without its compensations, since the boys of the Second and Third Grades would sometimes condescend to help us with our problems in arithmetic or geometry. And what was more, they taught us several new rude words, unknown in the Junior playground, and also instructed us in the art of smoking, while hidden behind a pillar of the colonnade, and dispersing the tell-tale smoke by fanning the air with our left hands. Lastly, they imparted invaluable information about our new teachers, by whom they had formerly been taught themselves, and revealed the real name of Poetus, our new Housemaster, for, much to our regret, we had been removed from the charge of our beloved Monsieur Payre.

This nickname bore no relation to the famous Pétomane, as Lagneau supposed. His real name was Leroux; but every winter, that is to say, during the period when bronchitis and influenza were rife, he took the place of those teachers of liberal studies laid low by illness. And every year, he dictated the same passage of Latin prose, entitled: 'The Death of Poetus Cecina', since the boys taking the dictation were different each year.

This fellow Poetus, a member of the Roman nobility, no doubt, was condemned to death by the Emperor Claudius for some unknown reason, but, as a special favour, the Emperor granted him permission to take his own life, and sent him a very handsome dagger for the purpose.

Poetus examined this weapon closely, tested the edge with the tip of his finger, shook his head, and, apparently, thought for a long time.

Seeing him thus, his wife Aria came up to him, took the dagger, and plunged it in her bosom, saying: '*Poete, non dolet*', meaning: 'It does not hurt, Poetus.'

Whereupon, Poetus seized the blood-stained dagger, stabbed himself in the heart, and fell upon the lifeless body of his spouse.

The astonishing behaviour of this Roman matron, who had spent her last breath in reassuring her husband, was one of the highlights of the winter term, the more so since our Poetus, obliged to use the grammatically correct vocative, would always say 'Pété, non dolet,' which invariably provoked gales of laughter, and furthermore, there was a story current that some wag in Form 1B, by the name of Périadès, had not scrupled, in his Latin exercise, to translate the heroic words in his own fashion as: 'Pété n'est pas douloureux' ('Farting does not hurt').

This earned him a full day's detention, and—considering that I am here referring to it sixty years after the event—enduring fame.

Our own Poetus was not a cheerful man. His obsession with that scene of heroic butchery was clear evidence of this, and because he was somewhat undersized, he tried to make up for it by severity. But severity, in his case, meant no more than threats muttered under his breath out of the corner of his mouth. These, however, were sufficient to restore silence in the classroom, no doubt on account of the aura of tragedy which surrounded him.

Needless to say, Lagneau and I were still sharing a bench, and the entire Fifth Grade had come up with us, all but Zacharias, who had been obliged to 'repeat'.

It was one evening, during the six to six-thirty study period, that I made an important discovery.

I had just completed my Latin translation. It was the sixty-third chapter of Book VII of Caesar: *Defectione Haeduorum Cognita*.

While waiting for the evening drumroll to sound, I was leafing through *Les Morceaux Choisis de la Littérature Française*, and, quite by chance, I came upon a poem by François Fabié, in which, referring to his father, a woodcutter of Rouergue, he promises never to forget:

'Que ma plume rustique est fille de ta hache'.*

This transformation of a hatchet into a pen struck me as the height of poetic felicity, and I experienced the sacred thrill of

* 'That my rustic pen is the child of your axe.'

303

responding to beauty. My eyes filled with tears, as I entered into the kingdom, under the very eyes of the unsuspecting Poetus.

I reread the masterpiece three times, until I knew it by heart. Lagneau, who had heard me whispering, asked anxiously:

'Is that tomorrow's recitation you're learning?'

'No.'

'When is it for, then?'

'It's not a set poem at all.'

'What are you learning it for, then?'

'Because it's beautiful.'

This explanation seemed to him so absurd that he was unable to repress a chuckle, which brought down a severe reprimand from Poetus upon the bewildered head of Schmidt.

After school, Schmidt always came with us as far as the stop where he caught his tram, the Cours Lieutaud terminus. On the way there, in a slightly quavering voice, I recited the sublime poem.

They listened as they walked, heads bent, ears cocked, and then Schmidt remarked idiotically that 'it wasn't bad', adding the crass comment that it must have been a very small axe to furnish no more than a single pen, and proceeded to point out with great seriousness that a woodman's axe weighed around three kilos, and that three kilos of steel were sufficient to provide two hundred boxes of *Sergent-Major* nibs.

The crudeness of these comments filled me with indignation, and I retorted that he didn't know what he was talking about, and that he had the soul of an ironmonger, and we left him all alone to wait for his tram, under a winking gas lamp. He did not seem much put out, for he was giggling as he watched us go.

As we walked along the Cours Lieutaud, I took Lagneau's arm, and began reciting the poem again, this time for him alone. He listened pensively, but said nothing, and it was plain to me that he had no very high opinion of it either.

We parted at La Plaine, on the corner of the Rue Saint-Savourin, and I went off down the Rue Terrusse, plunged in deep thought, and finally concluded that Schmidt's sniggers and Lagneau's lack of understanding could mean only one thing: they were not poets.

It was only a short step from this to the realization that I myself was a poet, and that it was stupid of me not to have realized this sooner, and that, if I wanted to be rich and famous by the time I was twenty, I should have to begin work on my masterpiece the very next day.

At once, I had a vision of myself being photographed in a sumptuous study, surrounded by priceless books, beneath a bust of myself crowned with laurels. With my inspired brow resting on my left hand, I was writing a poem to my father, using a pump-action fountain pen, which was the very latest thing, as used by no less a person than the Deputy Headmaster himself. This poem was to be a sonnet which would show Joseph in all his glory, first as a champion *boule* player and a crack shot with the partridges, and then as a beloved teacher surrounded by his grateful pupils. The sonnet would end with the following couplet, gloriously echoing the lines of François Fabié:

> '*Je n'oublierai jamais que je te dois le jour,*
> '*Et que mon stylographe est le fils de ta plume.*'*

Next morning, during the first study period, I told Lagneau of my plans. He congratulated me, and declared himself not in the least surprised, as, in his opinion, I had the right appearance for a poet. Besides, he told me, he already knew another poet, who was a stationer and newsagent in the Rue de Rome, and who was himself the author of the verses printed on his postcards. But I pointed out that such verses were never more than four lines long, and that anyway they were mere jingles, and not to be counted as real poetry.

So I was a poet. But what kind of poet? A Victor Hugo? No, not yet. An Alfred de Musset perhaps? No. He was too unhappy. What about La Fontaine, then? No. He was a poet for children. In the end I decided not to imitate anyone, but to compose a volume of at least fifty pages, entitled: 'THE BOOK OF NATURE'.

It was during the Latin class, while the Fourth Cohort of the Fifth Legion was wading through the marshes, that I began my first poetic work. To start with, I entitled it '*Melancholy*', because I liked the sound and rhythm of the word, but I found no inspiration in this title, and was moved, as if in spite of

---

* 'I shall never forget that I owe you my life,/And that my fountain pen is the child of your quill.'

myself, to write *La Chanson du Grillon*.* (Such is inspiration.)

By ten o'clock, just when Caesar began to interrogate Eporedorix, I had completed the first stanza.

During the ten to ten-thirty study period I completed the second, and then, after long and profound thought, accompanied by much mumbling and gesticulation, which greatly impressed Lagneau, I wrote the third verse straight off at one go.

At last, during the four o'clock recess, with a great show of reluctance, I allowed myself to be persuaded to give the first public reading of my work, that is to say, I went and sat on the bench at the end of the playground, with Lagneau and Nelps on either side of me, and mumbled '*La Chanson du Grillon*'.

But for my old Aunt Marie, this poem would have been completely lost. All her life she had hoarded postcards ('Greetings from Saint-Malo', 'Thinking of you here in Toulon'), receipted gas bills, tax demands, letters, in short, a mountain of odd scraps of paper, which she called her 'documents'. It was among these documents that, years later, I happened, quite by chance, to come across two stanzas of this poem.

Here they are:

> Je suis un petit grillon
> Noir, paisible, et solitaire. . .
> Au flanc jaune d'un sillon
> Loin du bec de l'oisillon,
> J'habite un trou sous la terre. . .
>
> Le soir j'en sors pour chanter
> Sous la lune mon amie. . .
> Je dis à l'astre argenté
> La splendeur des nuits d'été
> Sur la campagne endormie.†

The rest of the page, alas, was torn off, and with it the last stanza, my favourite, but I still remember the gist of it:

* *The Song of the Cricket*
† *I am a little cricket,/Black, peaceful and solitary. . ./On the flank of a brown furrow,/Safe from the beak of the nestling,/I live in a hole underground. . .   At night, I come out to sing/By the light of my friend, the moon. . ./I tell the silvery stars/Of the splendour of summer nights/Over the sleeping countryside.*

The Cricket's mate, jealous of the 'twinkling star', approached him, concealing herself in the grass, but the little singer spotted her:

> Et soudain d'une autre voix
> Je chante pour ma grillonne.*

Thus, it will be seen that the three first lines of this final stanza are lost for ever.

Well, what of it? Half of Aristotle's *Poetics* is missing, and of the thirty plays of Menander, the most famous of the Greek poets, only ten or a dozen lines have survived. The fact that Time, which consumes all things, has spared my first two stanzas at least, is surely a mark of favour.

When I had finished reading, Lagneau, obviously astounded, exclaimed breathlessly: 'It's terrific! It's terrific! I must get my mother to read it! It's terrific!'

Nelps's astonishment was even greater, since it manifested itself in the form of incredulity. He burst out laughing, and simply said:

'Where did you copy that from?'

Indignantly, I replied:

'I copied it out of my head!'

'I don't believe you,' said Nelps.

'What?' exclaimed Lagneau indignantly. 'I saw him with my own eyes!'

'You saw him write it down,' said Nelps, 'but that doesn't mean a thing. What I'm saying is that he read it in a book, and learnt it by heart. After that, it was easy enough to pretend he'd made it up himself!'

I considered this slanderous suggestion to be highly flattering.

'My dear fellow,' I said to him, 'you can't think how delighted I am to hear you say so. Yes, DELIGHTED! If you really believe that I am claiming to be the author of a poem by Victor Hugo, or Malherbe, or François Coppée, or even François Fabié, that means that you have a very high opinion of the poem! And to prove to you that it really is all my own work, I'll explain every word of it.'

Then, absurdly vain as I was, albeit deeply sincere, I set about analysing the poem in the manner of Zizi, that is to say, I

* *And suddenly, changing my tune,/I sing for my mate alone.*

307

expounded in detail the finer points of my work. And this is what I said:

' "*Je suis un petit grillon.*"

'This first line is simple and direct. The cricket speaks, which may seem surprising until we recall that in La Fontaine's poem, the Grasshopper speaks and the Ant replies. That is what is known as poetic licence. And, what is more, the word *grillon* is an evocative word. One has only to pronounce it to conjure up La Bastide-Neuve on a summer evening, and the last rays of the sun sinking behind the tops of the olive trees. One can even smell the clover in the fields.

' "*Noir, paisible et solitaire.*"

'There, in three words, you have the little creature described. It's called the presentation of character.

' "*Au flanc jaune d'un sillon.*"

'Obviously, a furrow doesn't have a "flank", since the word is applicable only to a living creature. But that is what is known as a metaphor. Metaphors are a very common poetic device, and "*sillon*" is a poetic word, an evocative word.

'For my part, when I read the word "*sillon*", I see my friend François driving the gleaming plough into the earth, and smell the newly-turned soil, and this awakens poetic emotions in me. And then I hear the blackbirds of Passe-Temps singing. That is what poetry is.

' "*Loin du bec de l'oisillon*".

'There's drama in that, because the little birds are watching out for the cricket, intending to eat him.'

'A nestling isn't a little bird,' said Nelps. 'The word means a very young bird, not yet able to leave its nest.'

'In a prosaic sense, you are right. But, in a poetic sense, I meant a rather small bird, like a sparrow or a chaffinch. That, as everything has to be explained to you, is what is known as poetic licence. Even Victor Hugo used poetic licence. Well, so do I.'

'You've said quite enough!' said Lagneau, outraged at this interruption.

I went on:

'But that's enough about nestlings.

' "*J'habite un trou sous la terre*".

'This instantly evokes a picture of a little, round hole, with

308

slender, black antennae poking out at the base of a tuft of dande-lions or, perhaps, poppies.'

I then proceeded, in the same pretentious manner, to analyse the two following stanzas, and concluded, with revolting hypocrisy:

'Remember that this is my first poem, and I'm not even sure that I shall publish it!'

Then Lagneau solemnly said:

'The extraordinary thing is how you managed to get in all those rhymes! Why, my dear chap, I don't think even Socrates could have done that!'

'One can't be sure of that,' I said modestly. 'And, for my part, I wouldn't presume, at this stage, to compare myself with him.'

'As for me,' said Nelps, 'I tell you in all sincerity that, if you really did write it all yourself, you're bound to end up as a member of the *Académie Française*.'

I was convinced that he was not mistaken. Modesty, if it comes at all, comes with advancing years.

All the same, I can understand and forgive this absurd vanity in a thirteen-year-old 'poet', especially as I have since become acquainted with a fair number of grown men and women who, long past puberty, have put their whole hearts into writing odes, sonnets and even epic poems. Their emotions are sincere, and their lyricism spontaneous. They are true poets at heart. When they read their works aloud to one, they cannot hold back their tears, as they experience again the feelings which inspired them, and which they believe they have succeeded in putting into words. To one, the name Françoise is the very embodiment of first love, the word 'grasshopper' evokes for him the little distant sound associated with the first night of his summer holidays. Fervently he breathes the words 'evening prayer', and sees again the little, dimly lit country church, where, one winter evening, he knelt beside his much-loved mother. But the hearer does not possess the key to any of these words. Often, indeed, he has quite different keys of his own. He has never been to evening prayers. For him, the word 'grasshopper' evokes a tall negro with a frying-pan full of the little creatures, urging him to taste at least one, and Françoise is the name of a cross-eyed cook who, on being dismissed, boasted that she had spat into the soup every

309

day. Which is why the bewildered listener hears nothing but a monotonous string of words, and finds the reader's outburst of emotion distressingly inexplicable.

That year in the Fourth Grade was entirely taken up with my labours as a poet. I wrote some thirty poems celebrating Mother Nature, as represented by the grasshopper, the spring, the wind, the nightingale, the shepherd, seed time and harvest. I spent every Thursday at Lagneau's house making copies of them on a cyclostyle machine, with the enthusiastic collaboration of his aunt, who regarded me as a budding genius. She sent copies of my work to various newspapers and periodicals, with covering letters written in her own inimitable style. As she never received any replies, she concluded that these people had entered into a 'conspiracy of silence', with a view to stifling youthful talent, and she wrote them further long screeds, full of scorn and sarcasm. Nowadays, I myself sometimes receive letters from madwomen, and when I do, I remember with affection Lagneau's aunt, so tormented by the swarm of bees buzzing in her bonnet, so prone to extravagant reasoning 'which reason knows not'.

In those distant days of my adolescence, on the benches of the old Lycée, in Marseilles, I wrote poetry, which is how almost all young writers begin.

Up to the age of fifteen, one is blind to the merits of prose, and unresponsive to the stylistic genius of a Montaigne or a Chateaubriand. What I admired about poetry was the technical difficulty of the craft, and I was of the naive opinion that the writers of prose had been forced to adopt that form because they were incapable of finding rhymes. Since this came easily to me, I considered myself vastly superior to Bossuet or Balzac.

My schoolmates were impressed by my talent, and my teachers encouraged me, believing that this passion of mine was an excellent way of learning to write good French.

Accordingly, I wrote a large number of little occasional poems, and rhyming declarations of love for my lovesick friends, who rewarded my genius with toffees from the *Chien qui Saute*, or sometimes with cigarettes.

By the time we had moved up into the Second Grade, I had decided to renounce madrigals, elegies and the like, and begin work on something more substantial, in the style of *La Légende des Siècles* or the *Iliad*. On a modern subject, needless to say. The outstanding hero of the twentieth century was undoubtedly Napoleon. So he was the one I chose. Having re-read my history notes with this end in view, it remained for me to devise a grandiloquent opening on the lines of *Arma virumque cano . . .* in the *Aeneid*, but it did not take me long to realize that I lacked the epic touch, and accordingly I abandoned the imperial theme.

I confessed my disappointment to Albert Cohen, who said:

'I knew you'd give it up.'

'Why?'

As our friendship was greater than our modesty, he replied:

'You are a great elegiac poet, in the manner of Racine or Alfred de Musset. What you could write would be a tragedy in the style of *Bérénice*, with one of the great love stories as your theme.'

Overjoyed to discover that I was a great elegiac poet in the manner of Racine—seeing that Cohen had said I was, I did not doubt it for a second—I borrowed from the library of the Lycée an anthology of Latin elegiac poems, edited by Monsieur Arnauld, a master in the Upper School of our Lycée. I discovered Propertius, Tibullus, Ovid and Catullus.

I was a reasonably proficient Latin scholar, because I spoke the Provençal dialect with my grandfather and my friends in the village of La Treille, near Aubagne. This dialect is much closer to Latin than is French, although, of course, many of the words have undergone changes over the centuries.

But at that time, although it is not really so very long ago, the people of Southern France still spoke Romance or, as it was called, the *Langue d'oc*. Provence had long survived as a Roman colony, a home from home for the Piedmontese, the Lombards and the Neapolitans, and the local primary schools were full of little boys who were the first members of their families able to read and speak French.

Common among the surnames of my father's pupils were Roux, Durbec and Laurent, but there were also numerous Lombardos, Binuccis, Renieris, Consolinis and Socodattis.

On one occasion a boy, an attractive little lad named Fiori Cacciabua, whose father was a stonemason, was absent from school for a whole week. When he reappeared, my father asked him for an explanation. He replied that he had been to Italy with his father to meet his grandmother, who was very old and who had never seen him.

'I'm sure you're telling the truth', said my father, 'but you'll have to bring me a note from your parents confirming it. It's the rule.'

That same afternoon, he handed my father a sheet of paper torn out of an exercise book, and folded in four. My father unfolded it, and was somewhat puzzled by the message it contained, which consisted of a single word written in capital letters in the middle of the page:

NAPATOR.

'What does it mean?' asked my father.

'It means', said Cacciabua blushing, '"*Il n'a pas tort*", in other words, that what I said was true.'

'That's quite all right,' said my father, with a very straight face. And he put the note in his pocket. But at dinner that night, he told the story to my mother and showed her the exotic word, 'worthy', he said, 'of being carved on the sarcophagus of a Pharaoh.' I insisted on being told the meaning of the mysterious word, having a great love for words, and I laughed heartily at the stonemason's ignorance. When one knows very little, one feels the greater contempt for those who know even less. I whispered the story to Florentin, who passed it on to Dubuffet, who told it to Davin. Henceforth Cacciabua became known as Napator, at which he himself enjoyed a hearty laugh. It just so happened that orthography was not his father's strong suit. Where he excelled was in carving garlands of flowers on marble tombstones.

SEVEN

Yves

Every morning, during the brief ten o'clock recess, I would pace up and down in the big day-boys' playground, under the lofty colonnades, musing and 'creating', with the appearance of one inspired. But if ever I caught sight of a belt hanging over the half-door of the earth closets, I would scoop up a handful of gravel from under one of the plane trees, then, hiding behind the trunk, with only one cautious eye showing, I would fling the lot over the top of the low door.

No sooner done than a raging bust would appear, a real bust without arms, such as are to be seen in museums, because the victim would be holding up his trousers with both hands. The bust would curse and threaten at the top of its voice, while I remained invisible, sheltering behind the tree trunk, and listening with glee.

When all was silent again, I would once more peer out cautiously with one eye, to discover that the bust had lowered itself out of sight, to complete its interrupted business. Presently, at my leisure, I would throw two more handfuls of gravel. I knew that the infuriated squatting figure, being trapped by the imperious call of nature, would not reappear immediately, but that his cries of rage would ring out from behind the door. It was then that I would throw a last handful of larger pebbles mixed with earth, and make my escape to the shelter of the colonnades. There, pacing slowly to and fro, I would pretend to resume my reverie, while in reality keeping a sharp eye on developments.

At long last, the victim would reappear, his twitching shoulders indicating that he was hastily pushing his shirt-tails down inside his trousers, and his furious gaze scouring the playground. Then he would grab hold of his belt, and emerge, fastening it as he did so, and fling himself upon some innocent bystander absorbed in a solitary game of marbles, who, having no idea what he had done to deserve a kick in the pants, would immediately launch a vigorous counter-attack.

These ludicrous skirmishes delighted me, ending, as they usually did, with the intervention of a junior master, who would haul the combatants off to the Deputy Headmaster's study.

But one day—I should have realized that the belt hanging over the door was unusually wide—a very big head, followed by a pair of hefty shoulders, appeared in response to my first volley of pebbles. It was one of the senior boys, who ought not to have been in our playground at all, but had come there in response to an urgent call of nature. This character did not hesitate for a second. Without saying a word, he hitched up his trousers with incredible speed, opened the door, grabbed hold of his belt in passing, and streaked towards me. He dragged me away from the tree-trunk to which I was clinging, and belted me on the buttocks. The junior master was a long way off. I ran towards him, feeling the lash of the heavy leather strap at every step. My buttocks were stinging, and my assailant nearly had me down, when I heard a furious oath, and saw the big boy sprawling face down on the gravel of the playground. Another boy, scarcely bigger than myself, had, by the execution of a skilful tripping manoeuvre, caused Goliath to bite the dust in shame.

My saviour was dark-haired, pale and hollow-cheeked, with high, square shoulders. He looked down at the fallen giant calmly, but with fists clenched.

The bigger boy scrambled to his feet. His chin was red and grazed, his eyes blazing.

'You little swine!' he said with feeling. 'You filthy little swine!'

The dark boy, in a slightly hoarse voice, replied:

'What are you doing in this playground, you great oaf?'

Stunned by the impudence of these words, the giant lunged at him and raised his arm, flinging the belt over his shoulder in preparation for the attack. But, while the leather strap was still in flight, I grabbed hold of it, to such good effect that the buckle was wrenched out of its owner's hand. The dark boy, lithe as a cat, leapt forward and, creating a diversion by pretending to aim

314

a blow of his fist at the enemy's face, kicked him sharply on the shin.

Once again, the brute shouted: 'Little swine!' in tones of anguished fury. But the kick he had received was not sufficient to deter him, for he was on the point of seizing the dark boy by the hair and pounding him in the face with his fists, when I swung the belt, and from behind, with all my strength, hit him with it. By an extraordinarily lucky chance, the heavy nickel buckle struck him a glancing blow on the top of his head with a muffled thud. It stopped him dead in his tracks. Holding his head in both his hands, he turned on me, towering with rage, thus enabling my ally to administer a splendid kick in the pants. But this further assault, successful though it was, had no effect but to redouble his fury against me.

He had already seized me by the hair, and I was shielding my face with both arms, when a powerful voice rang out:

'What's going on here?'

This question, to which no answer was required, was put by the junior master, who had come running on his long legs. With one hand he grasped the shoulder of the big boy, with the other he seized mine, and with long strides he marched us off to the Deputy Headmaster's study, while behind us a semi-circle of interested spectators was celebrating the downfall of the interloper at the tops of their voices.

When we reached the portals of Justice, I saw that the dark boy had followed us there. Despite the gravity of the situation, he had not lost his remarkable self-possession.

The junior master rounded on him abruptly, and shouted in his face:

'What are you doing here? Do you want to be put in detention as well?'

The boy replied, speaking very distinctly:

'I was in the fight as well. So I saw everything. I'm here as a witness. It was the big boy that started it.'

'That's not true,' shouted the interloper. 'I had gone to the lavatories in the junior playground because there was none free in ours, and so . . .'

But here an authoritative voice intervened, that of the Deputy Headmaster, who had just emerged from his cave.

'What were you doing in there?'

The big boy was just about to reply to this extraordinary question, when Monsieur the Deputy Headmaster angrily forestalled him:

'Be quiet! You're lying! You went there to SMOKE! You needn't think you can pull the wool over my eyes! You were SMOKING! Silence! This is the third time you've been caught reeking of tobacco! Four hours' detention! Silence!'

Then the junior master gave a brief description of the skirmish, as seen from a long way off. Whereupon I declared that the great brute had attacked me from behind, beating me with his belt, and that, but for the courageous intervention of the dark boy, I should now probably be in the infirmary. Great hypocrite that I was, I spoke in a broken, childish voice, trying to look as small and frail as I possibly could.

'And to make matters worse,' thundered the Deputy Head, 'he has the impudence to bully a little child! Eight hours' detention! If I ever catch you in that playground again, I will expel you from the Lycée. Silence!'

The big boy, who had long given up any attempt to speak, was rubbing the top of his head. His neck was extended like a giraffe's, and he was looking to the right and to the left with a glazed and bewildered expression.

'Get out!' said the Deputy Head.

The big boy turned on his heel, and then, with drooping shoulders and bowed head, went to meet his fate.

'And what about these two?' asked the junior master.

'These two,' said the Deputy Head, 'look thoroughly shifty to me. I wonder if an hour's detention might not do them good.'

He pretended to reflect for a moment, while we stood there with our hands behind our backs, and our gaze fixed on our toecaps. He repeated:

'Yes, I wonder! What do you think, Monsieur Poinsot?'

'That boy was a great deal stronger than these two,' said Monsieur Poinsot generously.

'Very well,' said the Deputy Head. 'We'll keep detention in reserve for the next occasion. Dismiss!'

We dismissed.

So that we could talk without interruption, I led my ally right to the far end of the playground. As we walked, I took a good look at him. He was rather thin, no doubt because he was growing too fast. His arms and legs were so long and loose-jointed that he seemed not fully in control of them. He had a few long hairs on his legs, and the shadow of a moustache under his slightly beaked nose. The expression of his dark eyes was dazzlingly open. To me he seemed virile and handsome, and it was love at first sight.

We went and sat down in a corner, half-hidden behind one of the pillars of the colonnade and the trunk of a plane tree.

I asked him:

'What's your name?'

'Yves Bonnet.'

'Are you a day-boy?'

'Yes.'

This was obvious. He was wearing very good fawn shoes, and a blue silk bow tie.

'What form are you in?'

'5A2.'

'I'm in 4A1,' I said with pride.

'I'm only twelve-and-a-half,' he said.

'You're very tall for your age.'

'I take after my father. He weighs a hundred kilos.'

I did not there and then refer to mine, for in this evaluation of fathers on the hoof, I should have lost hands down. He went on:

'He's Chief Engineer on the *Athos*, on the Marseilles–Yokohama run. Yokohama is in Japan, which means that he's seldom at home.'

'So you live all alone with your mother?'

'With my mother, and my two brothers. They are younger than I am. As my father only gets home once in three months, he hasn't time to scold us, and he always brings us presents.'

Presents such as chopsticks for eating rice, little cages, carved out of a solid lump of hard wood, housing a tiny monkey, itself carved out through the bars, and stuffed mermaids no bigger than a trout. For his wife, there were shawls, scarves, and silk carpets embroidered with dragons, breathing fire.

This style of life seemed to me very romantic. I gazed at him admiringly, not to say enviously, and pondered what I could tell him to make myself sound equally interesting.

'My father,' I said, 'is headmaster of a big school, the biggest in Marseilles.'

This was a lie, but Joseph had mentioned one day at dinner that he was hoping to be promoted to a headmastership in the not too distant future. It seemed only fair, therefore, to fulfil my father's hopes for him, on the grandest possible scale, especially in the face of a boy who owned stuffed mermaids, and walked barefoot on dragons.

Yves was properly impressed by this assertion, but, because I never felt really at ease when I was telling lies, I abandoned this topic for a more justifiable boast.

'But, most of all, he's a crack shot,' I said.

And thereupon I launched into the saga of his exploits, repeating yet again the tale of how he brought down two rock-partridges with a 'left-and-right'.

This epic, though I did not realize it, had become greatly embellished in the repeated telling. The right royal partridges had doubled in size and weight, my father had shot them down from more than a hundred yards away, and when they fell to earth, on my head, I had fainted in a lake of blood.

I added that this was a unique feat, for never in living memory had any other man achieved the 'royal double'. At this Yves gave a little smile, and said gently:

'There I think you are mistaken. I myself had pointed out to me, two or three years ago when I was on holiday, a man who had done just that.'

This assault on my father's reputation quite took my breath away.

'It's not possible. You can take it from me, it simply isn't possible.'

'All the same, it's true. I saw the man with my own eyes. He was a gentleman from the town, who spent his holidays in a little shooting lodge in Les Bellons, a village not far from La Treille. The *curé* actually took a photograph of him.'

I could scarcely contain my pride and joy. I sprang to my feet and cried:

'Well there you are then, it's him! Yes, it was my father you had pointed out to you, and as for the photograph, we have it at home. And every year we spend our holidays at La Bastide-Neuve in Les Bellons!'

'That,' he said, greatly excited, 'really is amazing. Because, you see, we too have a house in La Treille.'

'In the village?'

'No, just outside. It's on the left, on the road to Les Bellons, a big white house half-way down the hill leading to Le Ruisseau. It's called Rossignol . . .'

We were both temporarily struck dumb, for this seemed to us the most remarkable thing that had ever happened in all our lives. It was no mere coincidence, but a stroke of Fate. Yves was familiar with my own beloved hills! Every Saturday, he boarded the marvellous La Barasse tram! Why, then, had I never seen him before? Why had Fate prevented our meeting until this morning's epoch-making skirmish?

He was just about to explain, when I saw two huge black-shod feet advancing towards us, steered by the junior master on duty. He bore down on us, barking reproof, and we suddenly realized that the playground was empty, and that we had failed to hear the drum-roll summoning us back to work.

We fled towards our respective classrooms, pursued by a menacing volley of black threats about 'next time'.

Our Latin master, whom we called Zizi, sported a heavy moustache, and a little, white, pointed beard. He was looked upon as a bit of a swine, because it was almost impossible to get the better of him.

My late arrival was not well received, but Zizi said nothing, and I did not have to invent an excuse. Hastily, I opened my Caesar, and, with my head between my hands, and my brow furrowed with concentration, I assumed an air of passionate absorption.

While the Aeduans were vainly endeavouring to encircle the Second Legion, I thought only of my own personal battle, and of my miraculous encounter with my new-found friend. In vain I searched for an explanation of the great enigma: why had I not met him sooner? Why?

Into the midst of these questions, Zizi suddenly inserted one of his own. Pointing his forefinger at me, he said:

'Why is *oppido* in the ablative?'

I stood up, folded my arms, and said, very distinctly:

'Because he took a different tram.'

An expression of bewilderment mingled with indignation at

once overspread Zizi's pale face while I flushed scarlet, and the whole classroom shook with a great roar of laughter. Zizi banged three times on his desk with the flat of his ruler, and, like the beam of a baleful searchlight, his glance swept the room, instantly quelling the laughter. Silence having been restored, he said:

'Young man, I am prepared to tolerate stupidity, but not when it is combined with insolence. That answer of yours was sheer buffoonery. You will, therefore, translate Chapter IX of Caesar's *Gallic Wars* for me by Monday.'

Then, judging that I had received my just deserts, he abandoned me to my thoughts, and directed his barbs first at Picot, then at Albert Cohen. They had laughed louder than anyone, but he soon subdued the pair of them by means of the subjunctive.

Meanwhile, I was thinking of Yves, of La Bastide-Neuve, of Rossignol, and my head was full of grasshoppers. How soon would we be able to exchange further confidences? Yves, unfortunately, was a day boy, and would therefore be going home at four o'clock! Consequently, it would not be possible for us to meet again until the next day. This was unacceptable to me. I therefore made up my mind to make a dash for the classroom door at the first roll of the drum, and catch him as he was leaving his. This would have given us a few minutes, for a further precious exchange of secrets.

The martial antics of the Aeduans, bending their bronze swords back into shape over their knees after the first clash of battle, failed to make the hour of waiting seem shorter. Even centuries come to an end at last, however, and suddenly the drum roll sounded, echoing under the vaulted roof of the corridor.

At the very first stroke of the drumstick, I bounded to the door like a frog, and my hand was already closing on the brass knob almost before anyone else had had time to stand up. And then Zizi's voice rang out:

'Who is this jack-in-the-box? Oh, it's you again! Come here! What madness is this, sir? Is this all the interest you take in your work? Kindly go and stand in the corner, facing the blackboard, and stay there until everyone else has left the room!'

Then, having put me in the pillory, he turned to face the class, and said:

'Gentlemen, you may go!'

320

The harm could not be undone. I wished with all my heart that this scourge of a man might fall stiff and dead at my feet. But there was no point in wishing. There was now no hope of seeing Yves again before the following day.

When all the others had gone, Zizi, tormentor that he was, himself walked to the door with measured tread, and stood there waiting for at least half a minute. At last, he turned to me and said: 'You may go', and strode out.

I fled. The corridor was filled with boys streaming towards the exit. Inevitably, as I struggled against the tide, I jostled several boys who were unknown to me, and was rewarded by a torrent of abuse, and one remarkably skilful kick in the pants, which, if I had not been moving so fast, would have been very painful. But, when I finally reached the classroom occupied by Form 5A2, it was deserted, except for a drawing in chalk which filled the whole of the blackboard, and which was no doubt intended as a portrait of the Deputy Headmaster, since it was adorned with a top hat, a goatee beard, and a pair of ass's ears.

So thanks to the abominable Zizi, who would doubtless for-ever remain unconscious of the damage he had wrought, Yves had gone.

I hastened back towards the exit, still looking about me eagerly, but without much hope, for now all the boys I could see, every one carrying a bulging satchel, were beings from another world, that is to say, seniors in the Second or even the First Grade.

So I slowed down, and sauntered nonchalantly to the end of the corridor, where the daily boarders were formed up in two rows under the eye of another junior master, waiting for the order to proceed to their classrooms in the boarding house. This junior master was so thin that I used to think that his navel must be stuck like a limpet to the inner surface of his spine.

He had big blue eyes fringed with ginger lashes, and we called him Bluebeard.

I went and stood at the end of the line, still looking every-where for Yves. I had hoped that he might seek me out, or, at least, wait for me for a few minutes. But no. He had scampered off with the others, and I was more than disappointed, I was grieved.

Then suddenly, a hand was tugging at my overall. I turned

round, and there he was. I was so delighted that I burst out laughing.

'Were you waiting for me?'

'Yes, I'll go with you to the boarding house.'

'But that's forbidden, seeing you're a day boy!'

'I don't give a damn,' he said. 'If I'm caught, I'll say I've come to get back my *De Viris* from Chausson, who is a boarder. I lent it to him yesterday, and he's in the infirmary. And besides, it's worth taking a risk for something one really wants to do.'

At this point, Bluebeard coughed, and said in a gloomy voice: 'Straighten up, there!'

As he was looking straight at us, Yves bent his head and buried his nose in his handkerchief, to avoid being recognized as a day boy. Not that it was necessary to resort to any such stratagems, for Bluebeard would not have noticed even if a stag or an army colonel in full regimentals had joined our ranks. He was, and had been for several years, writing a thesis for a higher degree in mathematics, and his eyes had long been blind to the real world, seeing only that other world inside his bemused head, where figures crowded and jostled one another like ants on an anthill.

In a faint voice, he said:

'You may go.'

And we went.

At the end of the boarders' playground stood a long Roman colonnade, which afforded a very large play area for rainy days. The light was dimmer under the tall arches than out in the playground itself. A wooden bench ran the whole length of the back wall. It was here that we sat and talked.

That recess, though it lasted a whole hour, seemed very short to us.

First, Yves informed me that his maternal grandmother lived at La Treille the whole year round, and that she owned a very pretty pony trap—of varnished mahogany—which travelled at prodigious speed, drawn by a 'hinny'. When I asked him to describe this strange-sounding creature, he said that it looked like a pony, but that, scientifically speaking, it was 'the opposite of a mule', and that was all he could tell me.

Every Saturday, at four o'clock, he and his family set off by tram, not for La Barasse but for Saint-Michel, there to be met by the mysterious 'hinny', driven by one of the farm-workers, who would then drive them at a spanking pace as far as the village, and from there they would proceed on foot to Rossignol along a path bordered by a hawthorn hedge, and such sweet-scented herbs as sage, rue and rosemary.

Thus, the mystery was solved, and my explanation—which had seemed so ridiculous to Zizi—was proved to be correct.

Next, he told me that he was almost a stranger to my own beloved hills, having only once ventured as far as Taoumé. His own explorations had mostly been conducted in the area of the Plague Victims' Grotto, the Bec-de-Pugnaou and Allauch.

I responded with a colourful description of the real moors, my own. He gazed at me open-mouthed, eager and fascinated. Thus the men of the Middle Ages must have listened to the tales of Marco Polo. As for me, I looked forward to hours of intoxicating delight, introducing him to the distant gorges of Passe-Temps, the rocks of Precatori, where the only sound to break the silence of the stones was a gentle evening breeze, the dense green and sweet scent of the oak trees of La Garette, the ripple of wind over blue rocks, the triumphant echoes of my shouts, and, hovering in the domed sky, high above this vast kingdom, a single, solitary sparrowhawk.

I felt as if I were seeing it then, alive, a little wild, but serene.

EIGHT

Monsieur Sylvain

That day, I was walking with Yves along the rocky pathway which crosses the Vale of Passe-Temps. We were making for Precatori, a ravine where no trees grew, but where there were myrtle and juniper bushes over six feet high.

The previous day, we had set four concealed traps, hoping to catch a rabbit or two, not for love of the sport, but at the behest of our womenfolk, who had sent us to get something for the pot.

Even in the shade of the Vale, the heat was intense, recalling summers of long ago. Resin dripped like honey from red gashes in the black bark of the pines, and the crickets chirped louder than ever in the dry atmosphere. There were hundreds of them about, amplified to sound like thousands in that echoing place.

We sauntered along at our leisure, scraping our rope-soled shoes on the gravel, and stopping every ten yards for the pleasure of conversation.

Yves addressed me in English, and I replied in Latin.

'How do they call a *cigale* in English?'

'*Eheu! Cicadae autem Britannis ignotae sunt! Cum fabulam La Fontis traducunt, cicada "grasshopper" vocatur.*'

'This is nonsense!'

'*Optime! Quia "grasshoppers" locustae sunt!*'

We were very proud of these exchanges in pidgin-English and dog-Latin—but it must be said in fairness that all this pedantic clowning, keeping us, as it did, continually alert, resulted in our making great progress in both languages. We were forever striving to impress one another, and, for the young, there is no greater spur than vanity.

Just as I was groping for the Latin equivalent of 'je m'en fous', our footsteps were abruptly halted, and my concentration shattered by a brilliantly executed bugle call, coming from the far end of the Vale. The echoes expanded it into a fugue with variations, and two big blackbirds, a male and his mate, no doubt, swooped down to take cover among the clematis at the foot of the great wall of ivy.

This explosion of sound in the midst of solitude quite took our breath away, but not that of the unseen musician, who, as fluently as a gramophone, performed an unbroken succession of brazen fanfares, which, in their martial vigour, evoked a mental picture of the civil guard.

Because my satchel contained six partridge snares, I lost no time in hiding it in a clump of bushes. Then we left the footpath, and, under cover of a forest of ivy and myrtle, we crept noiselessly towards the source of the music, which re-echoed without intermission.

We crept on slowly until we reached the point where the Vale curved to one side.

Then, through the leaves, I saw a brass trumpet, then a pair of closed eyes above two puffed-out cheeks, and, finally, a fat man blowing into a mouthpiece.

He was not a policeman, for he was wearing blue denim trousers held up by red braces, and a white shirt, unbuttoned all down the front. Under an ancient walnut tree, on a ledge of rock, lay a black jacket, carefully folded, and an artist's floppy felt hat.

When he took the trumpet from his lips, we saw a face every feature of which was strongly marked, but finely drawn and noble. Beneath gleaming eyebrows shone a pair of fine, clear blue eyes. His hair was not grizzled but black and thick, and interspersed here and there with a few bright silver threads. One's total impression was of a reassuringly intelligent and kindly personality.

He drew a white cloth from his pocket, and carefully wiped the mouthpiece of his bugle.

I looked enquiringly at Yves. He responded with a wink. I emerged from the bushes, and we went forward towards the footpath.

The stranger raised his head and looked at us, taken by surprise at our unexpected intrusion; then he said, in a slightly hoarse but pleasant voice:

'Good day, gentlemen! I trust that you were not disturbed by my playing?'

'Oh! no, sir,' I said respectfully.

'We were a little surprised at first', added Yves. 'But once we got over our surprise, we were charmed by it!'

'As to your being surprised,' said the stranger, 'I can't blame you for that. It must indeed be surprising suddenly to hear a cavalry bugle sounding up here in the hills, because that's what this is, a hussar's regimental bugle!'

He looked closely at the instrument for a second or two, and then suddenly said, as if he had just discovered the fact:

'It's in the key of E minor!'

He put it to his lips and sounded a single, prolonged note.

'There', he said, 'you have just heard me play an E minor'.

'It's obvious,' I said, 'that you have served in the cavalry'. He opened his blue eyes very wide.

'Indeed not! I regret to have to tell you that you are woefully mistaken!'

He smiled broadly, winked, and said in a confidential manner:

'There are no horsemen in the navy, and I am a seaman! A seaman on leave, needless to say, since I am at present navigating among these hills, as you will have observed for yourselves . . . I see that this revelation surprises you, but:

"There are more things in heaven and earth, Horatio,
"Than are dreamed of in your philosophy".

'I trust that you will have recognized this quotation from *Hamlet,* for I can tell by your appearance that you are young townsfolk, and, judging from your age, I am led to suppose that you are sailing towards the rocky shores of the *Baccalauréat.* Am I not right?'

'We shall be moving up to Grade 2 in October!' said Yves.

'I congratulate you', went on the stranger, 'and I can promise you that you will have cause to congratulate yourselves. Grade 2 is remarkable in that it is a form in which NOTHING is done. For many, it is a period in dry dock, for others, a cruise, providing a panoramic view of the coast line and an opportunity of charting the reefs . . .'

He went to fetch his jacket, which he tucked under his arm, and put on his broad-brimmed felt hat.

'If you have no objection, I will walk with you, for the pleasure of your company, as far as your traps'.

He looked hard at us for a moment or two, savouring our astonishment.

'Yes', he said, laughing. 'I saw you laying them yesterday afternoon. I was lying down under a clump of juniper bushes, reflecting upon the complexities of human life, when you arrived, and I was an unseen witness of your poaching activities. I must confess that, after you had gone, I went and had a look at your work. Well, I congratulate you on your skill. The first three snares are well-placed and admirably constructed. All the same, I don't regret having been so indiscreet as to inspect your work, because I did not approve of the way in which the fourth snare was camouflaged, and I took the liberty of adding a few dead leaves, which—in my opinion at least—is an essential touch if the deception is to be lethal in its effects. I trust you have no objection to this spontaneous and wholly disinterested collaboration on my part.'

We thanked him most warmly, and the three of us set out together for the Vale of Precatori.

This fat man struck me as being at once agreeable and full of surprises. He walked ahead of us, making not the slightest sound, for, like us, he was wearing rope-soled shoes. Every now and then, he would turn round and smile at us.

'How is it,' asked Yves, 'that a seafaring man like yourself should have come and buried himself in this village?'

'Upon my word,' he said, 'I didn't come here to bury myself, but to find myself! And, since you ask, I'll tell you how it came about.

'I was, for several years, in command of one of those small vessels of war known as guardships, stationed in the Indian Ocean. I beat off a few pirates, whose only weapons were their reckless daring and a stock of old-fashioned muskets, and I read the novels of Pierre Loti under a continuous shower of flying fish. But they were not sufficiently thick overhead to provide shade on the bridge of my corvette, so much so that I was eventually struck down like a felled tree with a very severe attack of sunstroke. And, as a result of this, without having to apply for it, I was sent on long leave, and for very good reasons.'

He shook his head and smiled, a little sadly it seemed to me.

'But you'll be going back soon?'

'Any moment!' he said emphatically. 'My cases are packed,

327

and I only await a signal from the Admiralty. In my opinion, my recall is long overdue. But I am bound to admit—entirely between ourselves—that the effects of that attack of sunstroke have lasted much longer than anyone anticipated. From time to time even now—no doubt, it has something to do with meteorology, or more precisely, with sun spots—from time to time, as I said, I am not quite myself, or as the French idiom goes: *je ne me sens plus dans mon assiette*. In using the word *assiette*, you understand, I am not speaking ceramically, but nautically, in the sense of being "out of trim". Whenever I feel that I am beginning to keel over, I turn for help—very sensibly, I am sure you will agree—to the medical profession. I am then towed into dry dock, or, to put it frankly, incarcerated in what is inappropriately called a "sanatorium", considering that all the people you meet there are far from healthy. I have just spent four months in one, and I will tell you why'.

He paused to look about him, as if fearful of being overheard, and then, in a low voice, resumed:

'One morning, on waking, I was taking stock, as I always do, of all I had said and done the previous day, when I realized that I had developed a list of about ten degrees. Although a ship listing to that extent can still sail in good weather, the disadvantages are obvious. Accordingly, I did not hesitate to prescribe a refit. Which is why I was laid up until last week, and am now once again perfectly seaworthy. But in there, I was not able to play my bugle. It is an unsociable instrument, to be enjoyed only in the echoing solitude of such places as this.

'And that is why I came here this morning. I was feeling a little anxious, I must confess. I feared that, during these last four months, my lips might have lost their strength and suppleness, and stiffened to such an extent that I might have found myself unable, perhaps for a very long time, to produce a sustained *legato*. However, having now made the attempt, I think I can say, without false modesty, that I have not lost my skill. Tell me, you two—we are, after all, among friends—what was your impression?'

I had no idea what a sustained *legato* ought to sound like, but I assured him warmly that it was just that aspect of his playing which had so delighted us.

Yves hastened to agree with me, whereupon the stranger

immediately raised the instrument to his lips, and entertained us with a succession of military bugle-calls, followed by several tunes composed for the hunting-horn, entitled, he informed us: 'La Chamillard, Les Brisées, Le Laissez-Courre and L'Hallali.

We showered him with compliments, and his delight knew no bounds. He could not prevent himself from laughing out loud with pride and pleasure. Meanwhile, his lips retained the imprint of the mouthpiece, like a mould, and on his upper lip, in the very middle, there was a red protuberance about the size of a pea, which looked capable of picking up a coin from the ground, like the trunk of the elephant in the Botanical Gardens.

'Let's go!' he said, suddenly. 'Let's go! I'm wasting your time. It is not worthy of the captain of a corvette to fish for compliments on his skill as a bugle-player'.

He set off with long, even strides towards the Vale of Precatori. We had difficulty in keeping up with him. Yves whispered to me:

'He's a bit touched, but then so are all seamen who have served a long time in the Colonies. It's because of the climate and the whisky, my father says!'

With our four snares, we had only succeeded in catching one rabbit.

'It's the one with the three dead leaves!' said the stranger. 'You see the importance of attention to detail! It's important to you, in the first place, since you will be eating it in the form of a delicious stew, but even more important to this poor rodent, who was cruelly deceived by these dead leaves, so much so that it cost him his life! As I am responsible for his death, and as he is about to be eaten piping hot—albeit re-heated—I think it only fitting that I should "blow the quarry" in his honour.'

This he proceeded to do, with his eyes closed, and a mournful expression on his face, while I held the rabbit up by its ears.

Yves reset the snare, and our new friend himself replaced the fateful dead leaves.

Then, just as we were about to return by the way we had come, he suddenly slapped himself on the forehead, and said:

'I've just realized that I forgot to introduce myself! My name is Sylvain Bérard, your very humble servant!'

As he seemed to be waiting for a response from us, we, in our turn, told him our names and parentage: whereupon he removed his hat, and, with a deep bow and a flourish, shook us warmly by the hand. Next, though we could not quite understand why, he congratulated us heartily on being who we were. Then, during the whole of the long walk back, he talked, smiling and calm, with great authority, providing all the questions and answers himself, so that we could not get a single word in.

'I occupy my enforced leisure,' he said, 'by exercising my mind, a fascinating occupation, as you are no doubt aware.'

He was still smiling, as if to indicate that he did not take himself altogether seriously.

'To begin with,' he said, 'I have just completed a reconstruction of Euclid's system of plane geometry. He was a very wise fellow, that Greek, but his work is marred by his use of the famous Axiom. For that which is *Axiomatic* is, *ipso facto*, incapable of *Demonstration*. Thus, the reader is entreated to accept a principle which is in no way supported by reason. That's pushing it a bit, you must agree! I have attempted to fill this gap by a rigorous Demonstration of the Axiom, which I will impart to you in the near future!'

Seeing that we were shaking our heads, and that our eyes were sparkling with wonder and admiration, he gave a little gratified laugh, and said softly:

'This, needless to say, must remain a secret between the three of us, at least until the publication of my opus, the Need for which has been felt for the best part of two thousand years, and which will appear very shortly, for it is Section (a) of my masterpiece. Section (b) is also a demonstration. It concerns Fermat's Third Proposition. The sum of two squares can be a square, but the sum of two cubes can never be a cube. This work provided me with an agreeable pastime, and my only regret is that it took me so short a time to solve the problem which has exercised the minds of the world's greatest mathematicians for the past two hundred and fifty years.'

He went on to expatiate on Section (c), then Section (d), and so on right up to Section (z).

He informed us that Pasteur's theories were absurd, and that the great sage had denied the existence of spontaneous generation solely in order to be able to prove thereby the existence of God. He expressed severe disapproval of the operation for the removal of the appendix, and went on to state that if only pregnant women could be persuaded to walk on all fours, they would give birth to their babies without even noticing it, so much so that it would be necessary to follow them about at all times, so as to pick up the new-born infants from the grass, before informing their mothers of what had occurred.

Turning next to astronomy, he said that he could not bring himself to admire the genius of Newton, declaring:

'If apples were cubic instead of spherical, that Englishman would never have made his discovery, and it seems to me deplorable that the revelation of laws governing the universe should depend upon the shape of a fruit'.

He went on to claim that present-day ships were no better than sledges, and that they ought to be furnished with wheels instead of merely scraping the surface of the sea with their bellies. Then he proceeded to criticize the dairy industry, and revealed that he was on the verge of inventing a method of manufacturing milk directly from grass, without going through 'intermediary ruminants'.

'My method,' he said, 'though apparently simple, involves a number of somewhat delicate operations. It works as follows: I gather a quantity of grass, and subject it to digestion in a series of slightly acid baths heated to a temperature of 37 degrees centigrade. After leaving it to steep for two days, I extract . . . guess what?'

'Milk!' I said.

'Not at all! But your error is excusable, and I congratulate you upon it. In fact, I extract . . .'

He looked from one to the other of us with a triumphant air, and murmured:

'COW DUNG! And what is the residue left in my retort? MILK! It's as simple as Columbus's egg, once you have had the idea! As my experiments are still in progress, I should be obliged if you would refrain from mentioning them to anyone until they are completed. So, mum's the word, for the time being.'

We assured him that he could rely on our discretion, and he thanked us most warmly.

Then he was silent for some minutes, looking pensive, though smiling from time to time.

We had reached the plateau of the Adrets, and could hear a few stray notes of the Angelus borne on the breeze from some distant church. At this, he stopped, bared his head and affirmed his great admiration for the Roman Catholic Church.

It was, according to him, the greatest advertising agency that the world had ever known, having a representative in every village, with rent-free accommodation in its finest building, which, under its steep roof, was equipped with resonant bells, to summon those consumers of metaphysics who desired immortality.

This I interpreted as a condemnation of Uncle Jules's sacred religion, but he soon put me right by declaring that all this resounding publicity was fortunately deployed in the service of the noblest ideas ever conceived by man, that Christianity was the foundation of all civilization, and that only an imbecile could doubt the divinity of Our Lord Jesus Christ. Having thus solemnly affirmed his faith, he paused, and beckoned us to draw nearer. Then, in a low voice, he added:

'And yet, and yet, there is one thing he said that bothers me. He said: *Tu es Pierre, et sur cette pierre je bâtirai mon église.** Well, all I can say is no and no! The play on words offends me. Obviously, one could argue that our Saviour, when He took on human form, wished to assume it with all its drawbacks, and was even prepared voluntarily to demean Himself to the extent of uttering a pun. It could further be argued that He did so to place himself on a level with those lesser mortals who admire a play on words, a jingle or a spoonerism. Such arguments are not without weight. But all the same, all the same... This is my great stumbling block, and I sometimes dream about it at night...'

By now, we had reached the top of the ridge, where two roads meet.

'Here,' he said, 'is where, for the time being, we must part, though I hope we shall often meet again, at least if it is your wish that we should do so. But, before I leave you, I want to make you a present of a very profound idea, which came to me this morning. I wish you to commit it to memory, in case I myself should forget it. Listen:

'If you should ever, at any time, come across a plumb-line hanging out of true, be assured that SOMETHING IS GOING ON SOMEWHERE. Think about it.'

* *Thou art Peter, and upon this rock I will build my church.*

Looking solemn, he gazed at us for a moment or two in silence. Then he added:

'Permit me, now, to ask you one or two questions, and PERHAPS to confide a secret to you. If you have no objection, let us sit down on these three stones, which Destiny or Providence seems to have put here in anticipation of our meeting'.

These stones were set out in a semi-circle under a multi-stemmed ilex bush.

On our right, the huge summer sun was sinking imperceptibly down to the sea. Its almost horizontal rays, shining through the low branches of the ilex, shed a golden light on Monsieur Sylvain's noble face. The grasshoppers, sensing the approach of dusk perhaps, seemed to chirp more briskly.

'Come now, gentlemen,' he said, 'tell me the truth. Does my conversation bore you?'

I protested vigorously, and with great sincerity:

'On the contrary! For my part, it was a surprise to me to find how far we had come!'

'It's a rare treat,' said Yves, in his turn, 'to meet anyone with so many original ideas. It has been a most enlightening experience!'

'You weren't shocked by anything I said, I trust?'

'Not in the least!' I said. 'Naturally, I wasn't quite able to follow all your mathematical reasoning, but everything else interested me tremendously.'

'In other words, my line of argument seemed to you perfectly reasonable, sensible and logical?'

'Dazzlingly logical!' replied Yves.

'Good!' said Monsieur Sylvain.

His eyes sparkled with satisfaction.

'Good,' he repeated, rubbing his hands. 'That being so, I feel it my duty to reveal to you the mindless spite which exists towards me in some quarters in the village. To name but a few of those concerned, the woman who owns the grocer's shop, the *curé's* housekeeper, the postman, the turncock, the club secretary, etc. These people have seized on the notion'—he looked at us with a sad little smile—'of putting it about that I am MAD! Yes, quite simply mad!'

'That's only because your ideas are so original,' I said.

'Of course!' exclaimed Monsieur Sylvain. 'And people of that sort are scarcely qualified to judge the words and actions of someone so different from themselves. Among other slanders, they have spread the rumour that the dry-dock to which I occasional repair for refitting is nothing but a *Lunatic Asylum*, as the English call it. And that is why, if ever a child comes up to talk to me, its terrified parents call it back at the tops of their voices.

'And if ever, in the course of an evening walk, I should happen to encounter a woman in the village street, you may be sure she will turn tail, and disappear. Mind you, I must admit that I am partly to blame for this state of affairs, seeing that I have never attempted to prove to them that I am as sensible as anyone could possibly wish. On the contrary, I confess that on occasion, just for the fun of it, I have behaved towards them in a peculiar fashion, and talked a lot of gibberish, because it is my whim, from time to time, to confirm this absurd notion of theirs that I am mad, since it keeps them at a respectful distance, and thus protects my privacy.

'But in the company of such well-educated young gentlemen as yourselves—and I cannot congratulate you enough upon it—I have wished only to speak the simple truth, and to affirm to you that I am not mad!'

'It's an absurd idea', I said.

'Exactly!' cried Monsieur Sylvain. 'But self-evidently absurd as the idea is, as you yourself so aptly put it, I am nevertheless most anxious to prove to you just how absurd it is'.

'There is no need', said Yves. 'As far as we are concerned, you have already proved it!'

'Not yet!' said Monsieur Sylvain, glowing with pleasure. 'Not yet, but I very soon shall!

'This afternoon you have heard me state certain philosophic arguments and conclusions quite beyond the reach of anyone not of sound mind. I must now approach the question from the opposite end, and demonstrate that which I should be unable to prevent myself from doing if I were truly mad. Just wait here for a couple of minutes, will you? I should be greatly obliged.'

Laughing, he stalked off with long strides, and disappeared behind the ruins.

Yves looked at me thoughtfully, and said:

'He's a learned man, and he talks well. But he's a little bit eccentric, don't you think?'

'Of course he is,' I said. 'But don't forget, many great men were considered mad in their time, because ordinary people couldn't understand them. Obviously, those peasants in the village can't make out half of what he's saying, and so they think he's mad. But if you ask me, I think he's terrific!'

'So do I. He's a man to be cultivated, because one can learn so much from him.'

The truth was that we had been absolutely fascinated by his conversation, and had listened to him with unflagging attention. The adolescent is only too willing to accept new ideas, however preposterous, especially if they flout conventional wisdom, and the opinions taught in schools.

'Maybe he isn't a great genius,' I said, 'but he's certainly a character, rather in the style of *Pic de La Mirandole*. If you ask me . . .'

But Yves interrupted me, to whisper:

'Oy! Oy! What's he up to now?'

Monsieur Sylvain had just reappeared from behind the ruins, and he was coming towards us wearing a very strange get-up. He was naked to the waist, revealing a pair of fat, greasy breasts nestling in a thick pelt of black and white hair.

In place of his hat he was wearing an old bucket, riddled with rust, the handle of which hung down like a chinstrap. Two acorns, stuffed up his nostrils, made his nose look like a potato, and he had a sprig of thyme sprouting from each ear. A garland of ivy was hung round his neck, and he had rolled his trouser-legs up above his knees, so that his fat, furry thighs were exposed to view.

Intoning dramatically through his nose, he cried out:

'It is thus that a madman would be dressed, and this is how he would behave!'

Slowly, he came towards us, swaying like a gorilla, his arms outspread, his hands dangling, and suddenly, in heartrending tones, he broke into song:

> Avec deux glands dans les narines
> Et sa belle voix de ténor
> C'est un pauvre officier d'marine
> Qu'a complèt'ment perdu le Nord!*

* With two acorns up his nose/And his fine tenor voice,/Here is a poor naval officer/Who has lost his way and his wits.

335

Then, with a cry of 'Chorus!' he danced a little jig and sang:

> Et youp là là! C'est ça qui me désole!
> Je dérive en plein, je marche sans but,
> Et youp! Et youp! Où qu'est ma boussole?
> Je n'connais même plus mon azimut!*

All of a sudden, he began spinning like a top, yelling 'Hey ho!' in a strident voice, then he went off, dancing and capering, along the road to the village.

We watched him go, feeling dazed and a little frightened. Yves could find nothing to say but:

'Well, there you are, my dear fellow! There you are!'

I was very much shaken, but still I felt obliged to speak up for him.

'Listen, Yves, he did warn us. He told us he was going to act the madman; and that means that he's not really mad!'

'Be that as it may, if he behaves like that in the village, you can't blame them for thinking he's mad!'

'I agree, but he did warn us! He's an eccentric, certainly, and he does tend to overact, but you couldn't say that he was completely round the bend!'

Meanwhile, in the distance, Monsieur Sylvain, flinging his arms wide and taking great leaps into the air, was shattering the peace of the evening with his cries of 'Hey ho!'

* With a hey and a ho! My trouble is this!/I am all at sea, wandering aimlessly,/Hey ho! Hey ho! Where is my compass? /I just can't get my bearings!

NINE

The Plague Victims

And here is the story told to us by Monsieur Sylvain, seated on a red rock facing a clump of medicinal mint.

'In 1720, as you know, Marseilles was devastated by the plague. I congratulate myself on not having been there at the time.'

'Please also accept our congratulations on your absence,' I said.

'And we must congratulate ourselves as well,' said Yves.

'But the people of Marseilles,' said Monsieur Sylvain, 'had no such cause for congratulation'.

After the death of the great King Louis XIV, Prince Philippe d'Orléans assumed the regency of the realm. There was a great deal of intrigue at Court. But France, and in particular the town of Marseilles, was exceedingly prosperous. Historians of the period inform us that 'all these merchants are so rich and powerful that their support is eagerly canvassed by the aristocracy of neighbouring cities. They trade principally in the Levant, that is to say with Syria, Palestine and the Island of Cyprus, which are all in Asia, importing from them, by the Mediterranean route, cotton, wool, hides, silk and other merchandise'.

This was how Marseilles came to be so rich, and all its citizens (except for the idlers, and the galley slaves whose home port it was) enjoyed a very high standard of living.

Now there was, in this happy town, a tiny little enclave, even happier than the rest. It truly was a little bit of Heaven.

The Vieux-Port, known to the Greeks as Lacydon, was nothing more than a minute bay in which the sea was trapped between two small chains of hills at the end of a shallow valley, which sloped upwards from the seashore towards the heights encircling the town. On the hillside on the right, about half a mile from Lacydon, there was a small rise which later came to be known as Devilliers Hill. The foot of the hill was screened by bushes, but at the top of the slope there was visible against the sky a sort of hamlet, protected by a high wall, above which the tops of a row of plane trees—*umbrosa cacumena*—could be seen.

This 'hamlet' consisted of a small, rectangular 'square', surrounded on three sides by houses, of which the ground floors in several cases were shops.

Right in the middle, on a mossy plinth, stood a large stone fish, from whose head, emerging from a rock, a graceful jet of clear water poured day and night into a shell-shaped sandstone basin.

A street, which was in fact a thoroughfare leading from the Place Saint-Michel, on the right, down to the Rue de la Madeleine, on the left, crossed the square on its open side.

The owners of the houses, mostly prosperous merchants and professional men, had chosen to live there because the air was so pure, and the vast landscape to be seen from their windows so remarkably fine. In addition, the houses had large gardens at the back, enclosed by six-foot-high stone walls, and, beyond the gardens, ample stabling for their horses.

As was only to be expected, the inhabitants of this little hilltop enclave formed a close-knit community, and, in spite of being surrounded on all sides by the town, lived really more like villagers.

They came under the administration of the Marseilles magistrates, and had no parish council of their own. All the same, a certain Maître Pancrace was very much in control of affairs. He was a somewhat mysterious figure, in that no one knew where he came from, but he was a doctor, and, as such, very highly regarded. He went into town every day to minister to the ailments of the best families. Even Monseigneur the Bishop was among his patients. Maître Pancrace was sixty. He was still quite a handsome man, in spite of his white hair and wrinkles, and, although small of stature, he had great presence. He took the greatest care of his beard, which was very white and trimmed to a point, and, having beautiful hands, he had the habit of stroking it gracefully, so that the diamond on his ring-finger flashed. This diamond was a brilliant blue-white in colour, and was incontrovertible proof that he was, or had once been, very rich. He probably was a man of some considerable means, or at least had been in the past. His house, right in the centre of the row facing the street, was the largest of them all, notwithstanding that he lived alone, with two resident servants, Madame Aliette, who was reputed to be an excellent cook, and old Guillou, whose melancholy face was clean-shaven except for a grizzled moustache, and who was almost fifty years of age.

The other influential members of the community were Maître Passacaille, the notary, who wore black side-whiskers (or rather the colour of gunmetal, owing to his use of a lead comb), and had a long, quivering nose, and 'Young' Garin, who was at least fifty, but was generally known by this jocular sobriquet owing to the longevity of his father. He was very tall, with two deep, vertical lines in his cheeks, a thin moustache and a long nose. But he had a twinkle in his eye, and excellent teeth. There was also Maître Combarnoux, the cloth merchant, who was believed to be immensely rich, since he was contractor to the armed forces of the King.

He was a very tall man, in the prime of life, with a shining golden beard. His manner was uncouth. He spoke little, except to contradict others in a loud, hoarse voice. He was not much liked, because he set no value on friendship. But he was a sober and upright citizen, who attended first mass every morning, accompanied by his wife, three sons and five daughters.

In the house on the corner of the square, close up against the wall which overhung the steep hillside, lived the Captain, Marius Véran, who had crossed the Atlantic thirty times, trading in negro slaves with the Americas. Since he received a share of the profits from the shipowners, and since it was he himself who kept the accounts, these voyages brought him a much bigger return than he could have earned by honest means. He was open-handed with the ladies of the town who sometimes visited his house (after nightfall), and would occasionally throw a fistful of large coins down into the little square, for the pleasure of watching the children squabbling over them. As a result of some tropical ailment, he had lost nearly all his hair, but his bald head was adorned with a long, jagged scar, which gave him a soldierly appearance.

Besides these dignitaries there were a few small shopkeepers, such as Romuald, the butcher, appropriately stout and red-faced, but almost half-witted without a knife in his hand, Arsène, the haberdasher and dealer in second-hand goods, a tiny little man, and Félicien, the baker, whose brioches sprinkled with roasted almonds were famous throughout the town. Although he was already thirty-five years old, he was still popular with the women, because of his very white skin—due to his constantly handling flour, perhaps—and the soft golden hair on his chest. There were also Pampette, the fishmonger, Ribard, the lame carpenter, Calixte, the ships' armourer, and several others, whose names will appear later.

Naturally, there were also women, children and old folk, in all more than a hundred people, living peacefully together, apart from the Captain's fits of drunkenness, and the family quarrels, which, besides, were less common than they are nowadays.

During the summer, when the plane trees were in full leaf, great skittles matches were organized in the little square, to the accompaniment of much gesticulating and arguing.

The dignitaries, meanwhile, would forgather on the ramparts which dominated the entire town, looking out over the glittering bay of Lacydon. They would discuss politics or business or shipping. From time to time, those who had been eliminated from the skittles contest would come and listen to them, seated in a semi-circle on the ground, like spectators in an ancient amphitheatre, while the women filled their pitchers at the fountain, to the clatter of falling skittles.

Maître Pancrace, whose opinions were original but always sensible, had an answer to everything, whatever the subject under discussion. It was plain to see that he was a man with experience of the world, perhaps even of Paris itself.

One evening at the beginning of June in the year 1720, when the plane trees were in full leaf—the hotter the sun, the taller and shadier the trees, which proves that God is on the side of the skittles-players—the Captain saw the doctor returning from the town, in his pony trap, driven by Guillou. He went up to him, and invited him to join him on the ramparts to share a bottle of muscatel, which he had been about to open for himself.

'With pleasure', said Maître Pancrace, 'with pleasure. It's just what I need to dispel certain anxieties which are troubling me at the moment.'

'Heavens!' said the Captain. 'Surely politics aren't all that important. And as for all those things they're saying about the

Regent and the possible outbreak of war, I don't pay any heed to them. Because if ever the English . . .'

'It's nothing to do with the English, or with politics,' said Maître Pancrace.

The Captain, filling two goblets, asked:

'Is it a personal matter, then?'

'It's a matter of personal and general concern,' said Maître Pancrace.

He raised his glass, looked through the clear liquid, and drank it down in one gulp. Meanwhile, several other cronies, having seen the bottle, had come to join them, with goblets in their hands. The Captain roared with laughter, and hastened home to fetch another bottle, while the new arrivals exchanged greetings with the doctor.

'My dear friends,' said the Captain, when he had returned with a fresh bottle, and a corkscrew which he proceeded to use, 'let us drink three glasses in succession to the health of Maître Pancrace, for our good friend is troubled in his mind.'

'Why is that?' asked the notary.

'Say, rather, that I am a little uneasy,' said the doctor, 'and perhaps without good reason. At least I hope so.'

He drank a second glass of wine, while the Captain refilled the goblets of the others.

'Gentlemen,' he said, seeing that they were all waiting to hear more, 'I spent today in company with Monsieur Croizet, Surgeon-General to the Fleet, visiting the naval sick-bays. With us also was Monsieur Bozon, another distinguished surgeon, who has travelled a good deal in the Levant, and who has experience of tropical diseases, some of which are extremely dangerous. The magistrates had summoned us to examine the bodies of three naval sick-bay attendants, who they feared might be victims of the plague.'

At these words, all those present exchanged glances, wearing expressions of the gravest anxiety.

'And what then?' asked Maître Passacaille.

'Well, my colleagues were in no doubt! There was no question of plague, and they said so unequivocally in their report to the magistrates.'

'But what about you, what's your opinion?' asked the Captain.

341

Maître Pancrace hesitated, then said:

'I declined to express an opinion. Naturally, I'm not saying that those unfortunate men did die of the plague. But I observed certain swellings which left me in some doubt.'

He noticed that his friends had shrunk back from him, as if in fear.

'Don't worry', he said. 'Before even approaching the decaying bodies, we stripped to the skin, and put on overalls steeped in acetic acid so strong that I am still smarting from it. And, furthermore, before leaving, we bathed and disinfected ourselves from head to foot. And anyway, there may be nothing to worry about. After having drunk two glasses of wine, I'm beginning to think that my colleagues may be right.'

'One sees so many different diseases on board ship,' said the Captain. 'I know of a hundred different types of fever, all with the same symptoms, burning-hot skin, red and black blotches, pus, vomiting. No one really knows very much about them. When a lot of people die of fever it is called the plague, and the rest die of fright.'

'Especially in Marseilles!' said the choir master, who had just appeared on the scene. His name was Norbert Lacassagne, he was thirty years of age, and he regarded himself as a Northerner, because he came from Valence.

He taught scales, harmony, fugue and counterpoint. The people of Marseilles were not mad about music, which was why the choir master was so skinny. But he had a big heart, and a delightful twinkle in his eye.

'What have you got against Marseilles this time?' said Young Garin.

'Just this,' replied the choir master, 'that I've been here five years, and, ever since I got here, I've heard it stated at least three times a week that the plague has broken out in the Docks.'

'There's some truth in that', said Maître Passacaille, 'but you must admit our fears are well-founded!'

'It is a matter of recorded history', said Maître Pancrace, 'that there have been nineteen epidemics of the plague in this town. Three or four were fairly short-lived, but all the others raged for more than a year, and virtually decimated the population.'

'And the effects can still be felt in some families', said the notary. 'I have in my office a great many wills which were rendered ineffective because the testators and their heirs all died together.'

'And take my own family,' said Young Garin. 'It would have been completely wiped out in 1649, but that, by sheer chance, one of my forebears, who was a gunsmith in one of the King's regiments, happened to be stationed in Alsace when the epidemic broke out. Eleven Garins died of the plague, and it was only through that one exiled soldier that the stock was preserved.'

'I don't deny', said the choir master, 'that memories of that sort are a little alarming. All the same, we are no longer living in the Age of Ignorance, and ships are allowed into the ports much less freely than in former times. They have to have a clean bill of health, after being subjected to inspection and quarantine'.

'It goes without saying', said Maître Pancrace, 'that we are better protected than in the past, and that scientific knowledge has greatly increased. And I am convinced that, in the event of a fresh epidemic . . .'

At this point, a loud, harsh voice—that of the cloth merchant who had just arrived on the scene—broke in:

'In the event of an epidemic, as in all other circumstances, you may be sure that God will ordain the outcome, and that all your precautions will be in vain. All that matters is that one should be prepared to meet one's end, as I am, having just been to confession. . .'

He surveyed the company with a broad, self-satisfied smile. Then he added:

'Is it true that there is some cause for alarm?'

'It's no more than a remote possibility', said Maître Pancrace.

'God will look after his own!' said Maître Combarnoux solemnly.

Upon which, he turned on his heel, and returned to his house.

'Upon my word!' said the choir master, 'I envy that man! Such perfect faith! All the same, I wonder if he'll still be smiling, when it's his turn to go!'

'Come, now!' said Maître Pancrace. 'I feel quite myself again, and my advice to you is to give no further thought to the matter for the moment, because we can't change anything by worrying . . . You carry on with your skittles and I shall retire to my library and get down to some serious research just in case...'

For the next few days, there was an atmosphere of vague uneasiness, but no serious anxiety. The people of Marseilles are only too willing to forget their troubles, however grave. All the same, a number of rumours reached the little community from the town. It was said that the Surgeon-General to the Fleet— the very man who had denied that there was any cause for alarm—had died, and all his family with him. But, since these reports were no more than hearsay, spread by people who had no first-hand knowledge of the matter, they were not wholly believed, especially as, every evening on his return, Maître Pancrace would reply to all those who approached him, eager for news:

'There are no positive indications as yet. But, rest assured, as soon as I know anything for certain, you will be the first to hear'.

All the same, it was obvious that he was not easy in his mind, and no one any longer felt inclined to meet for a game of skittles.

It was the afternoon of the 10th of July when Maître Pancrace returned early from the town, driving his little pony-trap at a gallop. The Captain was alone on the ramparts, thoughtfully puffing at his churchwarden pipe.

'Captain,' called out Maître Pancrace. 'Be so good as to summon all the menfolk to meet at my house as soon as possible. I have grave news to tell them. Don't say anything about it, if you can avoid it, in front of the women and children.'

And so saying he went hurriedly indoors.

An hour later, the men were all assembled in the doctor's large drawing-room. They looked grave and thoughtful, for they already knew what they were about to be told, the more so in that the housekeeper had said:

'Maître Pancrace is taking a bath in vinegar and water, and he has instructed me to burn his clothes.'

'All his clothes?' asked the notary.

'All those he was wearing,' replied old Aliette. 'Yes, his linen shirt, his lace jabot, his long Scotch woollen hose, his handsome blue top-coat, and his shoes with the silk braid trimming. Yes, gentlemen, all those fine things have already been reduced to ashes in the kitchen stove!'

A sacrifice of such magnitude was proof enough of the gravity of the risk, and a gloomy silence descended on the assembled company.

At long last, the door opened silently, and Maître Pancrace appeared. He was draped in a voluminous bath towel, which gave him the appearance of a Roman senator. Those present who had been seated rose to their feet, while he went over to the fireplace, and stood there, with his back to it.

'My dear friends', he said. 'To begin with, I beg you not to lose your heads. You are men, and, I believe, capable of sustaining the shock of the very grave news I have to tell you. It is not only for your sakes but also for my own that I am giving you this warning. There is, alas, no doubt that the disease about which everyone is talking is the Plague.'

'If so, then it is God's will,' calmly said the cloth merchant.

For an instant, the others were silent, as if turned to stone—then the notary, sounding very strained, asked:

'Have you yourself *seen* any infected persons?'

'It is now realized', said Maître Pancrace, 'that the two sick-bay attendants, whom I mentioned the other day, were victims of the plague, since a third, who worked closely with them, has now died. Two distinguished physicians from Montpellier were brought here expressly to conduct the post mortem, and their findings admit of no doubt as to the nature of the disease.

'Furthermore, it has just been confirmed to me by the magistrates, who until now have been sworn to secrecy, that the rumour concerning the deaths of the surgeon and all his family is true. It cannot be doubted that these poor people also died as a result of the infection contracted by the surgeon who treated the sick-bay attendants'.

Norbert, the choir master, who had just arrived back from the town, then said:

'Maître, I think I can venture to reassure you, for I have just been speaking to a friend of mine, who is assistant to one of the doctors at the hospital. He told me that the disease was indeed rife in the Docks, but that this was by no means a rare occurrence. The Naval medical authorities are admirably equipped to deal with the plague, and it is quite certain that they will succeed in containing it.'

'It is quite certain,' said Maître Pancrace, 'that this time they have failed to contain it.'

Young Garin opened his eyes wide, and then his mouth, but no words came.

'What a plaguy business!' exclaimed the Captain.

'It certainly is that!' retorted the choir master.

'Where has it spread to?' asked Maître Passacaille, who had lost none of his self-possession.

'It's broken out in several places,' said the doctor. 'A waterman by the name of Eissalène, in the Place de Lenche, died over a week ago. More recently, a tailor named Creps and all his family died in the Place du Palais. Finally, this very morning, I myself witnessed the death of a woman named Marguerite Dauptane on the pavement in the Rue de la Belle-Table. The epidemic is not yet widespread, but you can take it from me that the whole town is at risk.'

Amid a deep silence, Maître Pancrace went and sat in an armchair, and proceeded to sip at a big bowl of soup, which old Aliette had just brought in to him.

At long last, the cloth merchant broke the silence:

'If the town is at risk', he said, 'it is because of its sins and its crimes, which are legion, and which have gone unchecked for far too long. God has been patient up till now—but it seems to me that His anger has at last been aroused, and that it will be slow to subside.'

'Perhaps,' said the choir master, 'our good friend Maître Pancrace is too much inclined to look on the black side of things.'

'If I look on the black side,' said Maître Pancrace, 'it is precisely because that woman whose death I witnessed was black all over.'

'If it's the Black Death,' said the Captain, 'it will spread to every corner of the town. For it needs no more than a glance from an infected person for the disease to be transmitted.'

'That is not quite accurate,' said Maître Pancrace, 'but it is true that the insidious agents of the disease spread at incredible speed when exposed to the lightest puff of wind.'

'But to return to the present,' said Maître Passacaille ,'what ought we to do?'

'For the moment, we are in no immediate danger. We are fortunate in that the air here is exceedingly wholesome, we being so high above the town, and benefiting periodically, as we do, from the cleansing effect of the *mistral*. All the same, we shall have to take some precautions. For instance, the children will have to be confined to the gardens adjoining the hillside, where they will be protected from the intrusion of any outsider who may be carrying the disease. As for ourselves and our womenfolk, we must avoid going into town except when absolutely necessary, and even then we must, at all costs, keep clear of the docks area. As regards food and other essential supplies, I suggest that they be obtained from the hillside villages, as far away from the town as possible, since the disease can also be transmitted through food. Finally, anyone who, for urgent business or personal reasons, is obliged to set foot outside our little community must, on his return, bathe in vinegar and water, and scrub himself very thoroughly with soap from head to foot. These few, simple precautions should suffice to protect us, at least for the time being. If the situation gets any worse, we may have to adopt more drastic measures.'

The following morning, Maître Pancrace held a meeting at his house, which was attended by the butcher, the baker and the grocer. To each of them he handed several gold pieces, saying:
'My dear friends, we have to think of the future. Go now and harness your horses, and make for the villages to the north of the town, which must still be entirely free of infection. Romuald', he said, turning to the butcher, 'you must bring back a few live sheep and five or six carcases of salt pork. And you,' he said to the baker, 'must lay in as many sacks of good flour as you can load onto your wagon. And you, Pampette,' he told the grocer, who was always so called, though his real name was Bignon, 'must stock up with dried vegetables, such as chick peas and lentils, and above all, with five or six casks, not of wine but of vinegar, the most concentrated you can find.'
'I already have four barrels in my cellar,' said Pampette, 'and I think . . .'
'I think', interrupted Maître Pancrace, 'that if the epidemic continues to spread, we shall bitterly regret it when our supplies run out . . . Furthermore, I want you to bring me several

bunches of rue, mint, rosemary and wormwood. By steeping these herbs in vinegar, we shall obtain a preparation known as the Vinegar of the Four Thieves, which worked miracles during the plague of Toulon, just seventy years ago. This lotion is not a cure for the disease, but it is a most effective prophylactic, since it destroys the invisible germs which propagate the infection. Now, my friends, you had better be going, not all together, for you don't want to draw attention to yourselves, and above all be sure to cover your wagons with tarpaulins, so as to conceal your loads.'

Within the hour, the three wagons were on their way, and they did not return until nightfall. The three men had carried out their missions to the letter. They had gone in different directions, the first to Allauch and the flour mills, the second to Simiane and the third to Aubagne.

They reported that they had seen nothing amiss in the countryside, and that the peasants from whom they had bought their supplies had asked no questions. But, at the same moment, Maître Garin junior, who had just returned from the town, where he had gone to buy powder, called out from a distance (for he had not yet bathed in vinegar and water) that the streets were almost deserted, and many of the shops shut, and that he had met a number of people muffled in hooded cloaks, steeped in vinegar. He would have said more, but that the doctor urged him to lose no time in taking the necessary sanitary precautions.

Young Garin's account of conditions was somewhat mitigated by that of the food merchants, and the members of the little community were not unduly alarmed, and were able to sleep easy in their beds, all except Maître Pancrace, who paced up and down his bedroom until dawn.

The following morning at eight, by which time everyone was up and about their business, they suddenly heard from the church of La Palud the tolling of the passing bell. This was followed by that of Saint-Charles and then that of Les Accoules. There was no cause for alarm in this, since ten or more funerals were a common daily occurrence. But it was not long before the sound of other bells, those of Le Pharo, Endoume and Les Catalans floated in on the breeze.

Maître Pancrace opened his front door and stood in the doorway, listening. Seated on the ramparts, the choir master and the Captain were also listening, when the mournful sound was heard again, from La Joliette, L'Estaque, Saint-Henri, and then from the distant chapel of Le Rove, whose contribution to this sorrowful concert was wafted in by a breeze from the sea.

'I don't like the sound of it,' said Maître Pancrace.

'It can't be denied,' said the choir master, 'that Monsieur Lully's minuets are easier on the ear, and a great deal more cheering to the spirits. All the same, I, for my part, still don't believe it's the plague. My friend, the hospital orderly, tells me that this is the season for malignant fevers, and that, at this very time, the marshes of the Huveaune are giving off a most insidious poison, which is causing the present little epidemic. And at the same time, there has been a fresh outbreak of smallpox, due to the recent arrival of those two regiments from Toulon, and my friend, the orderly . . .'

'Your friend, the orderly,' said Maître Pancrace brusquely, 'is little better than a fool, who thinks he knows everything because he can administer an enema. I tell you that the Plague is rife in the town, and that at least half the population will die of it.'

'I don't doubt your scientific knowledge,' said the choir master modestly, 'but I hope that, for the first time in your life, you are mistaken. In any case, as I have to go into town to collect my teaching fees for this month, I'll bring you the latest news when I get back in time for lunch.'

'Please God that is all you bring us,' said Maître Pancrace.

The choir master, unable to suppress a little smile, bowed courteously, and set off at a brisk pace.

The Captain, looking uneasy, watched him go, then stood up and, cupping his hands to his mouth, called after him:

'Hey, Norbert!'

The choir master stopped in his tracks, and turned round.

'If you catch the plague,' shouted the Captain, 'mind you don't come back here to die!'

The choir master raised his arms, curved, above his head, gave a little skip in the air, performed an entrechat, dropped down on one knee, and threw a kiss towards the little square with the tips of his fingers.

Then he put his hands on his hips, and tripped off down the hillside.

Maître Pancrace spent the day in his study, leafing through his medical and history books. At midday, old Aliette, without speaking a word, came in and laid a plate, knife and fork on the little table that stood near the window, and later reappeared with a long silver dish bearing a grilled perch on a bed of fennel.

As she went past her master, she murmured under her breath: 'It will get cold . . .'

Maître Pancrace, his nose buried in an enormous book, repeated her words, in a remote and toneless voice:

'It will get cold . . . but please say no more about it.'

The tolling of the passing bell could still be heard in the distance, as Maître Pancrace read: 'Take a sprig of rue from the very top of the plant, a clove of garlic, a quarter of a walnut, and a piece of rock salt, the size of a pea. Eat these every morning, and you may rest assured that you will be protected against the plague.'

He shrugged, turned over the page, and came upon the remedy recommended by the German doctor, Estembach. The recipe was extremely complicated and, it seemed to him, interesting, until he read the author's footnote:

'He prescribed this remedy for fourteen patients, who all died on the spot, which was why we would not allow this doctor to see any more patients.'

Still, he continued with his reading throughout the day, with his head between his hands, never pausing even to glance at the fine fish waiting for him on its bed of fennel . . .

He read at least two hundred recipes. All were much the same, consisting of treacle, black salsify, juniper, sal ammoniac, antimony, a diaphoretic, blanched onions and pounded slugs. The authors of the book spoke of 'good results', 'alleviation of suffering' and 'a few unexpected recoveries'. All the same, the authors stated, in conclusion, that 'the only really reliable remedy was to invoke the blessings of Saint Roch and Saint Francis.'

As the light began to fade, the good doctor shut his book, got up, and stood musing at his window.

In the little square, the children were playing at puss-in-the-corner, hopscotch and marbles . . . He was gazing sadly at these innocents, so full of life and fun, over whom hung the threat of a hideous death, when, all of a sudden, all games were abandoned, and all eyes were turned in the same direction, with an expression of mingled wonder and uneasiness. Then, suddenly, all the children dispersed to their homes, and the doors were slammed behind them.

Maître Pancrace opened his window, and leaned out to see what it was that had alarmed them.

Advancing along the road leading from the Plaine Saint-Michel there appeared a ghastly procession.

Leading the way were two men, dressed in long, grey overalls, their faces concealed by hoods, their hands covered in black gloves. In their right hands they held torches, and in their left, brass bells which they rang insistently. Behind them could be heard the creaking of axles and the clang of horseshoes on paving stones. As they drew nearer, Maître Pancrace heard the sound of liturgical chanting, and he was soon able to distinguish the words of the *Miserere*.

Before long, everyone was at their windows, gazing out as the seemingly endless procession went past.

There were four wagons, escorted by black mourners, each carrying a torch, and intoning the terrible litany under their black hoods.

The dead were piled up in untidy heaps, having been flung into the wagons, in some cases from an upstairs window. Arms and legs dangled over the edges of the flat wagons. Heads hung down, with their chins pointing to the sky, and their mouths open. Many were naked. In the last of the vehicles there was a dead man fully dressed, wearing a riding habit, with white leather boots, and a white lace jabot under a coal-black chin.

As a monk, intoning a prayer, went past his window, Maître Pancrace called out to him:

'Father, where are you going?'

'To the Charterhouse graveyard,' said the friar. 'There is no more room either in the Saint-Charles or the Saint-Michel cemeteries.'

'But how can that be, in so short a time?'

'It is so because the good people of the town are dying like flies. There is no longer time even to administer the last rites. Speaking for myself, I believe that my ordeal will soon be over, for I have a large swelling under my left arm. I think I shall be able to reach the graveyard, but I have every hope that I shall never leave it.'

As he spoke, black blood trickled from the corners of his mouth. Pancrace hastily shut his window, and ran to bathe his face in vinegar, as the funeral chanting faded in the distance. And there was no need for the doctor to summon his neighbours to him. They came pouring in, eager to place themselves under his protection. The entrance hall was not large enough to contain all of them, so Maître Pancrace suggested that they join him in the garden to discuss the situation.

While all these people were still sorting themselves out and finding somewhere to sit, they were joined by Maître Passacaille, the notary. Having just returned from the town, he was wrapped in a sheet steeped in vinegar. He was very pale and his face was contorted in a strange sort of grin, but his eyes were as frank and bright as ever, for he was a very brave man.

'My dear friend,' he said to the doctor, 'in order to get a clear picture of the situation, I have visited various parts of the town, wearing a cloak impregnated with vinegar, so as to avoid becoming infected, if possible. The procession which has just gone by has struck terror in all your hearts. Well, then, let me tell you that I have seen at least fifty such, several of which were made up of ten or more wagons. In the past two days, the disease has spread like wildfire, all the way from Les Catalans to L'Estaque. It has been found necessary to strike the fetters from fifty galley-slaves and to promise them their freedom, in return for their services in clearing the streets of corpses. I have been to see my friend Estelle, the Magistrate. He and his colleagues are in despair. Thirty-two surgeons and sixteen physicians have died in the last three days. An appeal has gone out for replacements to Montpellier, Toulon, Aix and Avignon. Sixteen have already responded to the call, I am told, and they arrived here this very morning. By three o'clock, one of them was dead. All the monks, nuns and priests in the town are working devotedly night and day. I have seen them myself, on their knees in the street, administering the last rites to the dying. Well, that is all I have to tell you. Now, as I cannot be sure that I am free from infection, I am going to shut myself up in my cellar for three days. I have already laid in a few provisions for myself. If I emerge on

352

the fourth day, it will be in the certain knowledge that I have escaped the disease. If, by ill-luck, I fall victim to the plague, leave me to die alone. Do not risk your lives in order to bury me. Just seal off the door and ventilator.'

'Do you mean to say,' said the cloth merchant, 'that you are prepared to die without receiving the sacrament?'

'I'm prepared to take the risk,' said Maître Passacaille, 'for the sake of the children, and I believe that the Good Lord Jesus, who loves them so dearly, will personally absolve me, even though I am a bit of an old rogue.'

Having made this astonishing pronouncement, Maître Passacaille turned on his heel, and strode off on his long legs to his cellar, where there awaited him four roast chickens surrounded by six bottles of wine.

'There goes a truly great gentleman,' said Maître Pancrace, 'and one who is an example to us all. Now, all of you, sit down on the grass, and listen to me.

'For the past few days, I have been wrestling with a very grave problem, asking myself whether I am not in duty bound, as a physician, to go into the town, and give my services to all those thousands of unhappy victims. It would probably mean sacrificing my life, but it would be an honourable death for a physician, would it not?'

'No! no!' cried several voices.

'Stay here with us! Stay with us!' implored the women.

'One moment!' said Pancrace. 'For I feel bound to justify, in advance, the course which I have decided to take.

'I am familiar with the plague, having cared for thousands of its victims during the epidemic in Hamburg in Germany. I have had frequent discussions on the subject with my medical colleagues, and I have studied everything that has been written on the subject, not only in French, but also in Latin, English and German. I have drawn my own conclusions, and these correspond with those of Monsieur Boyer, the highly distinguished Naval Surgeon of Toulon.

'"The plague", he wrote, "is a cruel and extremely infectious disease, for which there is no cure. The only means of prevention are fire and flight". This was also the opinion of the Greek historian, Thucydides, in ancient times. There are hundreds of remedies in existence, but it has been proved beyond a shadow of doubt that they serve no purpose, except perhaps to hasten the end of the victims, which, admittedly, is no bad thing, but not the solution which we are seeking.

'I therefore believe that to care for the victims of the plague is to care for the dead, whereas our duty, as physicians, is to protect the living.'

A prolonged murmur arose, as his audience sighed with relief. Here and there in the crowd, one or two people even gave a little laugh.

'Is it possible,' went on Pancrace, 'to preserve you from this scourge?'

He paused for a second or two, then said with conviction:
'Yes.'

At this point, the voice of Maître Passacaille came to them through the ventilator, saying:

'Estelle told me there was not a single plague victim in the Monastery of Saint-Victor, because they took the precaution of bricking up all the doors and windows!'

'I was just about to say,' exclaimed Pancrace, 'that whenever an epidemic has occurred, the enclosed religious orders have not heard so much as a whisper of the disease raging all about them. Well then, my friends, let us follow their example, for, although such conduct is far from creditable in monks, whose duty should be to make every sacrifice in the name of Christian charity, it is perfectly acceptable in men of the world with family responsibilities.

'For a start, we must all voluntarily subject ourselves to a rigorous discipline: from now on, no one is to set foot outside these walls.'

Angrily, the churlish cloth merchant intervened:

'And what about Mass? It is essential that I should attend Mass every day, with all my family, in the Church of La Madeleine. And my advice to those of you who scarcely ever set foot in a church is to make up for it now, by attending Mass at least once a day, if not twice!'

And he glared at Maître Pancrace, who could certainly not be held up as an example of piety.

'I insist,' said the doctor, 'that, for the time being, all church attendance must cease. The Good Lord, who watches over us all, will know that it is not through lack of zeal. It has not escaped

His notice that a church, like any other place of public assembly, is a dangerous hot-bed of infection. Everyone here acknowledges the strength of your faith, but if you were to come back here after attending Mass, and bring the Plague into our little community, would you really be behaving as a good Christian should?'

'It seems to me,' said the cloth merchant hotly, 'that only a hardened sinner could suggest that it was possible to catch the plague while attending Holy Mass! I say that a good Christian has nothing to fear from the plague! As for me, as long as my legs will carry me, I shall not allow a single day to pass without partaking of the Holy Sacrament. I have not missed a single day since my First Communion, and I do not intend to begin now!'

'In other words,' said Maître Pancrace, 'your decision is to return here bringing us infection and death?'

'It is not for me to decide such things,' said the cloth merchant, haughtily. 'It is for God alone to decide, and your efforts to thwart His will are not only ridiculous but impious. If it pleases Him to send us the plague, or death, it is madness to attempt to resist Him. I refuse to support you in this wicked enterprise, which, in any event, will avail you nothing. I warn you now that I and all my family will attend Church tomorrow morning, and I shall then go to Saint-Barnabé to visit my brother, of whom I have had no news for the past five days. And tomorrow evening, with your kind permission, I shall return home.'

Whereupon, he pulled his hat down over his ears, and strode away.

'There goes an honest fool,' said Maître Pancrace, 'whose folly may cost us our lives!'

'Surely not!' said the Captain. 'All we have to do is to lock him up in his cellar, with all his family.'

'If he comes back tomorrow night,' said Maître Pancrace, 'that is what we shall do.'

'Why shouldn't we lock him up straight away?' asked Young Garin.

'Because,' said the doctor, 'I hope that what he sees tomorrow will restore him to reason, and that he will come to us in fear and trembling, begging for a supply of lifesaving vinegar. But

355

now, let us discuss our plans. We shall have to live as if we were under siege. Have we enough provisions?'

'We have enough water, at any rate,' said Maître Garin. 'The fountain has never gushed more abundantly.'

'I think,' said the doctor, 'that we should do well not to drink from it. That water comes from the Charterhouse reservoir, which is fed by the Huveaune. If only one plague victim were to fall into the river, or even bathe his sores in it, it would be sufficient to poison the water. We shall drink nothing but well water.'

'There's a full twelve feet of water in my well,' said Maître Garin, 'which, according to my calculations, should fill at least a thousand pitchers.'

'There's only about six feet of water in mine,' said the grocer, Bignon, 'but the level remains constant throughout the year. Admittedly, if I use it too freely to water my land, it drops a little, but it always rises again during the night.'

'So,' said Maître Pancrace, 'as regards water, we have no cause for alarm. What about food?'

Bignon, the grocer, stepped forward.

'With all we brought back from our last trip, my cellars are well stocked. To begin with, I have at least a dozen barrels of anchovies, which I ordered from Toulon long before the disaster struck, and ten cases of salt cod. I have a cellar full of potatoes, five barrels of olive oil, two large crocks of spices, five or six sacks of chick peas (they have been somewhat damaged by weevils, but all we have to do is pick them over), and two hundred pounds of lentils. And in addition,' he said, laughing, 'I have my wooden pumpkins!'

He had, in fact, bought a small cargo of pumpkins from a Spanish sea-captain, which resembled pumpkins in nothing but name. They were spherical, wooden objects, like large cannon-balls, and they were very nearly as hard. But, when sawn in half, they were found to contain a tasty and nourishing white pulp. Patrice's customers, however, repelled by the appearance and resonance of this exotic vegetable, had left him with the greater part of the cargo on his hands. He consoled himself with the thought:

'Since the shell is watertight, the pulp will not deteriorate for at least four years!'

But his son, who was a bit of a wag, had suggested that they had better open a toy factory.

'Have you many left?' asked Maître Pancrace.

'Two cellars full, piled up to the ceiling!' said the son.

'They may yet be the means of saving our lives,' said the doctor. 'And what about you, baker? How are you off for flour?'

The handsome baker, who was somewhat slow-witted, thought for a long time, and then said:

'I have a dozen sacks of flour, which must weigh at least a couple of hundredweight.'

'How many pounds of bread will that make?'

'More than double that weight,' said the baker. 'But what I am short of is wood. I have barely a week's supply.'

'If necessary,' said Maître Pancrace, 'we'll burn our floor-boards. But we haven't come to that yet!'

'And besides,' said Young Garin, 'owing to the mild winter last year, we all have stocks left over in our cellars.'

At this, the notary called out through the ventilator:

'I still have at least two cart-loads in stock!'

'How are you feeling?' called out Maître Pancrace.

'A bit overheated,' shouted the notary. 'But I fancy that's because I have just drunk two bottles of wine, and a power of good they seem to have done me!'

'I'm sure it's the wine!' Maître Pancrace shouted back. 'Now you'd better try and get some sleep!'

'I couldn't possibly sleep!' shouted the notary. 'I'm much too interested in all you're saying. Go on! Go on! Ask the butcher what he's got!'

Fat Romuald stepped forward, looking a little overawed, and said breathlessly:

'I have a side of beef, a calf, and three sheep. There are about a hundred of us, so that should last us a fortnight, even three weeks perhaps, if the meat can be kept fresh.'

'My cellar is ice-cold,' said the doctor. 'It is at your disposal.'

'And what if the emergency lasts longer than three weeks?' said the notary.

'Heavens above!' said the doctor. 'There is a mule in my stable, isn't there, and one in yours, and then there are the butcher's two horses.'

357

'You're not suggesting we should eat my horses, are you?' said the butcher, horrified.

'We want to survive,' said the doctor. 'And so do you want to survive. If we are driven to eat your horses, we'll buy you better ones when all this is over.'

Finally, on a tide of goodwill, each housewife in turn revealed what she had in stock. In those days, it was the custom to store as many provisions as the larder would hold, for supplies of food, even in large towns, were not always as readily available as they are today.

The grandmothers led the field with such a huge number of jars of jam that Young Garin suspected them of exaggerating (in which he was mistaken), and, between them, the housewives contributed thirty strings of sausages, several dozen hams, sacks of dried chestnuts, maize flour, chick peas, lentils and haricot beans, all in such vast quantities that Maître Pancrace rubbed his hands gleefully and declared:

'My dear friends, I believe that, with the exercise of a little restraint, we shall be able to hold out for at least four months. By then, the vegetables which we shall be planting in our gardens will have ripened, which will give us another month or two of respite, should that be necessary. In other words, we are saved!'

At this, the Captain stepped forward and said, in offended tones:

'And what of me? Am I not to be invited to make a contribution?'

'A man living alone,' said Pancrace, 'does not keep much in his store-cupboard.'

'But you've forgotten the most important thing,' said the Captain. 'I am in a position to provide the community with four casks of good wine, which is the equivalent of close on a thousand bottles, not to mention two kegs of rum, a small cask of cognac, and more than a hundred bottles of liqueurs of various sorts, such as Maraschino, Aguardiente, schnaps, Kirsch and brandy, than which there is no better medicine on earth!'

This pronouncement was received with murmured acclamations.

'And now,' said Maître Pancrace, 'I suggest that you go home and eat a hearty meal. But afterwards, you will do me the favour of coming here to see me, one by one, so that I can examine you, and make sure that there are no wolves in our fold. Goodbye for now.'

The passing bell could still be heard tolling in the distance, but everyone was already greatly heartened by the doctor's plan.

The assembled company was beginning to disperse when the voice of Maître Passacaille was heard again, calling to the Captain. The slave-trader hastened over to the ventilator.

'What's the matter? Are you feeling worse?'

'No,' said the notary loudly. 'I have the feeling that I'm on the road to recovery. But I fancy I should get well all the sooner, if you were to bring me one of those bottles you spoke of just now!'

'That's a good idea,' said the Captain, and he hastened away to his cellar.

That evening after dinner, Maître Pancrace began by examining the children. As they had all been confined to the little square for the past two weeks, this did not take very long. Next, it was the men's turn. Almost all of them had been into town at some time, so the doctor subjected them to a very thorough examination.

He made them strip naked, and lie down on the table, and he began by examining every inch of their skin. Next, he smelt their breath, examined their tongues and throats, took their pulses, then palpated their bellies, buttocks and groins, by the light of four flaming torches. Every time he said 'This one is all right,' old Aliette would approach, and give the man a friction rub with that wholesome preparation known as the Vinegar of the Four Thieves. The man would then jump down from the table, laughing with relief.

It was nearly midnight before the women had their turn, followed by the unmarried girls. Four housewives held the torches. It was noticed that Maître Pancrace took particular care in examining these patients, sometimes spending more than a minute in stroking the white flesh of some blushing damsel. Then, with his nose to the ground, so to speak, he would search minutely for any trace of abrasion or swelling; for it is a fact that the plague is a most insidious disease, which sometimes begins with barely perceptible symptoms. At long last, by about three o'clock in the morning, it was all over, and the doctor was able to announce with absolute certainty that their little community was free of the plague. This news was received with joyful shouts.

Garcin, however, pointed out that Maître Combarnoux and his family had not come to be examined, and that the choir master was still absent.

'I'm very worried about that young man,' said Pancrace. 'His continued absence is a bad sign. As to the cloth merchant, we'll see what tomorrow brings.'

Whereupon everyone went home to bed.

While Maître Pancrace was getting undressed, he fancied he heard a kind of lamentation coming from the cellars. He felt ashamed of himself for having omitted to enquire after Maître Passacaille, who was perhaps writhing in agony on a pile of logs. He listened anxiously. Yes, that was the notary's voice all right, though it was not raised in lamentation, but in song.

> O bergère vola-age
> Dis-moi le secret de ton coeur,
> Je veux dans ton corsa-age
> Trouver le chemin du bonheur. . .*

At six o'clock the following morning, old Aliette came in to wake him, which was no easy task.

'Master,' she said, 'the cloth merchant is going out!'

Pancrace leapt out of bed, hastened to the window in his nightshirt, and flung it wide open.

Maître Combarnoux was engaged in adjusting the harness of his horse, which was between the shafts of a pretty little governess cart.

His wife was already seated in the front, and his five daughters installed on dainty blue cushions on the platform behind her.

'Maître Combarnoux,' said Pancrace, 'I had hoped that the night would have brought you better counsel.'

'On the contrary,' said the cloth merchant, 'it has strengthened me in my resolve to ignore the plague, and to submit myself humbly to the will of God, making no changes whatsoever in my daily routine.'

* Oh! fickle shepherdess,/Tell me the secret of your heart./I seek the road to happiness/In the bodice of your dress.

'In that case, since you intend to visit your brother at Saint-Barnabé, I think you would do well to remain there.'

'Why should I?' said the cloth merchant angrily.

'Because, in the interests of our own safety, we shall be compelled to take measures against you and your family which will be unpleasant for you.'

'I'd like to see you try!' said the cloth merchant, with a self-satisfied snigger.

'You will,' said Maître Pancrace. 'This very evening, if I'm not mistaken!'

Whereupon he shut the window, to the sound of the cloth merchant cracking his whip.

Pancrace devoted the whole morning to the completion of his preparations. First, he instructed the men to make breaches in their garden walls, to allow free access from one to another. While this was being done, he went from cellar to cellar, in company with the Captain, making a very careful inventory, in an old ship's register, of the amounts and types of food available. Finally, he had brought down from the attics a quantity of old palliasses, which he caused to be impregnated with dung and rabbits' blood. These were laid in the street, as if they had been thrown out of the windows . . . In the course of the afternoon, all shutters were closed, and all doors barred.

Then Pancrace went to the cellar where the notary, whom they had rather forgotten in the past few hours, was immured, and crouched down close to the ventilator.

To his great alarm, he heard what he took to be a death-rattle.

'Poor fellow!' he said.

All the same, he called out to him. At the third attempt, the 'rattle' ceased, to be replaced by a sort of quavering groan. Peering down, Pancrace saw the notary seated on a palliasse, with arms outstretched, yawning. Then he rubbed his eyes, and asked in surprise:

'Where am I?'

'In your cellar,' said Pancrace. 'How are you feeling?'

'I've got a thick head, and a foul taste in my mouth!' said the notary. 'And there's a terrible smell of rum in here. I can't think where it comes from!'

All day, the little community worked like bees in a hive. The

361

children played in the gardens under the supervision of their grandmothers. They had been told that there was a great big, wicked wolf in the neighbourhood, which would harm no one so long as it was left to sleep, but which any loud noise would bring running. Accordingly, the children played in silence, and when, from time to time, a burst of laughter escaped them, they would all take to their heels, and crowd in terror into the stables.

At dusk, a conference was held, to decide what was to be done with the cloth merchant on his return.

'He mustn't be allowed in,' said Young Garin. 'I have already put up the bar on his front door. Since he is determined to die of the plague, let him die somewhere else.'

'He won't take it lying down,' said the doctor. 'He's certain to go and complain to the authorities. And, if you want my opinion, we should do well to avoid drawing attention to ourselves. Better that we should be thought to have died or fled . . .'

'Well, then,' said Bignon, 'what do you suggest we do?'

'There are seven of them,' said the notary. 'We can't kill them all!'

'There's no question of killing anyone,' said Pancrace.

'Not yet!' said the Captain. 'But remember that the Black Plague means certain death for the victim, and possible death for his neighbours. For my part, I believe that, to save his life, a man has the right to kill someone who is dying anyway.'

'That's a reasonable point of view,' said Maître Pancrace. 'But Maître Combarnoux has not yet contracted the plague, not as far as I know, at least. If he comes back tonight, we'll try to reason with him, in the first instance. But if he persists in endeavouring to bring the infection among us, we shall lock him up in Garin's cellar, which is under the middle stable, with a ventilator opening on to the stable. If he attempts to cry out, we shall gag him. And besides, I'm convinced he won't put up much of a fight, because it will be a relief to him to be made safe by force, having done all he could to fulfil his pious duties, and having thus committed no sin.'

'I'll go and find a good heavy sack to put over his head,' said the Captain, 'and some rope to tie him up with.'

'And I'll go and clear out my cellar,' said Garin, 'because he's such a fanatic that I'm sure . . .'

But before he had time to complete his sentence, old Aliette suddenly burst in, saying:

'Maître Combarnoux is back! I saw him through the kitchen window!'

Maître Pancrace ran upstairs to the first floor of his house, followed by Garin, the notary and the Captain.

Stealthily, Pancrace opened a shutter.

The cloth merchant's pony trap was just drawing up outside his front door, a little to the left. There was no one on the front seat, but on the platform at the back the cloth merchant's wife and four daughters were lying together in a heap. Their faces were black and red and hideously inflamed. The mother was still holding in her arms the youngest child, who looked like a doll daubed with tar.

Maître Combarnoux was sitting bent double on the three steps leading to his front door. He was moaning loudly. Suddenly, he dropped on to his knees, and his hard blue felt hat fell on the pavement.

He made one more tremendous effort to insert the big, gleaming key into the lock of his front door, but his hand fell limply to his side, and the key dropped with a ringing sound on to the paving stones.

'Help! Help!' he moaned. 'Let me in!'

'Maître Combarnoux,' said Pancrace, in a somewhat tremulous voice, 'we can't let you in now.'

'For God's sake,' said the poor man, 'let me in, and take care of me.'

'For humanity's sake,' said Maître Pancrace, 'I beg you not to attempt to force your way in. Everyone here is in good health, every man, woman and child. You brought this calamity upon yourself, and I cannot permit you to infect others.'

The cloth merchant sighed deeply, and moaned:

'God has forsaken me!'

'You can't believe that,' said the Captain, 'since, at this very moment, He is gathering you to Himself.'

'My wife and children are dead.'

'Because He didn't want to separate you!' said the notary.

'At least, give me something to drink,' said the cloth merchant, with a heartrending cry.

'I'll lower a cordial to you,' said Pancrace, 'but I can't pretend that it will do any good.'

'I know,' murmured the cloth merchant. 'All the same, it's a terrible thing that a man of my standing should be left to suffer in the street.'

'Better perhaps than to die indoors,' said the Captain. 'With no ceiling between you and the sky, your soul will go straight to heaven!'

As he was speaking, Young Garin lowered a mug of chilled white wine on a piece of string. With a tremendous effort, the dying man crawled along the pavement on his stomach, and at last was able to grasp the mug in his trembling hands. After a further struggle, he raised it to his lips, but, retching horribly, he vomited up the first mouthful, followed by a stream of black blood.

'Maître Combarnoux,' said Pancrace, 'there is still a little life left in you . . . Make the effort, if you can, to heave yourself up my front steps, and sit with your back to the door.'

'What good will that do?' gasped the dying man.

'It would be an act of generosity,' said Pancrace, 'the last of your life, for the sight of your corpse would scare off any marauders who might come here to attack us. And thus you would be saving the lives of thirty little children, all of whom are well known to you. . .'

At this, the fat, churlish cloth merchant, retching in agony, and vomiting clotted blood at every movement, crawled up the steps, and then lay still.

'It's over. He's dead,' said the Captain.

But, in spite of the agony of his rotting body, the cloth merchant had merely paused to put all his strength into one last endeavour. And suddenly, with a supreme effort, he managed to turn round and, in four hideous spasms, he heaved his back against the door, and, for the last time, joined his hands in prayer.

Aliette, who was looking over her master's shoulder, suddenly cried out: 'Do you see the Angel? Look at the Angel!'

Neither Pancrace nor the Captain could see any angel, but as they watched in stunned amazement, the poor, black, swollen face broke into a radiant and joyful smile.

As soon as it was dark, Maître Pancrace began preparing

Young Garin and the butcher for the grisly task ahead of them. He made each of them put on three shirts, and cover them with overalls down to their feet. He then gave them linen gloves, and hoods which hung down to their chests. Finally, he sprayed them all over with the Vinegar of the Four Thieves. Then, equipped with two billhooks, such as are used to haul logs, they went out into the street.

The horse, still harnessed to the funereal trap, had crossed the street, and was leaning against the trunk of a plane tree, asleep on its feet, without a care in the world.

The two men led it back to Pancrace's front door, and, using their billhooks, they dislodged the five corpses from the platform, and grouped them artistically round the dead cloth merchant, whose jaw had by now dropped, and whose chin was resting hideously on a lace jabot steeped in blood.

In its self-imposed isolation, the little community observed an almost military discipline. The passing bell, which had replaced the Angelus, awakened them at first light, and the day began with a medical inspection. The doctor, installed beneath the notary's fig tree, examined all the members of the little colony, one by one. Any sign of fever, however slight, was considered suspect, any swelling, even if it were only a pimple, was regarded as a possible bubonic tumour. The sufferer was immediately placed in isolation in a freshly painted cellar, dowsed with vinegar like a pickled cucumber, and not allowed to emerge until three days had passed.

When the inspection was over, the women did the housework in total silence.

The small children played in the gardens under the supervision of the older girls, and the notary, seated under the fig tree, gave instruction to the older boys in undertones, assisted by the Captain, who held classes in geography. Meanwhile, Young Garin, to keep himself occupied, designed a new type of musket, the butcher pickled his meat, in order to preserve it longer, the grocer sawed his wooden pumpkins in half, and the baker kneaded his dough. He baked only every third or fourth day, always waiting till after midnight before lighting his oven, and then only if there was a breeze to blow away the smoke, which might otherwise have betrayed their presence.

Those who had nothing else to do cultivated their gardens, taking care to draw their water direct from the well by lowering hand buckets, to avoid the grating sound inevitable when winding a winch. Soon, the chick peas were brought out, then the lentils, then the haricot beans, and Maître Pancrace rubbed his hands in glee.

The doctor had converted his spacious stable into a communal refectory, and the whole community assembled there for the midday meal.

Then, after the siesta, which lasted until five o'clock, the women would sew and knit, and the men would play cards, draughts or chess, while the old grannies amused the children with bedtime stories.

At the same time, up in Maître Pancrace's attic—his house being taller than all the rest—there was always a man on watch at the skylight, to report on events in the docks and the town. He was relieved every two hours, and always made his report to the doctor on coming off duty.

At first, the watchers reported endless convoys of wagons, and people running or walking alongside. The Captain, looking at them through his spy-glass, recognized these men as galley-slaves freed from their chains. Each of them carried on his shoulder a long pole with an iron hook on the end.

Not a single ship now came into the harbour, though many were seen to leave. As time went on, there were fewer funeral processions, and the streets appeared deserted. No one now came to the little square, although, earlier on, there had been two or three potentially dangerous moments.

Every now and then, a starving man, armed with a pike, sometimes even with a pistol in his hand, would come sneaking into the square, in search of food or loot. He would get as far as the doctor's house, then freeze with horror and turn tail, and run away as fast as his legs could carry him. That good soul, the cloth merchant, black as a negro, his face crawling with worms, in the midst of his mummified family, was keeping faithful guard over the community.

Things went on in this way for almost a month, but, safe though they were, the morale of the people was declining day by day. The mournful tolling of the passing bell assailed their ears from dawn to sunset, and the need to converse in undertones gave them a feeling of guilt. The children, oppressed by the silence, lost their appetites, and their mothers grieved. The old people, who so feared death, were the first to show signs of dementia.

Mamette Pigeon, who was over eighty-five years old, disappeared one day. She was found hiding under a bed, and could not be induced to come out. When an attempt was made to drag her out, her screams were so terrible that it had to be abandoned, and her daughter was obliged to bring her food to her twice a day in this ludicrous hiding-place, where she lived flat on her stomach, wallowing in her own excrement.

Romuald's old father, who had always seemed so sensible, one day took to walking on all fours, and barking from time to time. He explained to Maître Pancrace that animals were never afflicted with the plague, and that, to avoid it, everyone had only to follow his example. Pancrace, judging him incurable, pretended to agree with him, only asking him to bark a little less loudly, which the old man willingly agreed to do.

Furthermore, boredom and fear were beginning to take their toll of the moral standards of these good people. Adultery was becoming rife, although this did not seem to cause anyone much anxiety, with the exception of Romuald, the butcher. He was furious at being cuckolded, but Pancrace consoled him so effectively with the noblest philosophic sentiments that, having made a present of his wife to the baker, he proceeded to set up house with the grocer's little servant girl. This pleased her greatly, for she had begun to fear, ever since the outbreak of the plague, that she was destined to die a virgin. These signs of moral decline greatly saddened the high-minded notary, the more so since he himself had fallen victim, having caught himself out one night *in flagrante delicto* with the fishmonger's wife, who, though neither young nor beautiful, was available and enterprising.

Maître Pancrace consoled him, explaining that fear of death always tended to stimulate the reproductive instincts, as if those who believed themselves to be about to die felt that, by striving to reproduce themselves, they could triumph over death.

On the evening of the fortieth day, when everyone was out taking the air in their gardens before dinner, headlong footsteps were heard on the stairs, and the watcher appeared in the doorway, his face alight with joy. It was Bignon's son.

'Victory!' he cried. 'The plague is over!'

All those assembled scrambled to their feet.

'How do you know?' said Maître Pancrace.

'They're celebrating by lighting bonfires!' said Bignon's son. 'The biggest is in the Vieux-Port, and I could see shadowy figures dancing round it!'

Several of the women broke into a dance, and began shouting with joy.

'Silence!' said Pancrace. 'Don't be too ready to rejoice. First we'll have to see for ourselves what it's all about!'

He hurried upstairs, to find that the Captain had already preceded him.

The Captain was no longer in the attic, but seeing that the skylight was wide open, Pancrace climbed nimbly up the ladder until his head was above the rooftops, on a level with the Captain's boots.

The town was spread out before him like a great black stain, but, here and there, he saw glowing patches of red, like the embers of a charcoal fire. Closer at hand, above the Vieux-Port, plumes of flame were dancing.

The Captain had extended his spy-glass, and was adjusting the focus. Maître Pancrace tapped him on the boot:

'What do you see?'

'I see a huge fire,' said the Captain. 'And, in front of the fire, shadows which, in their turn, are casting shadows on the flames.'

'I thought so,' said Pancrace. 'Those are funeral pyres. They are burning the bodies, because they no longer have time to bury them.'

Looking thoughtful, they began going downstairs, to find most of the men waiting for them on the steps.

Next morning, at first light, they heard knocking at Madame Nicole's front door. A discreet tapping at first, then louder knocking, breaking at last into ferocious hammering. Many jumped out of their beds and ran to their shuttered windows, though none ventured to open them. They peered through the slats, trying to see what was afoot. As they were doing so, they heard a voice shouting:

'Let me in! It's me! It's Norbert.'

They recognized the voice of the choir master, whom they had given up for dead.

But the only reply was a deathly silence.

Then he started to yell:

'I know you're there, hidden behind the shutters! Open up, or I'll break down the door!'

Maître Pancrace cautiously opened a window just above the distraught man's head.

'For God's sake!' he said. 'Stop shouting and making all that racket!'

'For God's sake', retorted the choir master, 'let me come in and get my things, or else throw them out to me through the window! I am leaving town, and I advise you to do the same, because, three days from now, they'll be coming in to burn down this whole area!'

'What are you saying?' cried Pancrace, who had turned as white as a turnip.

'Let me in, and I'll tell you everything,' replied the choir master. 'And it may be the saving of your lives.'

'So you came here with the best intentions,' said Pancrace. 'All the same, you have certainly brought the plague into our midst!'

'As for the plague, I have had it, and, by some miracle, I have survived. You know that it's impossible to get it twice!'

'If that is so, you will not get it again; but your clothes are no doubt infested with extremely pervasive germs, which will spread the infection among all your friends.'

'No doubt that's true,' said the choir master, 'because for the past two months, on the grounds that I was no longer at risk, I have been forced to collect hundreds of bodies which had been left rotting in the streets. So what do you want me to do?'

'For a start,' said the doctor, 'you must strip to the skin, and throw every stitch of your clothing over the ramparts. Next, I shall send you down some soap, and you must wash yourself from head to foot, especially your hair. When you have done that, I shall lower a big bottle of vinegar, which you will use to give yourself a friction rub lasting a full hour. You will also soak your toenails and fingernails in it. Finally, I will throw out a parcel of clean clothes for you to wear, after which you will be able to come in without the slightest risk to anyone.'

'So be it,' said the choir master.

And he began to undress.

It took him the best part of an hour to carry out these instructions, and while he was doing so, many of the women and girls crowded round to peer at him through the closed shutters, for he was a good-looking enough young man, and his naturally graceful figure had been fined down and much improved by the plague.

Standing beside the fountain in the deserted square, he scoured himself thoroughly from head to foot. When he was ready, Pancrace, holding a linen pad steeped in vinegar to his own nose, opened a door for him, and led him away to his study.

They talked for over an hour, while the other men waited in their gardens in total silence. They paced to and fro, with their hands in their pockets and their heads bowed. The women stood together in little knots, talking in whispers. Some were gathered round old Aliette, who was listening at the door of the doctor's study. She could hear nothing but a meaningless murmur of voices, but when Pancrace opened the door, he tripped over her, knocking her down, and exclaimed, 'A plague on the woman! Can't she mind her own business!' Whereupon she fled in horror, scarcely daring to breathe.

In silence, the two men walked into the middle of the big garden, and the choir master climbed up on to the cover of the well. Pancrace and the notary sat on the rim, and everyone else gathered round in a semi-circle. Then the choir master spoke to them:

'My friends,' he said. 'It is with great sorrow that I have to tell you that Maître Pancrace was right, and this town is beyond saving. Thanks to the Captain's spy-glass, you have some idea of what has been happening, I know. But that is only a tiny glimpse, one might almost call it a rosy picture, of the true situation. The fact is that they are throwing the corpses out of the windows, and the streets are littered with them. Everyone able to get away has fled into the countryside, but there are still a great many people left, although their numbers are decreasing by twenty a day, or more. The dead are no longer being buried, but burnt. Still, it is impossible to burn them all, in spite of the labours of over a hundred galley-slaves, and even they have to be almost entirely replaced by others every week, for their hard life has not inured them to this loathsome disease.

'You may be safe from it here, but not for very much longer.'

'Why not?' demanded the notary shortly.

'Because the authorities have decided to burn down the houses of the plague victims, whole districts, in some cases. The day before yesterday, they burnt La Tourette. Yesterday, they destroyed more than thirty houses in the Place de Lenche, and I'm told that today they're going to concentrate on the Plaine Saint-Michel, where the disease has wrought the most ghastly havoc!'

'That's almost next door to us!' said the Captain.

'Just so,' said the choir master. 'And what's more, there's been talk about our own little square. According to a police report, you are all said to be dead, and I fancy that, in two or three day's time, they'll be rolling up here, armed with firewood and torches.'

'In that event,' said the notary, 'we have only to show ourselves, and they won't burn anything.'

'That's true,' said the choir master. 'They wouldn't be so cruel as to burn healthy people. But, for a start, they'll steal all your stores, because food is so scarce that the town is on the verge of famine, and the authorities are confiscating all reserves. Next, they will compel the men to work alongside the galley-slaves, to bury the thousands of rotting corpses. You'll be supplied with a crook, a hood and gloves, and, just to cheer you up, you'll be called "crows". Admittedly, you won't have to worry after the first week, because by then you too will be a swollen, rotten corpse, with stray dogs fighting over your remains. That's the fate in store for you, if you should be foolish enough to remain here.'

Even before he had finished speaking, the women broke into weeping, and put their arms protectively around their children. The men stood motionless, helpless as blocks of stone, and the old people stared at one another in bewilderment.

The Captain was the first to break the silence.

'This young fellow is right,' he said. 'There's nothing for it but to clear out.'

'That's what we should have done, right at the start,' said the notary. 'I could have retired to my little place in Aix . . .'

'The plague has reached there already,' said the choir master. 'All the schools, law courts and churches have had to be closed.'

371

'In that case,' said the Captain, 'there's only one thing to be done: find a boat, and make for Corsica.'

'My dear Captain,' said Pancrace, 'that certainly would be the ideal solution. But where will you find a boat?'

The Captain shrugged, shook his head, and fell silent. Young Garin, the baker and the butcher each put forward impractical proposals, as people will do when the situation is desperate.

Maître Pancrace, whose self-possession never deserted him, reflected.

'The simplest thing,' he said, 'would be for us to go up into the hills. We could make for Allauch to begin with . . . I have a relation there . . . If the plague has already reached there, we could push on further . . . The likelihood, I must confess, is that the villages have already been contaminated . . . That leaves the hills. We might be able to shelter in some cave, or on the slope of a lonely ravine, where no one would think of looking for us.'

'But what shall we do for food?' said the choirmaster.

'We still have ample stocks in reserve . . . And, what's more, we have four horses and two mules.'

'The poor brutes are dreadfully thin,' said the butcher.

'There's no question of eating them for the present, but of harnessing them to our carts and carriages, to transport our provisions. We'll give them all the hay we have left, and our last remaining sack of oats. We'll spend the day loading up, and set out at midnight.'

'Hold on!' said the choir master. 'Do you really imagine it's as simple as all that? For one thing, as soon as your loaded wagons are spotted, you'll be attacked by the gangs of armed men who are scouring the town in search of whatever food they can find, and looting the cellars of the plague victims.'

'At midnight?' said the notary.

'Especially at night,' said the choir master.

'We have twenty-three guns,' said Maître Garin, 'thirty pistols, and more than a hundred pounds of gunpowder.'

'One shot will be enough to bring other gangs of looters rushing to join them. And besides, there are guards posted at every exit from the town, to prevent the plague from spreading all over the country.'

'What's to be done, then?' exclaimed the grocer, his face contorted with fear.

'We'll have to leave here one by one,' said the choir master, 'carrying as much food as can be concealed about our persons—and then it's every man for himself.'

'And what about the women?' said Pancrace.

'And the children?' said Maître Passacaille furiously. 'Are you suggesting that we should abandon the children?'

The women began to protest. The choirmaster spread out his arms, closed his eyes and shrugged, but said no more.

There followed a very long silence, which was broken at last by Maître Pancrace, who said:

'Come with me to my study.'

He led the way, followed by the notary, the choir master, the armourer and the Captain.

As soon as they had gone, the women started to say that the choir master would do anything to draw attention to himself. They were sure that he had never had the plague, but had very likely spent the past two months with some former mistress, who had ended up by showing him the door. They said that he had always been a great one for practical jokes, and that anyway he was not to be trusted. In conclusion, several of them declared that there was no need to take flight, and that the sensible course would be to stay put, as they had done hitherto.

The men were just beginning to come round to their point of view, when Pampette, the fishmonger, who had been on watch in the attic, appeared in the doorway.

'There's a huge fire raging in the Plaine Saint-Michel district,' he said.

Everyone was shaken, for this was what the choir master had predicted. The women began weeping again, and the men were on the point of going to fetch Maître Pancrace, when the doctor appeared in the doorway.

Pampette reported what he had seen.

'Our friend warned us of this,' said Pancrace, 'and there can no longer be any doubt of the fate in store for us. But all is not lost. Listen carefully to what I have to say, and obey my instructions without further argument. You can trust me implicitly. First, we shall load our stores on to the wagons, and cover them with tarpaulins. On top of the tarpaulins men, women and children will lie, half-naked, in the guise of dead plague victims.

I myself shall make them up to look realistically horrifying. Others among us, wearing hoods, will carry torches, ring warning hand-bells, and chant the *Miserere*. I am quite certain that our procession, far from attracting the gangs of looters, will put them to flight. As for the soldiers on guard at the barriers, I have no fear of them, and I give you my word that, if you do exactly as I say, they will let us through without any difficulty.

'The wagons must be loaded without further delay—and I warn the women, here and now, that there will be no room for family heirlooms, or childhood treasures, or any other knick-knacks that they feel they can't possibly do without. I myself shall be supervising the loading, and I will accept nothing that is not absolutely essential. Go to it!'

The preparations for departure lasted the whole day. They greased the wheels, tended the animals, loaded the wagons with sacks of food, barrels of wine, guns, gunpowder, shot and cloth.

Then Maître Pancrace gave orders that the unfortunate cloth merchant's cellars were to be broken into.

'At this time,' he said, 'he has no further use for his stocks, but they will be a great help to us.'

Next, he converted his own dining-room into a big garment factory, where some fifteen of the most skilful needlewomen were put to work. They began by making at least twenty black hoods, then the same number of long overalls, and as many pairs of mittens, that is, gloves without fingers. Finally, working from an engraving supplied by Maître Pancrace, and under the supervision of the notary, they made four military uniforms, or at least an approximation, to fit Young Garin, Bignon, Pampette and the baker, and a cassock for the choir master.

During this time, Pancrace had absented himself. An hour later, he reappeared in such an unfamiliar guise that the women shrieked, and even Maître Passacaille himself was thunderstruck.

And indeed, the man who stood before them was magnificently attired in the full dress uniform of an army officer. In his blue tunic, white doeskin trousers, red leather boots with silver spurs, sword with carved gold hilt, cloak lined with cloth of gold and trimmed with ermine, he presented such a splendid figure that the needlewomen, who had risen to their feet, lacked the courage to sit down again.

'Is it really you?' asked the notary.

'Alas! no,' said Maître Pancrace. 'And yet it is the man I once was.'

'But that's the uniform of a Captain of the Royal Guard!'

'Yes,' said Maître Pancrace, 'but with one small difference. The collar of my tunic is of yellow velvet, to indicate that I was Surgeon-in-Chief to that illustrious Company, with the rank of Captain.'

There was a murmur of admiration, and the doctor added in quiet tones:

'I even had the honour, during the campaign in Holland,' here he swept off his plumed hat, 'of attending His August Majesty the King himself.'

A little tear glittered in the corner of his eye, and the notary, in his turn, bared his head.

'His Majesty', said the doctor, with emotion, 'was troubled by severe attacks of wind, so violent that they frightened his horse. I succeeded in curing him, and from that day until his much-lamented death, I remained attached to His August Person.'

There was a moment's silence, then Pancrace, in a very different tone of voice, said brusquely:

'I'd be obliged if you would go back to your work, and don't forget the two silver stripes on the Captain's pea-jacket, to indicate his proper rank. . .'

After a hurried lunch, work was resumed in great haste, for already, close at hand, the sky was filled with billowing plumes of smoke, and a light film of ash was beginning to whiten the garden lawns. There was still no immediate danger, but the smell of burning was enough to underline the urgency of flight.

Meanwhile, Pancrace and Maître Passacaille had retired to the notary's study, where they had so often forgathered for a game of chess.

But, on this occasion, they did not touch the little towers mounted on ivory elephants.

Maître Passacaille began, with great care, to trim two goose quills into pens. Then he added a pinch of purified soot to his ink. Finally, he tore from a ledger a handsome sheet of engrossing paper, and proceeded to copy, in his fine, firm script, a few lines drafted by Maître Pancrace. The result was a correctly-worded *laissez-passer*, addressed to the Captain of the Guard at the barrier of La Rose.

He dried the ink with a pinch of powdered gold, which he caused to roll from one end of the paper to the other.

Finally, he extracted from one of his files a bill of sale signed sometime before, in his presence, by the magistrate, Moustier, and copied the signature with such astonishing ease and accuracy that Pancrace exclaimed:

'It's amazing! Anyone would think you had been doing it every day of your life!'

'No,' said the notary modestly. 'Not every day. But every craft has its own particular skills . . .'

Such a master was he of the skills of his craft, that he was able to produce a fine lead seal engraved with the arms of the City of Marseilles, which he proceeded to impress at the bottom of the page, on a blob of red sealing-wax, to which was attached a strip of blue ribbon.

Then, having closely examined his work, he rubbed his hands together briskly, and declared:

'This has come out particularly well. Even Monsieur the Magistrate Moustier would not dare to take his oath on its being a forgery . . .'

He rolled up the precious document, tied it with a blue ribbon, wider than the first, and handed it to Pancrace.

'And now,' said the latter, 'let us apply our minds to the creation of fake plague victims. We shall certainly enjoy that.'

They repaired to his study where, following his instructions, the choir master and the grocer had compounded a variety of preparations in at least a dozen saucers. There were burnt cork, glue, jam, honey, wax, powdered saffron, plaster, soot, tow and coloured pastes of all sorts.

Using these ingredients, Maître Pancrace with great artistry made up some forty faces and bodies, thus proving that, although he might not be able to cure bubonic swellings, he could certainly manufacture them splendidly. In fact, he succeeded so well that his unfortunate victims quite terrified one another, so much so that when the first two appeared in the garden, several women fainted, and Papet, still on all fours, barked plaintively.

When they had completed their work on the plague victims,

they turned their attention to the mourners. They dressed them in their overalls, hoods and gloves, and provided them with bells wrenched from the front doors of the houses. Finally, they spent several minutes lighting torches fashioned from the resinous branches of the garden pines.

Night fell, with a red glow in the sky over the Plaine Saint-Michel. In silence, the fugitives ate their last meal in the big stable, with everything securely closed, to shut out the acrid smoke which now lay in a heavy pall over the gardens.

Those disguised as plague victims were far from comfortable, their facial skin smarting under its dried coating, and their boils falling into their soup every time they moved their jaws.

The meal was soon over. Many of the woman wept at the prospect of leaving their homes and furniture. Left to themselves they would have taken everything with them, and the doctor, supervising the loading of the wagons, had had to reject a cat, two huge ancestral portraits, and five dolls, the property of an old crone who had never had any children of her own. Seeing that she was wailing at the top of her voice, Pancrace comforted her with a few kind words and a slap on the face.

After dinner, they could hear the roar of the fire, though it was still some way off. Maître Pancrace, with perfect composure, set about completing the staging of the show.

The wagons were lined up outside the carriage gateway, and the plague victims climbed on to the tarpaulins. Pancrace, disregarding considerations of modesty, insisted that one or two should be completely naked. Then he posed his actors, with suitably blackened legs, and bleeding arms daubed with lumpy jam, dangling over the skirting boards of the wagons. To some, he gave swollen faces, by stuffing their cheeks with bread. Then, in the middle of every boil, he painted a big red spot, ringed with black. Finally, he stuffed their nostrils with pulped black olives, which trickled realistically on to their upper lips.

When the hoods had all been steeped in vinegar, and the torches lit, they silently opened the double carriage doors.

Then Pancrace, in his magnificent uniform, got into his little chaise—Guillou had been holding the reins—at the head of the procession, and they set off without making a sound.

Marching two paces behind him was the braided Captain,

with his spy-glass slung over his shoulder. Next came four soldiers, shouldering their muskets. Finally, a priest, who was none other than the choir master, walking with an open book in his hand, preceded the wagons, which rolled slowly over the cobbles, flanked on either side by mourners bearing torches.

Seeing that there was no one abroad, the procession at first moved on in silence, until it came to the boulevard which represented the road to freedom, but, just as they reached it, Maître Pancrace turned round and raised his arm, whereupon the handbells rang out mournfully, and muffled chanting rose from under the hoods.

The choir master had spoken the truth. The town seemed deserted, and the street lamps had not been lit. But, by the light of their torches, they were soon able to see corpses stretched out on the pavement and in the gutter, or bent double in unnatural postures under the porches of the houses. They also, from time to time, glimpsed looters, but these shadowy figures would quickly disappear into the night, at the approach of the funereal procession.

They proceeded in this manner for more than an hour, down the long avenue, bordered with plane trees, their wagons shuddering over the uneven cobblestones.

As the town seemed deserted, except for those who fled at the very sight of them, their initial anxiety was transformed into a feeling of security, and the bogus plague victims on the wagons began exchanging pleasantries in undertones, and tickling the younger children, to such good effect that their joyful peals of laughter were subdued only with the greatest difficulty.

When they reached Château Gombert, where Pancrace was expecting to find guards posted, he sent the Captain back to restore order in the convoy, and reduce the corpses to silence.

This was just as well, because, round the next corner, he saw four lighted lanterns, and the gleaming window of a little wooden hut.

Two soldiers stepped forward, with guns at the ready.

'Halt!'

Pancrace halted, and turning round to face the convoy, repeated the order:

'Halt!'

Then, going up to the soldiers, he barked:

'Where's the officer in charge?'

'He's asleep,' said the soldier. 'And we don't need him to stop you. No one is allowed through this barrier, on pain of death.'

'Asleep!' exclaimed Pancrace furiously. 'With the town in torment, and the whole of France under threat of death, he's asleep?'

The soldiers, taken by surprise, could find nothing to say, but one of them raised his lantern, and advanced towards the doctor. For the first time, he took in the details of the glittering uniform, even more splendid by lamplight, and turning to the two others, he cried:

'Present arms!'

Which they promptly did.

'If he's asleep!' cried Pancrace, 'we shall have to wake him! Take me to him.'

But there was no need for them to go into the hut, for the sleeper, awakened by the shouted orders, was coming towards them, hurriedly buttoning his tunic, and with him another man carrying a lantern.

As soon as he saw Pancrace, he stood to attention, as was only fitting. Noting that the officer wore only one gold stripe, Pancrace assumed a very lofty tone:

'Lieutenant,' he said, 'I am displeased to observe that a man with your heavy responsibilities should take refuge in sleep!'

'Sir,' replied the officer, looking uncomfortable, 'I have been on duty for the past four days, and the human body has its limitations. And besides, if I do occasionally take a short nap, the ensign is here to relieve me.'

And he pointed to a figure, which stepped forward out of the shadows.

'Well, ensign,' said Pancrace severely, 'where were you, then?'

'Sir,' replied the ensign, 'the human body not only has its limitations, it also has its needs.'

At this, Pancrace smiled and said:

'A good answer!'

Then, adopting a more informal tone, he said:

'Gentlemen, come with me. I have something to say to you, which I would prefer your men not to hear.'

379

Whereupon he strode purposefully into the hut, and carefully shut the door. The hut was sparsely furnished with a camp bed and a deal table, on which flickered a single candle.

'Gentlemen,' he said, 'the mission with which I have been entrusted must be kept secret, to avoid spreading panic among the population. The plague which is devastating Marseilles is still the mildest form of the disease. But a medical report has just reached us, to the effect that there have been a hundred cases of the BLACK DEATH. Now, if this form of the disease were allowed to spread further, it would mean the end not only of our town, but perhaps of the whole nation. I have been instructed, with the help of those hooded galley-slaves out there, to bury those frightful corpses, by throwing them down a disused coal mine, which is to be found near Allauch.'

'Why were they not burnt?' asked the ensign.

'Because, according to medical opinion, before they were reduced to ashes they would give off sufficient poisonous gases to contaminate the entire town.'

He then took from his tunic a roll of paper, which he spread out carefully on the table.

'Here are the orders,' he said. 'I will leave them with you, since they are addressed to you by the Commandant, whose control of the situation is truly remarkable, and who happens to be a close personal friend of mine.'

The candle shone on the stamps, the seals, the signatures, and on Maître Passacaille's elegant, legal script.

As the two officers were gazing respectfully at the *laissez-passer*, Maître Pancrace added:

'I have only one fear, that my dear friend Andrault Langeron, our Chief Magistrate, whose devotion to duty drives him into the very hospitals, may himself fall victim to the disease. It would be a grievous loss to our city, and, indeed, to the whole realm.'

He went out, and the lieutenant hastened to raise the barrier, calling out to his men:

'Keep away from those wagons, if you value your lives.'

The procession moved off, watched by the two officers.

'Permit me to say,' said the Lieutenant, 'that I regret to see an officer of your standing exposed to such grave risks.'

'It's good of you to say so,' said Pancrace. 'But in such a crisis as this, everyone has to take risks.'

He offered them a pinch of snuff, and then climbed back into his chaise, whereupon six of the soldiers presented arms, and the officers drew their swords as a mark of respect.

He saluted the officers with a flourish, and the procession moved off into the night, leaving the soldiers, in terror of the Black Death, to crowd round the vinegar barrel.

As soon as they were out of sight of the soldiers, Pancrace silenced the bells and the chanting, and then ordered the torches to be extinguished. The deserted road was adequately lit by the stars. Finally, he urged the procession to move faster, fearing that the officers might have second thoughts about the genuineness of the *laissez-passer*, and come in pursuit of them.

They walked on in this way for two hours, before the sun rose, and they could be assured of the success of their expedition.

Beside the road, to their right, lay a great forest of pines and oaks. At the first foresters' footpath they came to, Pancrace urged his horse into the forest, and the entire procession followed him into the cover of the trees.

Before long, they came to a spacious clearing, carpeted in tough grass, and ablaze with poppies.

Pancrace reined in his horse, dismounted, and cried 'Halt!'

Soon the mourners were stripping off their gloves and hoods, the plague victims jumping down from the wagons, and the women rolling back the tarpaulins. They were all laughing with joy, like children, and pelting one another with their boils, and the horses, in spite of their bridles, were greedily cropping the grass.

Suddenly, they heard someone calling. It was the little haberdasher, who had wandered off into the trees, and found a pond. And they all made haste to wash in it.

Seated on a big stone, Maître Pancrace stretched out his legs to Guillou, who pulled off his boots, and massaged his aching toes. Meanwhile, old Aliette laid out her master's usual clothes.

The notary and Garin were sitting on the grass close by.

'My friends,' said Pancrace, 'the first half of our adventure has been a success. Nevertheless, there is a serious risk that those friendly young officers will be disabused by the first inspector to visit the post, which is why I am changing out of this all-too-conspicuous uniform. Those of you who are dressed as soldiers should do likewise without delay, and then we'll stuff all this tell-tale fancy dress into a sack and hide it. We are now only about half a league from Allauch. If you look through the trees, you will see a group of windmills at the top of the hill. Their presence tells us that the *mistral* blows steadily in these parts. The prosperity of this little market town depends upon it . . . and its health too. I am convinced that the plague has not reached here, and that it never will. We shall, therefore, appeal to its inhabitants for asylum.'

'I am very much afraid,' said the notary, 'that they will refuse to take us in.'

'But if we were to propose spending a period of quarantine in the forest,' said the Captain, 'they would have nothing to fear from us.'

'And besides,' said Pancrace, 'I have a great friend up there, who is a miller. His name is Léonard Gondran, and he is my foster brother. I fancy he must be a man of some standing in his village, and I am sure that he will put in a good word for us.'

The plague victims were returning from the pond very clean and in the best of spirits, and demanding something to eat. They were all very hungry. The little haberdasher got out his flute and began to play, whereupon the plague victims, glad of an opportunity to loosen up their stiff limbs, began dancing among the poppies, even as they ate.

The women had boiled some potatoes, and they had opened a barrel of anchovies, a drum of oil and two large jars of jam, which they spread on ships' biscuits. They ate very heartily, as the sun rose and gently dispersed the clouds on the horizon. As soon as it was shining in a clear sky, the whole company stood up as one man, and the notary, climbing onto a big stone, solemnly gave thanks to the Heavens. Then they set off for the village, like people going for a Sunday stroll.

In spite of its being so early in the morning, Pancrace had expected to see a few peasants already at work in this cool and pleasant countryside, and had intended to question them as to conditions in the village. But there was not a soul to be seen, and the doctor began to have an uneasy feeling that the plague might, after all, have reached these parts.

He was mistaken. It was not the plague which had banished the peasants.

It was fear.

They walked for more than an hour and, at last, at the top of a hill, sighted a cluster of windmills.

'There's Allauch!' said the doctor. 'It's possible that our troubles are now over. March on in an orderly fashion, and smile.'

A few minutes later, they saw a group of men watching their advance from the top of the hill.

The Captain extended his spy-glass, looked through it for an instant, and said:

'They've got guns.'

'To tell the truth, I was afraid of that,' said the doctor. 'But it's up to us to reassure them. If we sing as we march, they'll realise that they have nothing to fear from us.'

Immediately, they broke into a joyful Provençal carol, with everyone joining in, and the choir master walking backwards and beating time.

The group of men did not stir, but suddenly a loud voice rang out:

'Halt!'

Not twenty paces from the singers, a man stepped out of the hedge. The procession had halted, and the doctor advanced towards him.

'Don't come any nearer,' said the man. 'Where are you bound for?'

'Allauch,' said Pancrace.

'And where have you come from?'

'From the suburbs of Marseilles,' said the doctor.

'In that case,' said the man, 'you are infected with the plague. We can't possibly admit you.'

'We are not infected,' said Pancrace. 'We have been in isolation in a perfectly healthy little enclave. I am a doctor, and I can assure you ...'

'Nothing you can say will make the slightest difference. Everything that comes from Marseilles is tainted. We cannot admit you. And don't attempt to come any nearer. That big olive tree is the boundary. If you overstep it, we'll shoot.'

Maître Garin stepped forward a pace, and said:

'We have guns, as well.'

'So I see,' said the man. 'But our look-outs have only to sound their horns for five hundred men to come running, and kill every single one of you. There's nothing you can do. It may seem cruel, but then so is the plague cruel, and we have a thousand women and children to protect.'

'I understand,' said the doctor. 'But we could camp out in one of these fields, where you could keep an eye on us, and if, at the end of a week, there was not the slightest sign of illness among us . . .'

'It's just not possible,' said the man. 'If we were to let you stay, in a fortnight there would be hundreds more demanding the same facilities. We get these requests all the time. You'll just have to turn back.'

'So be it,' said the doctor. 'But before we leave, I should be much obliged if I might have a word with my foster-brother, whose name is Léonard Gondran. Would that be possible?'

'Oh! so you are the foster-brother of Gondran, the mill-owner, are you?'

'Yes,' said the doctor. 'Be so good as to tell him that the Marquis de Malaussène wishes to speak to him.'

The sentry bared his head, and said:

'I will go at once, my lord.'

And he went off at a run.

It was a great surprise to everyone to learn that the doctor was a nobleman, and a member of one of the oldest families in Provence.

'What!' exclaimed the notary. 'Are you really the Marquis de Malaussène, who was for so long physician to the King?'

'Well, yes,' said Pancrace. 'I did have the great honour of looking after the health of His Majesty, our gracious King Louis XIV, and I also, to my great grief, attended him in his last illness. His death was such a severe blow to me that I left the court after his funeral, to devote the rest of my life to scientific research.'

The bogus plague victims crowded round him, bursting with pride at the realization that they had been receiving medical attention from the Great King's personal physician, and completely reassured as regards their future.

After an hour of waiting, they saw two pack-mules, led by

two men, coming towards them in the distance. It was the sentry accompanied by Gondran, who began to run as soon as he caught sight of the Marquis, in spite of being an old man of fifty, whose hair was completely white. But he still had most of his teeth, and seemed to have retained all the strength of his youth.

TEN

Lagneau's Love Life

Lagneau was sixteen, and had earned his nickname* by virtue of his angelic serenity. He was fat and round, with pale, pendulous cheeks, a very shapely little nose, black eyes and black, curly hair. The reader must have a clear picture of him in his mind, if he is to understand the violent passion which Lagneau inspired in a delightful child known as Inidos. It was Easter time, and Lagneau was preparing himself for the dreaded *baccalauréat* examination. He and I always sat together in our study periods, and, after a game of cards on a playground bench or between two conversations, he would apply himself to such formidable mathematical problems as variable functions. From time to time he would complain that he could not make head or tail of them, and would tell me in whispers that he was a 'slacker', that he was bound to be 'ploughed', that his father would force him to become apprenticed to some trade, and that he bitterly regretted all the time he had wasted. None of this, however, deterred him from wasting more time every evening between seven and eight, in taking a stroll along La Plaine, which, as everyone knows, is the most beautiful and spacious square in Marseilles, and famous for its magnificent plane trees.

One morning, he arrived at the Lycée, resplendent in a white flannel suit, wearing a straw hat with a wide, curly brim far back on his head, so that it looked like a halo. He told me in a whisper that, as a gesture of gratitude for the munificent generosity of his father, he was resolved to shine in the *baccalauréat*, and that, as a first step, he had made a firm resolve to begin work in earnest the following week.

* In the first few pages of the manuscript of this chapter, written between 1919 and 1920, the name of Lagneau was written as l'Agneau (the lamb). For the convenience of our readers, we have restored the spelling used in the preceding chapters.

386

I ventured to point out that he would do better to begin at once, but he assured me that this was impracticable, and for the best of reasons, namely, that he had a timetable already worked out.

This timetable, due to come into force on 26th May, divided the examination syllabus into sections, with one week to be devoted to each. By this means, he would have covered the entire syllabus by 20th June, thus leaving himself six days for general revision before the start of the examinations on 1st July.

'You must understand,' he said, 'that it's all worked out, down to the last detail. If I were to start work today, as you suggest, it would be disastrous! It would throw the whole timetable into utter confusion! Failure would then be inevitable! As to starting on general revision right away, that's out of the question. One can only revise subjects one already knows something about, and I know nothing about anything.'

This was unanswerable, and I could not but concur.

As he still had four days in hand before giving up all pleasures, he decided then and there that it was essential to make the most of them. He got out his elegant fountain pen, and a handsome sheet of bristol board which he had brought with him for the purpose, and, in a flowing hand, wrote a chit, informing Monsieur the Deputy Headmaster that Lagneau's mother was desperately ill, and being in grave need of the services of her son that very evening, she begged the Authorities to release him from school at four o'clock.

Lagneau, having stowed this chit away in his satchel, settled down with me to a game of *écarté*, which, though briefly interrupted by the ten o'clock recess, continued right through the study period which ended at midday.

The Deputy Headmaster was always to be found in his office after one o'clock.

Lagneau accordingly parted from me at five to one, to deliver his masterpiece. He went off carrying it in a hand which did not tremble. Would to Heaven that the man had discovered the fraud! Lagneau would have got off with a long period of detention, whereas . . . But I will not anticipate events.

At four o'clock, having carefully polished his shoes with an overall belonging to an absent boy, he emerged from the building. He spent some considerable time combing his hair, then, having jammed his hat on the back of his head, he walked briskly away.

Next day, which was a Wednesday, Lagneau told me of the marvellous adventure that he had had. He had gone for a stroll on La Plaine, and indulged in the voluptuous pleasure of smoking English cigarettes.

'I was thinking of you, old man. I was just saying to myself what a pity it was you hadn't come with me, when, all of a sudden, I sensed that someone was watching me. I looked up and saw, at the first floor window of a palatial mansion, the face of a girl looking shyly in my direction. And then she dropped the curtain. The whole incident had lasted no more than a second. But I just stood there, dazzled by her beauty. Just imagine, two huge eyes, black and melting, framed in long brown curls, and a little, white hand holding the curtain. You will understand that I couldn't bear to go away without seeing her again, so I went on strolling up and down. I went past her window about ten times, but there was nothing to be seen. Still, I could tell by the way the curtain shook, that those beautiful eyes were still there behind it. Who was she, this lovely young creature? I pondered this question for a long time, never taking my eyes off the window. I could discover no clue, no clue whatsoever. But then, all of a sudden, I felt a hand on my shoulder. I turned, and there was Peluque of Elementary Maths. He was smoking that huge, crackling pipe of his with the long curved mouthpiece, reaching down to the top button of his waistcoat. He passed a few remarks about the smartness of my turn-out, and then asked me what I was looking for.

'"Peluque," I said, "I want to ask you a great favour".
'He made a face, waggled his ears and said:
'"Go ahead."
'"Who lives in that house over there?"
'"My sweetheart," said Peluque, sounding very smug.
'"Your sweetheart?" I repeated, choking. "You mean. . . ?"
'"Just so. It started three months ago, and I see her every evening. She's a bit of all right, isn't she?"
'"Yes," I said. "She's gorgeous. All that lovely black hair!"
'"Black?" he said. "You can't have got a proper look at her. She's a blonde."

' "What do you mean, blonde?"

' "What I say. She has fair hair and blue eyes. A lovely creature from Normandy. She's twenty years old, and she's crazy about me."

' "There must be some mistake," I said. "The girl I'm talking about was looking out of that window up there just now. She can't be more than sixteen, and she's dark, with eyes like deep black pools."

' "That's the kid," said Peluque. "The boss's daughter. I'm talking about the maid."

' "What's her name? What does she do?"

' "Have you got a crush on her, or something?" said Peluque. "You're making a big mistake. There's no question of love, where girls like that are concerned. If you take my advice, you'll find yourself a nice little servant-girl."

' "What's her name?" I repeated.

' "Lucienne," said Peluque. "Her father is an engineer. He's over six foot tall, and reputed to be very fierce. She goes to the Lycée, and the maid always goes with her. I always follow them at a distance, and then I walk the maid back home. And that's why I never get to the Lycée before two o'clock, and why I'm always kept in on Thursdays."

'He drew deeply on his pipe, spat with great force, and stuck his thumbs into the armholes of his waistcoat:

' "But then, what can you expect! That's love!"

' "Peluque, that girl has looked out of that window at me more than once!"

' "Are you sure?"

' "Absolutely."

' "But how did she look at you?" said Peluque. "There are ways and ways of looking at people. I'm looking at you now, but I haven't got a crush on you. I'd have to see for myself."

' "That's easy enough. I'll turn my back, and walk away, and you keep an eye on the window."

'We carried on in this way for about ten minutes, and then Peluque waved me off in the direction of the Rue Bergère and joined me there.

' "Well," he said. "That's that. It's love, all right. Now, do you know what you have to do next? Write her a letter. And be sure to lay it on thick, see? With plenty of frills ... Nothing frightening, mind. Something in verse, perhaps . . . Plenty of soft soap, what? If you give it to me, I'll get the maid to pass it on . . ."'

'So, you see,' concluded Lagneau, when he had come to the end of his story, 'the important thing now is to write the letter.'

And he drew from his satchel a splendid sheet of delicately scented, mauve writing paper.

'Very well,' I said, 'get on with it. You've got plenty of time between now and this evening.'

'The trouble is,' went on Lagneau, 'that I'm a bit bothered. French composition is not my strong suit. . .'

This was true enough. French composition was not his strong suit, but then, neither was any other subject.

'I do think you might offer to help. You could write a little sonnet for me. You're good at that sort of thing.'

Flattered, I agreed to do as he asked, on condition that he spoke not a word to me while I was in the throes of composition, and that he kept himself occupied with something else. Accordingly, he opened his algebra book and vainly endeavoured to immerse himself in it.

For my part, I invoked the Muses, and settled down to work. I had barely completed two lines before Lagneau began to show signs of restiveness. As soon as I had completed the first quatrain, he came and looked over my shoulder, and went into ecstasies. He read it twice, and then said joyfully:

'It scans!'

At the end of half an hour, I had completed the following masterpiece:

> Je marchais à pas lents sous les platanes frais.
> La Plaine, après l'hiver, semblait enfin renaître,
> Je rêvais à l'amour, hélas, sans le connaître
> Dans mon sang rajeuni tout le Printemps courait. . .
>
> Et j'ai senti soudain comme un bonheur secret,
> Un effluve d'amour enveloppa mon être
> Et j'ai levé la tête: à la haute fenêtre
> Un visage divin sourit et disparaît. . .

O les beaux yeux, plus purs que les pures fontaines!
Beauté pensive, à peine entrevue et lointaine,
Je restai là, muet, insensible, hagard. . .

Je suis parti très tard, sous la nuit embrumée,
Mais de cet ineffable et magique regard
Je sens encor, ce soir, mon âme parfumée. . .*

It scanned, of that there was not a shadow of doubt.

Lagneau, under my supervision, composed the prose offering which was to be dished up with the sonnet.

Lagneau was minded at first to portray himself as a consumptive young millionaire. I dissuaded him. On my advice, he claimed to be an accomplished sportsman, and an occasional poet.

He implored the young goddess to show herself at her window every evening at five, so that he could gaze at her from afar.

When I read of this proposed assignation, I protested, pointing out to Lagneau that it would severely disrupt his timetable. He replied that he would rearrange it. He would leave school every afternoon at four o'clock, thus losing two working hours. But he would make them up in the evening, between ten o'clock and midnight. He would work every night until midnight. It was as simple as that, and I respected his strength of mind.

Through the good offices of Peluque and the maid, the letter was delivered. Two days later, Lagneau received a reply, couched in the following terms:

Sir,

I was surprised and delighted to receive your charming letter. I did, indeed, see you when you were taking your evening walk in La Plaine, and I cannot conceal from you that I am highly flattered by your attentions. I am only sixteen, and I attend the

---

* I sauntered slowly under the shady plane trees./La Plaine, after the winter, seemed at last reborn./I dreamed of love, unknown to me, alas!/All the Spring flowed in my rejuvenated blood. . . And I was suddenly seized with a kind of secret happiness,/A flood of love enveloped my being,/And I lifted up my head; at the window above/ A divine face smiled and disappeared. . . Oh! those lovely eyes, purer than the purest fountain!/Pensive beauty, remote and briefly glimpsed./I stood there mute, stunned, distraught. . . I retreated at long last into the misty night,/But even now I feel that ineffable and magic glance/Like a lingering scent in my heart. . .

Lycée, and am in the Fourth Grade. My father hardly ever allows me to go out, because we have a large garden, where I can day-dream to my heart's content. I shall be at my window, as you ask, every evening at five o'clock. It has, anyway, long been my custom to do so. Till tonight, then.

                    Your little friend.

The letter was not signed, but this in no way abated Lagneau's delirious transports of joy. During the study period, he opened a book, and appeared deeply absorbed in it. But, all of a sudden, he would burst out laughing, and rub his hands until the desk shook. Then, oblivious of the glare of the duty master who had been woken up by these antics, he would lean over to me, and whisper confidentially: 'Things couldn't be better!' I would reply with a smile. I envied him.

This exuberance earned him several detentions, but he only laughed the more, and declared that it was good to be alive.

At one o'clock, he went off to see the Deputy Headmaster, armed with another chit, supposedly signed, as before, by his mother, which claimed that that robust lady was sinking fast, and that, for an indefinite period, her son's presence was required at home from four o'clock onwards. Permission was granted.

Alas! I was dragged downhill with him. Eager to have some-one with him to witness his happiness, he incited me to forge my father's signature to a request that, one afternoon, I should be released at four o'clock, which I duly did.

My hand shook a little as I proffered the visiting card, with its forged signature, to the Deputy Headmaster, but the wretched man suspected nothing, and, at four o'clock, having spent a long time sprucing ourselves up, we set off together. Lagneau was delirious with happiness. He kept on repeating: 'Just you wait! You'll see! She's so beautiful! Those eyes! That hair! She's angelic!' and so on and so forth.

He went and sat on a bench, facing the window of which I had heard so much.

Also sitting on the bench was an old man, who coughed and spat with abandon, but we paid no attention to him, and at five o'clock the window opened.

Lagneau turned scarlet, and gazed down at his shoes, murmur-ing: 'We don't want to seem too . . .', and failing to complete the sentence. But it was plain to me that he was simply longing to take flight. As for me, having no scruples about seeming too . . . , I took a good look at her. I saw a pretty little creature of sixteen, rather slight, with a pink and white complexion, framed by a mass of dark curls. A tiny mouth, a small, straight nose, and, above all, a pair of magnificent eyes, huge eyes which glowed with a soft radiance, like black pearls.

At first, she pretended not to see us. Then, growing bolder, she turned her gaze on Lagneau, who, somewhat restored to himself by my reiterated insults, raised his head and looked at her.

Seeing him once more wreathed in blushes, I muttered between my teeth:

'Stop staring at the ground, fathead, and look at her! Stir yourself, you peasant, and don't be such a ruddy coward. . .'

But Lagneau had already taken to his heels, and I could do no more than follow him, cursing loudly.

Next day, however, not a whit discouraged by this anti-climax, he requested me to compose another poem. I wrote a second sonnet, the final sextet of which, I confess, pleased me a good deal.

> Au ciel clair, déployant mollement ses longs voiles,
> La nuit aux yeux d'argent allume ses étoiles,
> Je vois se dessiner un visage moqueur.
>
> O je les connais bien, ces larges yeux. C'est elle.
> Et cette voix lointaine et douce qui m'appelle,
> C'est mon amour caché qui chante dans mon coeur.*

Once again, Lagneau was highly satisfied. I read his letter, which was suitably ardent. I had never seen any French composition of his so eloquently expressed. He was carried away by his subject, as they say. With a pen in his hand, he was bold enough, even going so far as to yearn tenderly for an unattainable kiss.

The letter was dispatched, and Lagneau spent the rest of the day asleep at his desk, to compensate, he told me, for the sleepless night he would be spending, poring over his books.

The following day, pink-cheeked and refreshed, he told me

* As the silver-eyed night lights its stars/And softly trails long streamers across the sky,/I see the outline of a mocking face. Oh! I know those great eyes so well! It is she,/And that soft and distant voice calling out to me./It is my hidden love, singing in my heart.

that he had got through a terrific amount of work, and he crossed out two sections of his timetable. He was really bearing up remarkably well under the load, and, to look at him, one would have thought he had had twelve hours' sleep.

He gave me a lively account of his assignation the previous evening. She had smiled three times, she had thrown him down two flowers, she had gazed at him, first with tenderness, and then with passion. Returning home, he had been faced with the task of writing her another letter, in reply to the one he had received from her that morning, which entailed cancelling the ten to eleven work session. As this would leave him only the last hour of the day, he had had to re-arrange his schedule, fitting in the extra hour between one and two in the morning.

Having resolved upon this, he had proceeded to write his letter. And so it went on, for a month.

Lagneau suffered no ill-effects from these immensely arduous nocturnal labours. His French compositions showed some improvement, as a result of the letters he was writing every day. As for me, I was giving birth to a sonnet almost daily.

Little by little, the tone of the correspondence was growing more passionate. The first timid mention of an unattainable kiss was superseded by the suggestion that it was, after all, not such an impossibility. Perhaps Lagneau wanted to prove, once again, that to a Frenchman nothing is impossible.

The girl, having begun with a few timid expressions of affection, was gradually emboldened to declare that he came to her in her dreams and showered her with long, burning kisses. Lagneau replied that she was his whole life, his beloved mistress, his priceless treasure. He even went so far as to say that he had seen her in a dream, stark naked beside a mountain spring, and praised her 'alabaster throat' and intoxicatingly shapely calves. She spoke of sleeping with her head on his breast. He addressed her by the familiar 'tu'. She responded by confiding in him that she had a mole on her right shoulder, and another extremely fetching one on her left breast. In the process of showering kisses on the envelopes, Lagneau swallowed a fair amount of glue. He browsed on the flowers that her lips had touched. All in all, these two innocents inflamed one another's imagination to an alarming degree.

In spite of all their endeavours, her father's vigilance pre-

394

vented them from meeting. Occasionally, by some happy chance, they would brush against one another in the street. On those days, Lagneau was beside himself. He laughed uproariously in the classroom, and walked on his hands in the corridors.

And Peluque, who performed the office of postman, frequently admonished him for writing so many letters, and warned him that, sooner or later, the girl's father was bound to intercept one.

Lagneau, for his part, kept a sharp eye out for any tall stranger, and he had only to catch sight of one in the distance to decamp at speed, realizing that discretion was the better part of valour.

One morning, I saw that Lagneau was engaged in drawing up a new timetable.

'What are you doing?' I asked.

'Well, it's like this,' he replied. 'I've noticed that in the *baccalauréat* there are only a limited number of questions, and they're nearly always more or less the same. In the French literature paper, for instance, it's always Racine and Corneille. In Physics, it's Ohm's Laws, Gramme's generator and so forth. So I reckon it's just stupid to learn anything else.'

I agreed.

'So', he went on, 'I'm crossing out all the subjects I won't be asked about, either because there's never a question on them, or because there was one in last year's paper.'

I remarked that that surely meant that there was precious little left.

'Practically nothing,' he said triumphantly. 'Practically nothing.'

'But supposing there's a question on one of the subjects you've crossed out?'

Lagneau looked at me scornfully.

'That would be their mistake. It would just prove that they were idiots. And besides, I refuse even to consider such a possibility.'

There was no possible answer to this, and Lagneau went on to say that he would be starting work that very evening in accordance with the revised timetable.

Two weeks went by. Every evening, he went and sat on the famous bench, to wait, as it were, for the curtain to rise. Sometimes, on a Thursday, I would go with him. The lovers, frozen in an attitude of mute adoration, gazed at one another. The pair of them seemed to me to have attained the Hindu state of Nirvana. The tone of the correspondence was growing ever more intense. Lagneau's locker was overflowing, and Peluque, the postman, would say to me from time to time:

'They're overdoing it with all those letters. It isn't real love any more. It's bound to lead to trouble...'

The day of the *baccalauréat* arrived. Early that morning, we forgathered in the playground, to undergo the first phase of our ordeal.

There was Peluque, smoking his pipe as usual. There was Polype, the inventor. Barbeille, of Form 1A, was wearing a bowler hat, and smoking an Italian cigar as twisted as a vine tendril. Houille was smiling, and his ears stood so far out from his head that they appeared to be stitched to the brim of his hat. He was carrying a sealed bottle of ink, and smoking *Three Castles* cigarettes. Havet, uneasy and tremulous, was going from one group of boys to another, asking: 'What will the questions be like, do you think? Do you know anything about Ohm's Laws? Have you revised optics?' Belloche, a towering figure, responded with a shrug and a beaming smile: 'I don't give a damn. I don't give a damn. I don't care what the questions are...I don't know anything...It's all one to me...'

Every new arrival would be greeted with noisy shouts: 'Here comes Pédorka! Come over here, me old mate! There's Merlau. Just look at that hat!'

In the midst of all this hubbub, I saw Lagneau.

'Well?' I said. 'How are you feeling? Ready for the off?'

'If you say so,' he replied gloomily.

'What do you mean, if I say so?'

At this point, Peluque accosted him:

'Hi there, lover-boy! You've got a nerve, turning up for this exam. You're certainly not lacking in cheek! No, indeed! Oh! dear, no!'

He went on in this exclamatory vein, until he had exhausted every possibility.

'What do you mean?' said Lagneau. 'I'm no more stupid than anyone else!'

'I'm not saying you are,' said Peluque, coming nearer. 'All I'm saying is that three months spent in gazing up at a window is

396

no recipe for success in examinations. What do you think, Panier?'

'I think,' I replied, 'that, put like that, you're probably right. But what you don't know, I daresay, is that he's been working hard every night.'

'Is that what he told you?' retorted Peluque. 'He doesn't look to me as if he's been burning the midnight oil. Oh! no! Anything but!'

He put his pipe back in his mouth, and, after a brief silence, said:

'To be serious for a moment, Lagneau, how much of the syllabus have you actually missed out? You surely can't have covered all of it,' he added in a conciliatory tone.

'To tell you the truth,' said Lagneau, somewhat nonplussed, 'it would take less time to tell you what I have covered. I'm very well up in Gramme's generator, Corneille and variable functions, and I can describe a sunset in English. And that's the lot.'

I was more than a little startled at this. Peluque roared with laughter.

'You don't say! Is that what you call being prepared for the *baccalauréat*? Getting up the answer to one question in each subject! One solitary question!'

Lagneau's reply, spoken with calm conviction, deserves to be recorded for posterity. Coldly, he looked Peluque in the eye and said:

'They only set one question.'

At that moment, the great door was flung open, and the invigilator, reading from a long list, began calling the roll. We all rushed forward to respond. Then, one by one, he let us in. Two retired masters showed us to our seats at the long tables. The candidates were seated six feet apart, to prevent cheating, every Arts student being flanked on either side by a Scientist.

The examination hall was vast, with a vaulted roof about forty-five feet high. The sun poured in through the open windows. When we were all seated in our appointed places, one of the two old gentlemen solemnly mounted the dais at the far end of the hall, and, picking up a buff package, held it out to us at arm's length. His lips then began to move energetically, and, although I myself could not hear a word, I presumed that he was talking to us. It was not too difficult, in the circumstances, to guess that he was requesting us to take note of the fact that the wax seal on the packet of examination papers was intact. This was a matter of indifference to me, and I sat waiting for the papers to be handed out.

The Latin translation was easy, and I quickly disposed of it.

Looking up, I caught sight of the disconsolate figure of Lagneau, three tables away. No doubt the examiners had failed to set his question, the only question in the entire syllabus to which he knew the answer. Seeing that the invigilators were at that moment talking to one another, I took advantage of the opportunity to ask my neighbour about the Science paper.

'It's on the same subject as last year,' he said.

So, according to Lagneau's view of the matter, the examiners had proved to be idiots, and had set him a question on a subject about which he knew nothing.

In the English paper, that same evening, he was asked to give his opinion of *Macbeth*. When we got outside, he told me how he had worked in his description of a sunset.

'How's this for ingenuity?' he said. 'I began as follows: "Macbeth is a much-discussed play. But the only proper way to read this famous work is seated under an oak tree with the book on one's knee as the sun is setting . . ." and so forth. Two pages of description of the setting sun. D'you get the point?'

'And what about Macbeth? How did you fit him in to all that?'

'I summarised the play near enough. You know . . .'

'So you do know the play?'

'Vaguely. Hang it, everyone knows the plot . . . The Moor who smothers his wife . . . The indelible blood stains . . . Thou shalt be king hereafter . . . To be or not to be . . .'

I could see no point in disabusing him.

'I handled it all very well,' he said. 'I can safely rely on getting at least 25 marks.'

He looked so confident that it was a pleasure to see.

Next day, he emerged from the mathematics paper looking radiant. The examiners had obliged with the only question to which he knew the answer. It was the same in the evening, after the French Literature paper, in which he was able to paraphrase and comment on a set passage from Corneille. He was rubbing his hands with glee. Peluque and I were waiting for him outside.

'It's in the bag,' he told us, 'I'm sure I've passed. I've failed in Physics. Let's say five out of forty. But I can count on twenty-five in English. That makes thirty. And thirty in Maths. That makes sixty. I don't want to seem over-optimistic, so I'll say twenty-five for French Literature. That makes a total of eighty-five, which gives me a pass, with five marks in hand.'

This was pitching his hopes high indeed.

It was then that Peluque handed him two letters from his beloved.

'I've had one of them since yesterday,' he said. 'I didn't give it to you, so as not to take your mind off your work.'

Lagneau hastened to open them, and, as soon as he had read them, passed them over to me. As he did so, he leapt high into the air several times, threw up his hat and caught it, then jammed it far back on his head and cried:

'I shall be talking to her! I shall be taking her in my arms! Hurrah! Three cheers! It's all fixed! Heigh-ho!' and so forth, in the same exclamatory vein.

The reason for all this became clear to me when I read the second letter. Lucienne, full of ardour, informed him that on the 8th of July she would be attending a big fête to be held in aid of several charities. All the pupils of the Lycées were to be invited. Her father would be unable to accompany her. Instead she would be attended by a sprightly old aunt. At last, they would be able to meet, and perhaps even wander off together into the shrubbery in the Park. Oh! rapture!

For the next three days, we turned up, as usual, at the Lycée, although the First Grade classrooms were all deserted. There, provided we took reasonable care, we were able to enjoy complete freedom. From eight o'clock to twelve, safe in an empty class room, Lagneau and I played cards and smoked cigarettes, in company with Houille and Peluque. As it was very warm, we took off our shirts and vests, so that we were naked to the waist under our overalls.

At midday, we had lunch in the school dining-room. From half-past twelve to two, we strolled about in the playgrounds. From two to four, more cards. At four o'clock we all left, because, as *baccalauréat* candidates, we were officially on holiday from the 1st of July.

Lagneau went to take up his vigil on the bench.

As for me, I was taken by Peluque to a billiard hall, and initiated into the secrets of making breaks and running through.

At last the great day came. It was a Thursday. Lagneau came to fetch me at home, where, already dressed, and with my hat on, I was attempting to revise, or rather to learn for the first time, some part of the history and geography syllabuses.

He had scarcely time to press the bell before I was downstairs, and, wearing light jackets and straw hats, we set out in the blazing summer sunshine.

He was a splendid sight, in white flannel trousers with wide turn-ups, a long grey jacket, and a white waistcoat with most of the buttons undone. He was wearing a magnificent tie, light brown shoes, light gloves, a blue silk handkerchief peeping out of his breast pocket, and a carnation in his button-hole.

As we walked side by side along a broad avenue, with great spreading trees on either side, he told me his plan of campaign, which provided for every eventuality.

I had a part to play, albeit an insignificant one.

Our first task would be to survey the Park, with a view to marking down in advance two or three secluded spots where, according to circumstances, the meeting could take place.

We would then track down the young charmer and, when a suitable opportunity arose, indicate, by expressive gestures, the chosen rendezvous. Finally, after the couple had retired together, I was to mount guard, a role at once inglorious and unrewarding.

I showed our tickets at the gate, and we at once made our way into the Park.

In the midst of a veritable forest of pines and oaks stood a magnificent chateau. Around the chateau, a great many fairground booths had been erected. There was a roundabout, a white elephant stall, a shooting gallery and a tombola. In one corner of the Park, which was criss-crossed by carefully-raked gravel walks, was an open-air theatre. Seeing that this was obviously unsuitable for our purpose, we made for the most densely wooded part of the grounds, where the broad walks gave way to narrow footpaths. This area was all we could have wished for, and we soon came upon an artificial grotto, well-hidden behind a luxuriant clump of brambles, with a little path leading

400

up to it. Lagneau's only comment was that if they should be surprised in one another's arms, there was no way of escape. When we explored the grotto, however, these fears were dispelled. It had three exits, so that, in the event of discovery, the lovers could safely take flight in opposite directions.

Lagneau made a thorough inspection of the site. He found an old, overturned bench, which he restored to its upright position, and dusted. Then he showed me the place where I was to stand guard; and I practised coughing in a special sort of way, which was to be the warning signal.

When all our preparations were completed, we returned to mingle with the crowd.

The guests were pouring in. Two anaemic girls, wearing shell-pink, accompanied by enormously fat mothers, dressed like young girls, with flowers pinned to their bodices; gentlemen, looking bored and solemn, wearing cream-coloured gloves and dazzlingly glossy shoes.

Schoolmasters in pince-nez, old ladies with reticules. Head-mistresses of Lycées and high schools, their hair so elaborately dressed that they scarcely dared move their heads. Flat-chested junior schoolgirls and, finally, a sizeable contingent from our own Lycée. Belloche, with his generously rounded stomach, Barbeille, permanently smiling, Havet, going over in his mind all the salient dates in Polignac's period of office, and, last but not least, Peluque, unrecognizable in patent leather pumps, a cravat as big as a flag, and a straw hat with an immensely wide brim. His hand was in his pocket, twisting and turning his pipe, which he dared not take out, because, as he put it, it would be indecent! All the same, how he longed to light up! A great crowd had gathered round all the little booths, and every boy from the Lycée had already marked down the charmer of his choice, and was pursuing her with sugared almonds and flowers.

Lagneau was twitching with impatience. He confided to me in a whisper that he intended to elope with her, for he could no longer live without her . . . Havet came up to us, and asked us how we felt we had done in our exams. He then proceeded to give us an account of his own performance, totting up his achievements down to the last half-mark. Then, seeing that we were scarcely even pretending to listen, he buttonholed Polype, who had just arrived, and poured it all out to him.

Suddenly, Lagneau exclaimed: 'There she is!' And there, indeed, she was, dressed all in blue, with a white collar, which made her look like an enchantingly pretty child. She was with two girl-cousins, and towering over the three of them was a very fat lady, dressed in gleaming silk, which seemed to beg for mercy every time she moved. The three girls turned to the lady and conferred with her. Then the little group threaded its way through the crowd to the open-air refreshment stall. The fat lady subsided into a garden chair, and one of the girls brought her some lemonade. Then she handed out money all round, and, straightway, the girls ran off towards the booths. We followed at a discreet distance. Peluque joined us, whispering: 'I'll give her the message. Where is it to be?'

Lagneau pointed in the direction of the grotto:

'In the grotto,' he said.

'Off you go, then,' said Peluque. 'She'll join you there.'

Lagneau, trying hard to behave naturally, walked away very slowly, darting so many glances in all directions that one might have imagined that he was inviting all those present to follow him.

The three girls, surrounded by a crowd exuding the freshness of youth and Pivert scent, were shooting at clay pipes, which the detonation of the rifles alone was enough to shatter. Each shot won them two macaroons, which they paused to eat. Then they stood down to give others a turn, but remained in the crowd to admire the skill of their successors. Peluque, making free use of his elbows, managed to reach Lucienne and, in an undertone loud enough to be heard by everybody, said: 'In the grotto, over there, near that clump of pines.' Having said his piece, he at once assumed an innocent expression, and gazed in fascination at the shooting gallery.

The love-lorn girl emerged from the crowd, accompanied by her two cousins. They conferred together, then Lucienne, followed by one of them, walked slowly towards the trysting place. I noticed that she was very red in the face, and giggling in an affected manner. I was off like a streak of lightning. I found Lagneau sitting on the bench. He was sneezing dreadfully, for it was chilly in the grotto, and looking very uncomfortable. As soon as he saw me, he sprang to his feet, and asked, in a strangled voice:

'Is she coming?'

'She's on her way,' I said.

He looked anxiously along the footpath, and turned pale, with happiness no doubt.

I went to my post, and saw the two charmers approaching. Behind them came Peluque, smoking a cigarette.

I felt quite emotional. What will happen? I asked myself. At the point they've reached, on paper at least, they're not likely to hang fire. They'll fall into one another's arms, and the grotto will re-echo to their kisses. I hope it won't get out of hand . . .

I promised myself that I would not so much as take a peep, but would carry out my part with exemplary selflessness.

But, why the devil had she brought her cousin with her? That really bothered me. Peluque also must have disapproved, because, while they were still some little way off, he went up to them, and I heard him suggesting to the cousin (my goodness, what a delightful girl!) that they should take a stroll round the Park. The way he put it, one would really have thought he owned the place, and his manner was so persuasive that she readily agreed, and they went off together into the wood, while Lucienne approached nearer to the grotto. From my hiding-place, I heard Lagneau sneeze.

She went in.

I could hear nothing. I longed to turn round, but resisted the impulse. Then I heard a voice, Lagneau's:

'So you . . . you . . . you decided to drop in on this fête?'

'Yes.'

'Oh! Ah! That's good. That's very good.'

It was no good, I simply could not resist taking a look.

Lagneau, scarlet in the face, was standing up facing Lucienne in the entrance of the cavern. He was fidgeting clumsily with his hat, which he was holding with both hands, and gazing fixedly at his left shoe. The young lady, her cheeks burning, was nervously stripping off the petals of a flower.

'There are a lot of people here,' Lagneau remarked.

She did not reply.

'They'll have taken a lot of money,' he went on. Then, emphatically: 'Well, that's a good thing, seeing it's for charity...'

I was appalled. As Peluque would have said, this was not real love.

403

Lagneau was turning from scarlet to purple. He tried to think of something else to say. He moved further into the cavern.

'It's a grotto,' he said. 'There's a bench over there.'

She still made no reply.

At this point, I poked my head through the bushes, and stared intently at Lagneau. He spotted me, and the sight of me gave him courage. He threw himself upon his Dulcinea, pressed her fiercely to his heart, and cried:

'I love you . . . Come. Come, I adore you.'

And he endeavoured to lead her into the grotto. But she burst into tears, and began tearing her handkerchief to shreds. Lagneau took a step backward, and stared at her. He got out his splendid blue silk handkerchief, and wiped the perspiration from his forehead. Then, suddenly seized with panic, he bolted.

I was dumbfounded. The girl remained there for a moment longer, weeping, whimpering and tapping her foot. Then, from Heaven knows where, she got out a little powder compact, which had a mirror set in the lid, and proceeded to repair her ravaged face, and to calm her ravaged heart with a few consoling reflections. Presently, looking pensive, she left.

Cursing volubly, I went in search of the Swain. I was just in time to prevent his escape, and I promptly berated him, calling him a fool, and a squanderer of love.

'And another thing,' he said. 'What did you have to show yourself for?'

'Oh! no!' I cried. 'You're not suggesting, are you, that I am to blame for this catastrophe? Whatever possessed you to run off like that? Idiot! Peasant! Much good it did you, going into raptures over the roundness of her hips! A fine specimen you are! Some Don Juan!'

He listened to my reproaches in silence.

'You surely don't think that all is lost?' he said.

'It certainly looks like it to me,' I replied. 'We'll have to see what Peluque advises. But you can be sure of one thing, he'll curse you up hill and down dale, when he hears how brilliantly you rose to the occasion!'

I shepherded him through the milling throng. So dazed was he that he offered no resistance. As we went past the drinks stall, I saw the sprightly aunt seated between Lucienne and one of her cousins. The three of them were swilling down great

404

quantities of lemonade. The loved one blushed as she caught sight of us. As for Lagneau, the sight of her threw him into such confusion that he bowed to the little group as if they were old acquaintances. The old lady returned his salutation, and stared at him through her lorgnette. Then she turned to her niece, no doubt to ask: 'Who is that young man?'

After much pushing and shoving, we managed to get through the crowd, which was by now very dense, and made towards the bushes. This part of the grounds was no longer quite deserted, for, here and there, we saw one or two timid couples strolling along the footpaths, with poetry in their hearts and flowers in their hands.

We searched for a long time, and were just on the point of giving up when we heard, behind a clump of bushes, a voice that sounded very like Peluque's. I beckoned to Lagneau to follow me.

Through the branches, in the middle of a little clearing, we saw Peluque. He and Lucienne's pretty cousin were sitting very close together on a mossy tree stump. She had her head on his shoulder, and was smoking a cigarette. Peluque had one arm round her waist, and there was a cigarette in his other hand. Every now and then, between puffs, they exchanged the tenderest of kisses.

'What a brute! But he certainly knows what he's about!' I murmured.

Then Peluque spoke.

'I wonder what they're doing at this moment?'

'Oh! Lord!' said the cousin, with a little, frightened titter. 'The thing is that those letters of theirs were so . . . passionate.'

At this, Peluque showed himself to be no mean psychologist.

'Pooh!' he said. 'That doesn't mean a thing. I doubt if they've even got as far as we have.'

They kissed.

'I bet you five francs,' said Peluque, as the scent of tobacco and kisses became once more intermingled, 'I bet you five francs that he hasn't even got as far as putting his arm round her waist!'

They kissed again.

'Do you really think so?' said the cousin.

'I'm sure of it,' went on Peluque. 'I know Lagneau. He's a mug.'

The crestfallen Swain gripped my arm. Oh! misery. He mumbled incoherently. With the sound of kisses and youthful laughter rising from behind the bushes, I dragged him back towards the hubbub of the fête . . .

Two days later, we were at the Lycée awaiting the results of the written examination. The boarders' playground was full of examinees, strolling about and chatting. I was with Lagneau, and we were discussing his love life.

'I wrote her a splendid letter,' he said. 'I hope it will do the trick. And next time, I shan't waste my opportunity. Oh! no!'

He said this so emphatically that he succeeded in convincing himself.

Houille came up to us.

'Ho! Ho! Lagneau. So he's got his reward at last!' he said, looking envious. 'His little lady was at the fête. I saw her making for the bushes, where her Don Juan was no doubt awaiting her . . . You're blushing, Lagneau! So I guessed right! I guessed right! Oh! What a devil with the girls! The things he must have said to her! Such transports of ecstasy! I bet you weren't in the least backward in coming forward, what!'

Lagneau did not know where to put himself, the more so since Houille was being wholly sincere, and truly believed that a perfect orgy of kissing had taken place.

At this point, Peluque appeared. He was the bearer of a letter. Lagneau proceeded to read it. While he did so, I put Peluque in the picture as to what had occurred at the fête. He raised his hands to heaven, and cried repeatedly: 'Oh! what a mug! What a mug! What a double-dyed, twenty-four carat mug! You certainly have made a proper fool of yourself!'

Then, catching sight of the Swain, who was looking utterly crushed, he stopped abruptly.

'What's the matter?' he asked.

Lagneau held out the letter, and I read it half-aloud.

It read as follows:

Sir,

I don't know how to begin this letter, and I feel almost as embarrassed as we both were the day before yesterday. I fear

406

that our love *cannot survive that meeting, which taught me a lot about my state of mind which I had already begun to suspect. I do not believe I can really love you, because, I must tell you frankly, I had not the least desire to let you kiss me. The main reason why I was attracted to you, I think, is because I am very lonely, and your love was a bit like something out of a romantic novel. If I have hurt you, I beg you to forgive me. I shall never forget you, and, for the rest of my life, it will always give me a little thrill to think of our exchange of love letters.*

Yours,

P.S. I should be grateful if you would either burn my letters or return them to me. I return yours herewith.

'Oh! yes,' said Peluque. 'There was a parcel with the letter. But it was too bulky, so I left it at home. I don't think there's anything in it but letters. It must weigh over ten pounds!'

'I wrote to her every day for three months, letters of twenty pages each.'

'What a tragedy!' declaimed Peluque.

At that moment everyone began rushing headlong towards the corner of the playground, where two masters were putting up the examination results.

We joined the throng.

In a flash, the whole playground underwent a strange transformation. Some looked serene, others shattered, yet others were swearing horribly, and threatening to break the chief examiner's b . . . neck, and others again were capering about in the wildest fashion. Havet, for instance, was hooting with shrill, hysterical laughter.

As for me, I had passed. I searched for Lagneau's name. It was not there.

He had already looked, and slunk away. I found him alone leaning against a plane tree, the very picture of desolation. Peluque, who had also passed, took me by the arm, and we went over to comfort him as warmly as we could.

He greeted us with a gesture of despair.

'So that's what it's come to!' he cried. 'No love and no *baccalauréat*. It's too much! Honestly! Oh! no! Those cretins of examiners!'

For, as every reader will know, whenever anyone fails an examination, it is invariably the fault of the examiners.

'If only *something* had gone right! But nothing! Nothing!'

He slouched off unhappily, his shoulders hunched, his hands in the pockets of his elegant white trousers and, characteristically, his hat jammed down over his eyes.

Peluque lit his pipe:

'It's all his own fault,' he concluded. 'Those sorts of love affairs are for kids. They're not serious. He'd have done better to listen to me, and take up with a servant-girl.'

Marcel Pagnol and The Time of Love

by Bernard de Fallois

The foregoing chapters were written by Marcel Pagnol between 1959 and 1962. They were intended for inclusion in the fourth and last volume of his already famous autobiography, entitled *Souvenirs d'Enfance*.* The title he had chosen for this volume was *Le Temps des Amours*. But although the author did not die until 1974, it was never published.

This book, therefore, tells a story, as do all books, but it also tells another and more singular story, that of a work abandoned by its author.

It is a great pity that Marcel Pagnol himself did not tell these two stories. For not only did he love to create, he also loved to explain himself. Had he done so, with reference to the work acclaimed by the public as his masterpiece, he would have shed a fascinating light on many topics, such as the art of prose writing, the nature of memory, childhood and the craft of authorship.

But besides all this, he would undoubtedly have taken the opportunity, as he did in regard to *Les Marchands de Gloire*, *Topaze* and *Marius*, of describing the circumstances in which these *Souvenirs* were conceived, the sort of life he was leading, the friends he was seeing, and Paris as it was then, contrasting it, no doubt, with the Marseilles of his childhood. This second viewpoint, much more important than the first, imbues the prefaces to the earlier volumes with as much flavour as if they were little novels in their own right; they are every bit as enjoyable to read, or rather they constitute a natural sequel to the *Souvenirs d'Enfance*, equalling them in verve, tenderness and humour.

At the time when these prefaces were being written, however, the *Souvenirs* were still very fresh, whereas the thirties were already long past. And, in writing of those years, he was, in a

---

* The first three volumes were published in English in two volumes, entitled *The Days were too Short* and *The Time of Secrets*.

way, describing his own youth. And it is pleasanter to look back on one's twenty-fifth year than on one's sixtieth. And this is, no doubt, the reason why Marcel Pagnol chose to preface *La Gloire de Mon Père* with a mere two or three pages, comparing the task of the author in preparing a book for publication with that of the dramatist preparing a play for performance on the stage— all very interesting, admittedly, but not very nourishing fare.

Thus, it seemed to me necessary to provide a brief sketch of Marcel Pagnol as he was during those years, and to explain how he was inspired to write his *Souvenirs*, and why he never completed them.

He has just reached the age of sixty, and he looks barely forty. He is of medium height, rather stout, and blooming with health, genuine health, which in no sense derives from regular exercise. He is occasionally to be seen wearing a green suit and, on Thursdays, a trilby, but more often, he does not even wear a tie, but only a fisherman's jersey, such as *boule* players also wear. The most impressive thing about him is not his voice, magnificent but all too easy to mimic, but the expression of his eyes. It is ambiguous, one eye forever twinkling with mischief, the other a little sad. But it is the twinkling eye which is tentative, and the sad one which is very steady and direct. He is a sight for sore eyes. To sum up, there is nothing of the Parisian about him. He has the air of a Roman senator who has read Dickens.

No trace remains of the slender, enterprising, dazzlingly daring little schoolboy from Marseilles, who, more than forty years earlier, founded the magazine *Fortunio*. Nor of the young author, gnawed with anxiety, who is about to stake his all on a play which he believes to have merits, and which was originally called *La Belle et la Bête*, until, recalling that all Molière's major works bore the names of their principal characters, he renamed it *Topaze*.

And besides, he no longer needs such writers as Musset and Molière either as sources of inspiration or as patrons. Thanks to the cinema, he is known today to a far greater number of his fellow-countrymen than any other French writer before or since. His name is Marcel Pagnol.

The fifties, which are just coming to an end, have not been

410

particularly memorable years. Those years concluded the second post-war decade of the twentieth century, but without the changes, discoveries, challenges and euphoric illusions of the first. Those ten years, which had just come to an end, had thrown up very little that was new or spectacular. The stars of the inter-war years still held the stage, and the younger generation seemed in no hurry to dethrone them. A decade of giddiness? No, rather a decade of sobriety, even sadness.

And what is happening to our Marcel as the year 1955 draws to a close? He is a man loaded with honours. What more can he wish for? He wanted everything that life had to offer, and that is precisely what he has got.

To begin with, fame. He had experienced it for the first time at an age when others have to be satisfied to dream of it, with *Topaze*. And again, but less spectacularly, in 1945, when he was elected to the Académie Française, his friend Henri Jeanson having surreptitiously slipped a letter of application among the papers on his desk, while he was opening a bottle of champagne to drink to the victory of the Allies. He had made a jest of it, but it had not displeased him. Like so many wholehearted anarchists, he had a liking for established institutions.

But he saw to it that fame did not prevent him from having fun, and he did indeed have fun, glorious fun, with the latest toy, which was to become the most exciting toy of the century, namely, the cinema. With the arrival of talking pictures, he was the first to realize, contrary to popular opinion, that a new era had dawned in the history of entertainment. This realization earned him ten years of happiness, with his own studios, constant new discoveries in sound and photography, and experiments with the latest types of film. There were the scripts, often completely rewritten in a single night, the actors, who were his friends, and who loved one another, and quarrelled, and made up their quarrels. It was all a tremendous adventure, shared with a band of followers, whom he was able to lead in his beloved Provençal hills, like the bandit chief that he sometimes imagined himself to be.

Having fun, however, was not to be allowed to interfere with earning money, and earn money he did. A great deal. In the early days, he still kept count, with a sort of gleeful innocence. It was still possible to keep count then. He would say: 'If my

411

play runs for a month, it will make me as much as a senior Civil Servant earns in three months; if it runs on into the summer, it will make me the equivalent of two years' salary in the Civil Service.' Towards the end, he must have made the equivalent of a couple of hundred years of earnings in the Civil Service, but by then he no longer knew, he had stopped counting. He was rich.

Best of all, neither money nor fun nor fame prevented him from getting his heart's desire, that is to say, from falling in love and being loved in return. After a somewhat stormy youth, soon after the end of the war, he married a delightful young actress, who appealed to him because she was the very image of all the heroines of his stories, and who delighted him, above all, 'because she was herself'. Her name was Jacqueline, and she bore him two children, whom he adored.

There was only one tragedy to mar his perfect happiness. His little girl, Estelle, had recently died. But his reserve was such that he never spoke of it, even to those closest to him.

It was, in fact, for this reason that he had just moved house, abandoning forever his villa in Monaco where, hitherto, he had liked to spend several months of the year. Since his Paris flat in the Rue Jean-Goujon was too small, he had moved to a handsome private house near the Bois de Boulogne.

There, as was his wont, he settled down to a stint of hard work. He had a reputation with the press of being a very lazy man. He made no effort to correct this impression, totally false though it was. Had anyone succeeded in gaining admission to the little study on the second floor, to which he chose to retire several times a day, what would he have found on his desk, and on the bookshelves behind, which were piled high with papers? The manuscript of a play: *Le Petit Ange*, which he had written many years ago, and which he had recently decided to revise. His translation of the *Georgics*, long projected, in tribute to his Latin teacher, Monsieur Leprat. A medical article on the respiratory functions. A thick file of mathematical material, containing all his work on prime numbers, and his attempts at proving Fermat's last theorem, in which he believed he had succeeded. This was something known to very few people; it was virtually a secret. In any case, it was not just a hobby, it was an obsession. He used to smile occasionally at the recollection that, at the age of thirty, even before *Topaze* and *Marius* had reached the stage, he had decided to make a clean break with literature, to devote himself entirely to the pursuit of science. He had even gone so far as to write a preface announcing this dramatic decision, which he intended to publish as a foreword to his *Eléments d'une Thermodynamique Nouvelle*.

And what else? The beginning of *Manon des Sources*, which he had filmed in 1953, and was now in the process of turning into a novel. Another Manon, *Manon Lescaut*, whose memoirs he was tempted to write, in the form of a refutation addressed to the Abbé Prévost. According to Marcel, the good Abbé had totally failed to understand the nature of her relationship with the handsome *chevalier*. Another fascinating puzzle, that of the Man in the Iron Mask, concerning which he had already begun systematically to assemble a vast quantity of material, with a view to writing a historical work.

It will be obvious to the reader that there was a spate of work in progress. Never had the inventive Marcel, the immense range of whose interests was not even suspected by most people, had so many projects on hand at the same time. He was as happy in his work as in his life.

And yet, however good things looked on the surface, they were less so in reality. Was it that his creative powers had diminished with advancing age, or was it simply that he had lost that fire, that will to overcome all obstacles, which hitherto had so triumphantly and splendidly suffused all his work? At any rate, nothing that he had written since the end of the war had been such a resounding success as his earlier plays and films.

He had remained faithful to the cinema. He had shot *Manon des Sources* in his native Provence, and he had a great affection for this fine, lyrical work which, portraying as it did the land-scape so dear to him, was, in a double sense, a love story. He had returned to the theatre with a play, *Judas*, which had been maturing in his mind for a very long time. Both, though very differently received, were ambitious works, and yet both left him feeling somehow dissatisfied. *Judas* was a very good play, but it was a total failure on the stage. *Manon* was enthusiastically received by public and critics alike, yet he was unable to believe wholeheartedly in its success.

The fact is that, by now, Marcel was a little weary of the

cinema. He no longer had his own studios and distribution network. The funds needed to make a film were now considerable. The great star Raimu was gone, and several of the others had also vanished. There had been a sort of magic about that little company, and now it was disbanded.

As for the theatre, the trends which had lately become fashionable seemed to him more than a little foolish and pretentious.

To sum up, Marcel Pagnol, at the age of sixty, loaded with honours and fame, could still look forward to a distinguished career as a member of the Académie Française.

But the fires of his youth were beginning to die down.

It was at this point, when he was least expecting it, that a miracle occurred, and creativity welled up in him again, as powerfully as it had ever done before. And Marcel, abandoning all other work, launched, almost by accident, into a little story of an entirely different kind. A story so simple and modest that, when he began it, he had no idea that it would fill a book, still less that it would bring him greater fame than all his other works put together. A book for 'all people everywhere, and for all time', in short, a true classic.

And so, all unawares, yet knowing that artlessness is at the very heart of creative genius, he took a new folder, and inscribed upon it a title so simple that no one else would have dared to choose it: *Souvenirs d'Enfance*.

The *Souvenirs d'Enfance* were born in the spring of 1956, during luncheon at the home of Hélène and Pierre Lazareff.

Memories are short, and today the influence of these two remarkable people has already been forgotten. In those days, communications were dominated by the press, and Pierre and Hélène dominated the press, he as editor of the principal national daily, and she as editor of the principal women's magazine. But their influence depended much less upon power than upon personal gifts. They were interested in everything, valuing talent above all else, contemptuous of, if not hostile to, all forms of intolerance. They built an extremely valuable bridge between their own brilliant pre-war generation and that which followed it.

Once a week, almost everyone who was anyone in Paris could

be found at their home, actors, writers, leading politicians and journalists.

From his youth Pierre had had two major passions, a love of the theatre and an intense loyalty to his friends. Marcel Pagnol was one of his favourite guests, because their careers had begun to flower at about the same time, and he looked upon Marcel as the brightest star of that brilliant era.

'But,' he would say, speaking of his wife, 'of the two of us, Hélène is the genius.'

She was about to prove it.

During luncheon, Marcel, as was his wont, had 'told a story'. On this occasion, however, it was not one of his inexhaustible anecdotes about the theatre or the cinema. It was a slight, though tragic, tale of his childhood, the story of the four chateaux that he and his parents used to walk past on their way to La Treille when he was little, and of the appalling misery he experienced when, confronted by a bailiff, he had, for the first time in his life, seen his father broken and humiliated.

By tradition, the magazine *Elle* always printed a short story in its Christmas number. Scarcely had Marcel finished speaking than Hélène Lazareff was asking him to write down for her readers the story that he had just told.

Marcel promised to do so. He was free with his promises.

Weeks went by, and he forgot. The story of the four chateaux would have been lost forever, but for the intervention of a second agent of destiny.

For, if Hélène Lazareff deserves the credit for having suggested that the *Souvenirs* be written down, it was another employee of the magazine who was responsible for compelling Marcel actually to produce them. He was a very humble member of the staff in the office in the Rue Réaumur, none other than the messenger, in fact.

The name of this literary benefactor has not come down to us, so we cannot thank him personally, but he deserves a place in history for his astuteness. One morning, round about eleven, he rang Marcel's doorbell, and announced that he had come to collect the promised short story. The Master received him very civilly.

'My dear friend,' he said, 'I realise that Madame Lazareff is anxious to have the story as soon as possible, and nothing would give me greater pleasure than to oblige her. However, I regret to say that I have not quite finished it.' (In fact, he had not even begun it.) 'I still have a few more lines to write, and I don't want to keep you waiting. I would therefore be obliged if you would go back to the office, and tell Madame Lazareff that I will call in myself tomorrow morning with the manuscript.'

'Sir,' replied the messenger, 'I have a wife and two children. It seems that the management set great store by this story of yours, since they made it clear to me that, if I returned to the office without it, I should be dismissed on the spot. With your permission, therefore, I shall be quite happy to wait in the garden while you write the last few lines. There's always maintenance work to be done on a bicycle, so I shall have plenty to occupy my time. And, besides, I'm in no hurry.'

And so saying, he turned his bicycle upside down, and began dismantling one of the wheels.

Caught in a trap, and perhaps even secretly delighted at finding himself thus outwitted, Marcel had no choice but to return to his study and pick up his pen, not a fountain pen, for he disliked all such new-fangled toys, but his best *Sergent-Major* pen.

And so it came about that a few weeks later, on 3rd December, to be precise—for in the world of women's magazines, for some reason that escapes everyone except the advertising manager, Christmas falls not on 25th December, but much earlier—the readers of *Elle* were able to read for the first time the following memorable words, which were later to delight millions of readers. As they have been edited out of the definitive edition, I have no hesitation in quoting them here:

This incident occurred in 1905, and, according to my calculations, the aggregate age of my family at that time was seventy-three: two for my little sister, six for my brother Paul, nine for myself, twenty-six for my mother and thirty for my father, our patriarch. He was at that time a schoolmaster in Marseilles, and we admired him for his strength, his good looks, his skill at boule, his talent as a flautist and, above all, his casual habit of sharpening his razor on the palm of his left hand . . .

Divided into five instalments, the story of the four chateaux appeared in the magazine between 3rd December, 1956 and 7th January, 1957.

The response was so immediate, the enthusiasm so great, the

readers' letters asking for more so numerous, that Marcel was in no doubt that he could not stop there. And besides, he himself had so much enjoyed writing it that his pen seemed now to have taken on a life of its own. He decided to expand it into a book, and he worked on it all that year. It was soon evident that here was material for more than one volume. Accordingly, he split it into two, the volumes being entitled *La Gloire de mon Père* and *Le Château de ma Mère*, titles which have since attained immortal fame.

This, at any rate, was how Marcel Pagnol frequently described to his friends the three stages in the birth of his *Souvenirs*. Was it an accurate account? Contrary to the opinion of many, to whom it seems too good to be true, I think it probably was. Marcel, much as he was given to embroidering, did not tell lies. In the same way as his fits of rage were not spurious, but simply performances, so his stories were not so much inventions as dramatic productions. In short, he practised what might be called 'Provençal mendacity', which is no more than a tendency to give a tiny jolt to reality, in order to extract the poetic truth inherent in people and events, as different from lying, in its commonplace and vulgar form, as generosity is from wastefulness or holy faith from hypocritical piety.

Be that as it may, *La Gloire de mon Père* and *Le Château de ma Mère* were published a year later, at a few months' interval, in November, 1957 and April, 1958.

But Marcel already knew that there were more childhood recollections to come.

No sooner had he completed the last page of *Le Château de ma Mère*, in fact, than he realized that he had dealt with only one phase of his childhood, the earliest, which covered the period preceding his years at the Lycée.

Those years at the Lycée, for some so sad, so meagre and so empty, were for him full of beauty, richness and illumination, and were the inspiration of many of his works. It was inconceivable that he should leave them out of account. It would therefore be necessary to devote to them a third volume of his recollections. Once again, just as *Marius* had engendered *Fanny* and, later, *César*, he found himself engaged in writing a trilogy.

He was the more inclined to continue his work, in that he had gradually come to realize something of which he had hitherto been unaware, namely, that, with the passing of time, real people become transformed into characters, and that, in describing events which really happened, the writer of memoirs experiences the same pleasure as the novelist, and, in giving free rein to his imagination, finds himself scarcely more circumscribed. Pagnol himself remarked on this in an unpublished draft preface:

In this book, he wrote, I shall say nothing either good or bad about myself. It is not I who am the subject, but the child I used to be and am no longer. He is a little fellow I once knew, who has melted into thin air, as birds do when they vanish, leaving no skeleton behind. And besides, he is not the hero of the book, but merely a witness to a series of very small incidents.

I trust, therefore, that the reader will find no trace of histrionics in this little tale . . .

Thus, he started work on this third volume under the provisional title—perhaps in tribute to his beloved Dickens—*Les Grandes Amours*, which, before long, he changed slightly to *Les Belles Amours*.

At the outset, as can be seen from the notes he made at the time, Marcel did not think there would be much to tell:

Le Château ends with the ten-year-old boy about to enter the Sixth Grade at the Lycée.

What happened during the next two years in the Sixth and Fifth Grades?

Nothing, or very little.

The summer holidays, that first year, with Lili.

Then, as the outline of the book began to take shape, he jotted down a few sketchy chapter-headings:

General Outline:
The holidays following Le Château.
The Isabelle episode. Admission to the Lycée.
The story of Lagneau (detentions).
The meeting with Yves.

And, little by little, the creative process which had already manifested itself in the earlier volumes took over once more. The characters materialized, the anecdotes filled out, chapter succeeded chapter. Instead of being too slight, as he had feared, the narrative was now too long to be contained in a single volume. When it came to considering publication, Pagnol

Moreover, the book was meant to have a very different ending, as we know from Marcel's own account, which he never modified. Having escaped death, the plague victims' manner of life became so riotous that they were driven out by the inhabitants of Allauch. Thereafter they took refuge in the famous *Grotte des Pestiférés*, where they were exterminated by the villagers.

It is of interest, at this distance in time, to note that three great Provençal writers, Camus, Giono and Pagnol, were all inspired to describe cataclysmic historical events and men's reactions to them in terms of the plague.

Chapter X, entitled *Les Amours de Lagneau*, has an even more intriguing history. The account of the episode printed here, unlike all the other chapters of *Le Temps des Amours*, was not written between the years 1959 and 1962. It goes back much further, to the year 1919, and was discovered by a miraculous stroke of luck, in one of those little exercise books in which Marcel Pagnol, at that time a schoolmaster teaching English, carefully noted down the homework and learning tasks he had set his pupils, the corrections he had made to their proses and translations, and the marks he had awarded for their compositions, etc. Yet, every detail of this little tale, with its intrigues and reverses of fortune, corresponds exactly with his notes on the subject written in 1960, and with the two or three versions of the opening paragraphs also written at this time.

Thus we learn, to our surprise, that, as much as forty years earlier, Marcel Pagnol had already conceived the idea of telling the story of Lagneau, whose name, incidentally, is already to be found by the observant reader in *Pirouettes*, a slight, early novel published in 1933 by Fasquelle, and itself a reworking of two tales, *Le Mariage de Peluque* and *La Petite Fille aux Yeux Sombres*, published ten years before in *Fortunio*. It is clear that, even at that early date, he was contemplating writing his memoirs, since the piece was included under the general title of *Mémoirs de Jacques Panier*.

But, for Marcel Pagnol, a manuscript in progress was infinitely adaptable. It could never be regarded as definitive. The author was free to make modifications right up to the last moment, and even after that, since it was always possible to make changes in a new edition.

This, therefore, is how matters stood, *Le Temps des Amours* being virtually completed, when Marcel was suddenly struck with a new idea. He had just noticed something which worried him. The book was far more concerned with portraying people, friends, teachers and relations, than with retailing amorous adventures. In fact, it was really an account of his schooldays rather than a collection of love stories.

For the second time, therefore, he considered a complete reconstruction of *Le Temps des Secrets* and *Le Temps des Amours*, by a redistribution of the contents. He would remove the story of the meeting with his first love, Isabelle, at the age of ten from *Le Temps des Secrets*, and rewrite *Le Temps des Amours* around three main episodes: the encounter with Isabelle, Lagneau's love life, and the story of Blanchette, his first real experience of love.

Hence the numerous jottings, shunting the chapters from one volume to the other. For instance:

In Le Temps des Secrets, *the story of Isabelle occupies 150 pages.*

It must be replaced by L'Affaire des Pendus *and* La Tragédie de Lagneau, *and possibly also the* boules *competition and* Parpaillouns.

Isabelle to be transferred to Le Temps des Amours, *with Lagneau, Blanchette and Pomponnette.*

Admittedly, the first volume was already in print, but Marcel Pagnol was not the man to let such a trifle stand in his way. Another page of notes:

Le Temps des Amours will begin with Isabelle. This will be in the collected edition. In the ordinary edition, I shall begin with Lagneau, followed by Blanchette, then Madame ... Yves and Rose? Open with Yves and Monsieur Sylvain; Zizi; Poetry.

However, the artist proposes, and art disposes. In spite of all these good resolutions, neither the ordinary nor the collected edition was ever to appear. Shortly after this, Marcel abandoned his *Souvenirs* as suddenly as he had begun them, turning his attention to other matters, and gently but firmly telling his friends to mind their own business, whenever they urged him to finish *Le Temps des Amours*.

The ways of the creative artist are mysterious indeed. What was it that prompted Pagnol to abandon his book when it was almost completed, and he had already several times announced its forthcoming publication?

There is probably more than one answer to this question.

In the first place, he was assailed by doubts. As we have seen, he had decided to end *Le Temps des Amours* with an account of his first real experience of love. Now, although he cannot be said to have written the book specifically for children, Marcel had been greatly struck by the immense popularity of *La Gloire de Mon Père* and *Le Château de Ma Mère* with young and very young readers. He had received a great number of enthusiastic letters from friends, fellow-writers and critics. But also he had received many thousands of letters from children. Such letters poured in ceaselessly from every corner of France, some from individual children, some from children and their parents, some from whole classes, asking whether this or that anecdote or character was based on fact. The thought that his concluding chapter might shock the sensibilities of these young readers was distasteful to him, and he often said as much, when pressed to finish the book.

Secondly, he wanted to turn his thoughts and efforts to other things. Unlike many writers, he loved making a fresh start, because of the challenge involved, which was, indeed, the reason why he was undeterred by failure. His failures interested him. He enjoyed analysing them, and finding reasons for them. Success, on the other hand, palled very quickly.

Thus, no sooner had *Le Temps des Secrets* appeared in print than he resumed work on the biographical novel *Manon des Sources*, which he had abandoned in 1956. To this he added *Jean de Florette*, and the two stories appeared in November, 1962 and March, 1963, under the title *L'Eau des Collines*.

At about this time, also, under the stimulus of his childhood recollections, he began work on the long prefaces referred to above, and on a whole series of articles on the cinema, the collected edition of which was entitled *Cinématurgie de Paris*. All these pieces obviously represented a kind of sequel to the *Souvenirs*, evoking, as they did, the scenes of his early manhood as a young dramatist and film-maker. These he intended to include in his *Oeuvres Complètes*, of which he had recently drawn up yet another list, and which began to appear in 1962.

No doubt the *Oeuvres Complètes* project owed something to

the acclaim accorded to the recently published *Souvenirs*, for Marcel Pagnol must by now have realized that he had written his masterpiece. But the project itself throws an interesting light on his temperament as a writer, which was essentially ambivalent.

On the one hand, he never regarded any of his work as finished. He was not one of those artists who consider that their work is engraved in marble. From his work in the theatre and the cinema, he had learnt that, in response to the claims of an audience, it is always possible to modify a script, to condense or expand a scene, and this was a lesson that he was never to forget. There are at least five or six versions of *Marius* in existence, and, as we have seen, he had made plans for a complete reshaping of *Le Temps des Secrets* and *Le Temps des Amours*. On the other hand, he was as proud as he was modest, and held his craft in very high esteem, which was why the notion of publishing his *Oeuvres Complètes* delighted him.

Moreover, it was an idea that he had had in mind for a very long time, since the prime of his youth, in fact. Among his papers are to be found a dozen different schemes formulated at various periods of his life, and indicating his changing views on the subject. One can smile now at his first scheme, drawn up when he was about twenty, and comprising some thirty works, none of which, with the exception of *Catulle* and a few poems, had yet been written, or were ever to be written. But he was certainly not lacking in self-confidence. So much so that it would be no paradox to say that the reason he worked so hard all his life was in order one day to have the satisfaction of seeing his *Oeuvres Complètes* in print.

In conclusion, the final obstacle to the completion of *Le Temps des Amours* was another project which had long occupied his mind, and to which he now returned to the exclusion of almost everything else, a study of the mystery of *The Man in the Iron Mask*. This historical enigma, endlessly regurgitated and vulgarized in popular magazines, was coming more and more to fascinate Marcel. Adopting the role of examining magistrate, he scoured the official records, studied the depositions of witnesses, and read all the relevant books. He amused himself endlessly in constructing novel theories on the subject, somewhat to the consternation of his friends. The unfortunate prisoner in the

Bastille left them cold. They were keenly aware of how much was being sacrificed to this project, to such an extent that they could seriously have wished that Louis XIV had executed summary justice upon him.

When, having published his conclusions, Marcel immediately announced that he was starting work on another book on the subject, which, as well as being a radically revised and corrected version of the first, would contain a number of entirely new and startling revelations, they could not contain their disappointment. All to no avail. Marcel, who liked nothing better than to infuriate his friends, declared, with the imperturbable aplomb of which he was such a master:

'In a hundred years' time, all my books will be forgotten, except this one.'

Be that as it may, the fact remains that he was to devote himself for another ten years to his beloved *Man in the Iron Mask*.

The last time he and I ever discussed *Le Temps des Amours* was one night in January, at the beginning of the year 1974. He had just returned from a brief stay on his 'estate' near Cagnes. He was by now in a permanent state of exhaustion. The sky was overcast, the drawing-room damp and somewhat chilly, and, reclining on the big couch, he looked like a forlorn child, left behind in the house by his family.

'This time,' he said, 'I give you my word, you shall have *Le Temps des Amours* by the spring. It isn't as if it was yet to be written. It's finished. I have only to go upstairs and fetch it.'

The next day, he went into the American Hospital to undergo tests. Three days later, he returned home in a state of intense nervous excitement, declaring that while it was occasionally possible to survive an illness, it was never possible to survive the attentions of one's doctors. Then he went to bed, set to work on a series of algebraical equations, smoked innumerable cigarettes, kissed his wife, and died.

After it was all over, and he was laid to rest in the little cemetery of La Treille, close to La Bastide-Neuve and not far from 'le Château de ma Mère', the chateau which his mother did not own, we had not the heart to give much thought to the works of Marcel Pagnol.

As far as the public was concerned, nothing had changed. His books were as much in demand as ever, his films and interviews were shown repeatedly on television. In fact, he remained very much with us. Through the magic of the cinema, it was possible repeatedly to experience the miracle which he had described, that of the little lamp which 'rekindles extinguished geniuses, reanimates dead dancers, and touches our hearts by restoring to us the smiles of lost friends.'

But for us, his friends, things were a little different. We knew that it was no longer possible to telephone him at six o'clock in the evening, to let him know that we intended calling on him, for the pleasure of listening to him for hours on end. We could not forget those marvellous evenings in his company, his heartfelt welcome, that smile of his, which ill-health never succeeded in quenching. The poignant 'nevermore' of death—the fearful power of which lies in its being not an abstract idea or universal sentiment, but a feeling constantly reawakened by the thousand trivial details of daily life—had us in its grip, and plunged all of us who were his friends into a deep silence.

Nevertheless, after several months had passed, I began to feel the need to tidy up the loose ends. Had Marcel been speaking the truth that night in January, when he had said that his book was practically finished?

His wife, Jacqueline, and his brother, René, were inclined to doubt it.

'It's possible, you know,' they told me, 'that he said it just to please you.'

There was only one way to find out, and accordingly we repaired to Marcel's study. It was no easy task, since his passion for hoarding was equalled only by his untidiness. Little by little, however, we found everything, the stirring story of the plague victims, which we had all heard him tell, and which we had so often regretted that he had not written down, the pieces which had been published in magazines, and those other stories which he had never mentioned to anyone. Next, we found his notes, his chapter-headings and his rough drafts. Then, whole chapters came to light, and the book began to take shape under our very eyes. And we knew that Marcel had not lied.

Is it ever right to publish an author's work posthumously?

Work, that is to say, that the writer, given the time, would have extensively modified, extended and improved.

There are many who still doubt the wisdom of doing so. But they forget how many great works would have been lost to us in that case, beginning with the *Aeneid*, which Virgil expressly asked his friends to burn, because he had not had a chance to revise it, and ending with *Le Temps Retrouvé*, which Marcel Proust also did not live to revise.

Of course, it is always right to publish posthumous works, even minor works, whose only merit is that they enlarge our understanding of their author. How much more so if they represent a significant contribution to his *oeuvre*.

This is certainly the case with *Le Temps des Amours*. This last volume, for all its faults, contains some of Marcel Pagnol's finest writing, some of the most moving and entertaining stories he ever wrote. The style, at once so highly seasoned and so limpid, stamped with the simplicity of genius, speaks to us, as we silently read, in his uniquely personal voice.

The book also affords us some fascinating insights into the craft of writing.

First, the subject-matter, derived from his earliest experiences, so that we find that the whole of the writer's creative life has its roots in those early years. How intriguing it is to discover little Lagneau and his love life, featuring in a story written in adolescence, and to realize that these *Souvenirs*, apparently recalled haphazardly by a man in his sixties, had, in reality, both in style and in subject-matter, been germinating all his life.

Revert to his childhood though he might for his themes, his style grew ever richer and more mature. One has only to contrast the last chapter, written by a young man of twenty-five, already showing so much innate talent, such a wealth of joyful fantasy, such a love of clowning, such youthful high spirits, so much burgeoning imagination, with all the earlier chapters, to realize how far it falls short of the masterly clarity and economy of his mature style. Art does not progress, but artists do.

In conclusion, *Le Temps des Amours* demonstrates more clearly than any other of Pagnol's works his genius for realism. What he loved best to describe all his life were things, people and places. Whether he was retailing the babblings of a lunatic or the misadventures of his school-fellows, his concern was always to portray things as they were, to pay homage to that which is.

There is a jotting in the margin of one of his exercise books which admirably sums up the philosophy of life that pervades all his works:

I love many people, and even those whom I do not love I find interesting. No landscape, however beautiful, matters to me as much as a man or a woman. 'Nothing human is alien to me', said Terence. I would add: 'Nothing that is not human is close to me'.

If I had been a painter, I should have painted nothing but portraits.

I do not intend, by these brief remarks, to append a critical footnote to a work that can manage very well without it. My only purpose is to right an injustice, and to point a way.

For many years, Pagnol was admired more for his success than his talent. He was better known as a personality than as a writer. And, since his death, more and more stress has been placed on Pagnol the man, with his talent for conversation, and his many delightful quirks of character. Certainly, Pagnol the public character existed, and should not be forgotten. He has his place in a sort of legendary poets' corner in a waxworks show, sitting in the *Bar de la Marine* in company with his friends Vincent Scotto, Raimu and Tino Rossi, about to play a hand of cards. But there is another Pagnol, and his kindred spirits are Rabelais, La Fontaine and Molière. The time has perhaps come to speak of him. And in reassessing Marcel Pagnol, to recognize him as one of the truly great classical writers of France.

Elements of a New System of Thermodynamics
(Preface, 1930)

When one has made a decision, one is overwhelmed with happiness and relief. But making one's choice, and organizing one's life accordingly, is difficult. As far as I am concerned, the die is now cast.

I have completed *Topaze, Marius* and *Fanny*, to the best of my ability. I am now retiring from the stage, for there is something I have long been meaning to do, but for which I have never found time. I want to tell my readers about it, and explain my reasons.

I received a liberal education, and, like everyone else, was instructed in the 'humanities'. That is to say, by the age of twenty-five I had several university degrees, and was able to read Homer, Virgil, Goethe and Shakespeare in the original. But I believed, in all good faith, that the square of three was six.

Needless to say, I had attended classes in mathematics and science at the Lycée, but these classes were tailored for the use of 'arts' students. The syllabus was sketchy and truncated, consisting mainly of formulae, and omitting the reasoning on which these were based, for it was thought that we were incapable of understanding it, and besides, two hours a week was scarcely time enough in which to learn all there was to know about geometry, algebra, arithmetic, physics, chemistry and astronomy. Our teacher, a kind-hearted man called Monsieur Cros, had his class notes cyclostyled, and sold us copies at a loss. He looked upon us with a mixture of warm affection and profound contempt. When expounding some elegant formula to us, he would say: 'I can't go into explanations as to how it is arrived at, you wouldn't understand. All the same, do try to learn it and remember it. You can take my word for it that it is correct, and based on sound logic.'

In other words, it was not science that we were being taught, but rather scientific theology, consisting of a series of mystical revelations.

Which is why when, ten years later, I happened one day to open a text-book on physics, I read it from beginning to end.

Occasionally, when asked a question by one of the boys, Monsieur Cros would attempt an explanation, but this was always dismissive, sketchy and misleading. He never got to the heart of the matter, but, like a well-bred man telling a dirty story in mixed company, skated over it.

Some of the formulae he taught us were delightful. Towering above us on his rostrum, he would declaim:

> 'La circonférence est fière
> D'être égale à 2πR,
> Et le cercle est tout joyeux
> D'être égal à πR^2.'*

Then he would smile, as if to say: 'Since you are students of literature, I give you a poem'.

Having delivered himself of this poem, he would beam delightedly upon us, as if to say: 'Ha! You've never heard that one before, have you?' And the whole class, amazed at the pride of the Circumference, and charmed by the unalloyed delight of the Circle, expressed its appreciation by prolonged bellowing.

Whereupon Monsieur Cros would bang the desk with a huge pair of wooden compasses, and say: 'Come now, gentlemen, do not mock the Muse, when she comes to the aid of Science.'

He would also recite:

> 'Le volume de la sphère,
> Quoi que l'on puisse faire,
> Est égal à $\frac{4}{3}\pi$R^3.'†

And then he would pause—for a full twenty seconds—subjecting the whole class, from Yves Bourde at one end of the room to Avérinos at the other, to a sweeping glance. Then, softly, with forefinger raised and eyes half-closed, he would add:
> *'La sphère fut-elle de bois.'*‡

* The circumference is proud/To be equal to 2πr,/And the circle is overjoyed/To be equal to πr^2.
† The volume of the sphere,/Do what one may,/Is equal to $\frac{4}{3}\pi$r^3.
‡ Even if the sphere is made of wood.

He laid great stress on this last line, which he delivered with a kind of triumphant severity. But he was no longer addressing us, he was talking to the Sphere Itself. He was warning it, he was giving it notice that, whatever subterfuge it might resort to, whatever dishonest intentions it might have, whatever Protean guise it might choose to adopt, whether solid or hollow, heavy or light, made of steel, graphite, chalk, manganese, copper, plaster or a compound of zinc and tin, or even (the supreme attempt at evasion) if it were '*made of wood*', it would not escape the ineluctable formula imposed upon it by the laws of geometry. Merely by squeezing the trigger of that fearsome weapon: $\frac{4}{3}\pi r$,^{3} even if it were made of wood, one had it pinned down, measured and vanquished.

To reduce the plump, round sphere to a flattened corpse on a sheet of paper, one had only to press this nickel-plated trigger: $\frac{4}{3}\pi r^3$.

EVEN IF IT WERE MADE OF WOOD.

After this triumph, Monsieur Cros would pause once again. His expression would relax, then, good-naturedly, beguilingly and generously, now rolling his 'rs' less ferociously, he would add:

'One might also say:

Quand bien même elle serait en bois'.

He pronounced *bois* as 'boa'.

We were taught Physics and Chemistry by Monsieur Oneto.

He had a little black beard, which made him look like a younger version of Mephistopheles. He had great authority, and was immensely kind.

Like Monsieur Cros, he rolled his 'rs', and like Monsieur Cros, he held us in affectionate contempt.

A completely crazy syllabus laid down that we should be taught the whole of Physics and Chemistry in fifty lessons, we who came to him fresh from the Philosophy course, and who did not even know how to solve a simple equation, we who had given of our best to Berkeley, *Fichte-grain-de-sable*, the categorical imperative, pragmatism, Auguste Comte and Baralipton.

Then, with immense patience, and to entertain this class of blithering idiots, he would carry out experiments. Whenever I think of those science classes, I see a piece of wire burning in a retort full of oxygen, a mercury lamp turning Monsieur Oneto's blackest of black beards green, a test-tube which he was wont to shake, saying: 'Watch now, and you will see it turn blue' (whereupon it would turn bright scarlet), and—the apotheosis of my physics classes—a piece of sodium, completely out of control, erupting in deafening explosions on the surface of a kind of chamber pot, spitting angrily and throwing off sudden flashes at the vortex of a submarine conflagration.

Monsieur Cros's epic poem and the explosive prestidigitation of Monsieur Oneto enabled me to pass my *baccalauréat* examinations, without understanding the first thing about mathematics or physics. But these two excellent teachers did teach me—although I was not aware of it at the time—the one thing that I was capable of learning, which was the most important lesson of all. They instilled in me the desire to learn.